Richard G. Hodgson
A.D. 1962 Spring

THE MOON

The Moon, age 12 days. E. A. Whitaker, Greenwich Observatory

THE MOON

A COMPLETE DESCRIPTION OF THE SURFACE OF
THE MOON, CONTAINING THE 300-INCH WILKINS
LUNAR MAP

BY

Dr. H. PERCY WILKINS, F.R.A.S.

AND

PATRICK MOORE, F.R.A.S.

THE MACMILLAN COMPANY
New York

Printed in Great Britain

CONTENTS

ILLUSTRATIONS

The 25 numbered sections of the main 300-inch map will be found before the detailed description of each section.

ACKNOWLEDGMENTS

The authors wish to express their appreciation for assistance during the compilation of this work.

The choice photographs include some taken by Mr. E. A. Whitaker, F.R.A.S., with the 36-inch 'Yapp' reflector at the Royal Observatory, Greenwich, reproduced by kind permission of the Astronomer Royal, Sir Harold Spencer Jones, F.R.S. The Director of the Pic-du-Midi Observatory and Mme Lyot kindly consented to the reproduction of some of the superb photographs taken by the late Dr. B. Lyot. We also wish to thank Lyle T. Johnson for allowing us to reproduce his photographs, and to Dr. Ira Bowen for the splendid photograph of Clavius taken with the 200-inch Palomar telescope.

Our gratitude is also extended to Dr. D'Azambuja, Dr. Bertaud, Dr. Dollfus, and Mme Hermann for not only affording us the use of the great 33-inch refractor at the Observatory of Meudon, near Paris, but for their assistance during observation. Many of the drawings were secured with the aid of this magnificent example of optical skill, and show much minute detail, previously unrecorded. These observations were supplemented by others obtained by the aid of the 25-inch 'Newall' refractor at Cambridge University Observatory and the 30-inch reflector belonging to Dr. W. H. Steavenson. Our gratitude to Prof. Redman and Dr. Steavenson is very great.

Among the many eminent observers who contributed drawings and notes, mention must be made of Prof. A. Paluzie of Barcelona for details of lunar maps, K. W. Abineri, B.Sc., F.R.A.S., H. Hill, F.R.A.S., E. J. Reese, R. M. Baum, F.R.A.S., D. P. Barcroft, E. Hare, E. A. Whitaker, F.R.A.S., F. H. Thornton, F.R.A.S., D. W. G. Arthur, F.R.A.S., and Dr. J. Q. Gant.

In addition to supplying photographs, Mr. E. A. Whitaker, F.R.A.S., most kindly assisted in the rather tedious task of proof reading.

The complete Map of the Moon contained in the work is the latest and revised edition of the 300-inch diameter map drawn by the senior author and first published in 1946. It includes all details discovered at Meudon and Cambridge, while the special charts of selected formations include all detail visible in the finest instruments.

Our thanks are also due to Mr. R. T. Wardleworth for assistance in preparing the drawings, and to Messrs. Faber and Faber for undertaking the publication of the work.

FOREWORD TO THE SECOND EDITION

Much has happened since the first edition of this book appeared some years ago. The first earth satellites and planetary probes have been successfully launched; rockets have been sent past the Moon and to the Moon; photographs have been obtained of much of the averted hemisphere, and the first manned orbital flight has been made.

All this research has necessitated modifications in the original text, but most unfortunately the senior author is no longer with us to carry them out. H. P. Wilkins died suddenly in January 1960, only a few days after retiring from his official post in the Ministry of Supply with the intention of devoting the rest of his life to astronomy. His death was a tragic shock to his friends all over the world—the more so, perhaps, because it was so completely unexpected.

Wilkins was never a professional astronomer; he remained an amateur, though his status in the scientific world was acknowledged in many countries. His enthusiasm for selenography was unquenchable, and he was still hard at work up to the moment when he was taken ill with a heart attack. He had, in fact, just finished plans for a full revision of his lunar maps.

He would have been the last to claim that his charts are free from error. Of course they are not; but the best comment upon them was, I feel, given by the Russian astronomers in mid-1960, when they used Wilkins' maps of the lunar limb to correlate the photographs of the Moon's far side with the features already known by direct observation from Earth. It is a fact, too, that no entirely satisfactory photographic atlas has so far been produced. The latest effort, by G. P. Kuiper and his colleagues in the United States, is a notable contribution—but even so, many of the plates, particularly those of the limb regions, are too blurred to be used for detailed studies, and there is as yet no complete substitute for direct lunar observation made at the telescope.

For this revision I have not altered the maps, but I have done my best to bring the text up to date and to incorporate the results of the latest work. My main regret has, of course, been that Wilkins was unable to do so himself, and to take part in the new studies of the world to which he devoted so much of his life. My part in the compilation of this book has been very minor; the credit must go to Wilkins alone.

PATRICK MOORE.

26th April 1961.

INTRODUCTION

Ever since the invention of the telescope, when the celestial wonders first burst upon the astonished gaze of men, the Moon has been a favourite object for scrutiny and study. Despite its small size and its secondary rôle as a satellite, this beautiful silvery sphere, richly covered with markings, across which the effects of light and shade play in an ever-varying panorama, remains the most fascinating of telescopic objects. For while its broad features may be clearly discerned with the naked eye, forming the rude out-lines of a human face, that of 'The Man in the Moon', observed throughout the ages, the interest is infinitely enhanced by the use of the smallest telescope; even the most casual observer confesses that our satellite possesses an appeal and presents a spectacle full of charm, and always new.

This especial interest in 'that horned maiden whom mortals call the Moon' arises from its proximity, as it is the only celestial object of which the actual surface features can be seen in their more minute details. Their vivid distinctness is largely due to the absence of any appreciable lunar atmosphere. Whatever atmosphere the Moon may possess, it is more attenuated than the most perfect vacuum ever formed by man. From this absence of an atmospheric screen, every detail is sharply presented, the effect of hill and hollow being heightened by the brilliancy of objects in sunlight and the intense blackness of shadows. Aerial perspective is totally absent; also any traces of twilight, indeed of all half-lights. Any such graduation of light is masked along the terminator (the dividing line between the illuminated and the unilluminated regions), by a shadowy border, due to the source of light, the Sun, being an object of appreciable apparent size. The shadows also are not always an impenetrable black; faint glimmerings and ghostly outlines can often be traced, rendered visible by reflection from adjacent sunlit cliffs or ranges, or even, in certain circumstances, from the light of the Earth itself.

Even the smallest telescope will reveal the broader features of our satellite, the sombre plains, the glittering highlands, massive mountain ranges, isolated hills, often of surprising brightness, with the principal characteristics, the grand peculiarities of the Moon—the crater-plains. Everywhere, save on the dark plains, will be seen rings, isolated or crowded together, often encroaching and distorting each other, the whole surface resembling a gigantic pumice-block or honey-comb. A good 3-inch refractor will reveal not only all the broader features of these ringed structures but many exceed-ingly delicate objects, especially to an observer familiar with them under superior optical power. With instruments of from 6 to 12 inches in aperture, valuable work may be done, and it is to such apertures in the hands of amateur observers that most of our knowledge of the lunar surface features is due.

HISTORY OF SELENOGRAPHY

Before the invention of the telescope and its application to the study of our satellite by Galileo, Marius, Lower and others in 1610, various views and opinions were held and expressed regarding the Moon. In a sense observation of the Moon began when men first noted her changes and motion from night to night. In ancient times she was worshipped as a goddess, under such names as Artemis, Ashtaroth or Diana. The ancient Egyptians had two goddesses of the Moon, Khonsu and Thoth; and the observers of those days, priests rather than astronomers, together with the Chaldeans, noted her appearances with such exactitude that they were able to predict eclipses, not indeed with the precision of modern times, but with sufficient accuracy to be able to announce the day when an eclipse would take place. In the Middle Ages the mediæval philosophers delighted in such follies as to declare that the Moon influenced the growth of some forms of vegetation. Both animals and men were brought under her sway; she was supposed to rule over all who worked by night, such as thieves or spies, while the eyes of cats or the spots of the panther were affirmed to vary with the changes of the Moon.

All these ideas were swept away by the invention of the telescope, and the study of the lunar surface details, or Selenography, dates from the spring of 1610. Galileo not only recognized the existence of mountains in the Moon but made estimates of their altitudes, and constructed the first lunar map. Sir William Lower, observing with his 'perspective cylinder' at Traventy, in Pembrokeshire, was probably the first telescopic worker in England. He describes the contrast between the sunlit mountain peaks and the blackness of adjacent valleys, still enveloped in night, and the rugged nature of many portions of the lunar surface.

Lagalla, Scheiner, Malapert, Mellan, Gassendi, Langrenus and Rheita followed the path thus laid down by Galileo and Lower, the map of Rheita showing very well the outlines of the plains, the principal 'craters' and the chief systems of bright rays.

To Hevelius, City Councillor of Danzig, we are indebted for the first map of the Moon worthy of the name. This chart, which was published in 1647, was laid down by eye estimates, and contained 250 named formations. Hevelius named the various objects after supposed terrestrial resemblances. Thus the great ringed-plain now known as Copernicus was called 'Mount Etna', and the beautiful ring-plain Plato, 'The Greater Black Lake'.

In addition to his map, Hevelius also published shaded drawings of the Moon in various phases; the book containing his observations, *Selenographia*, remained the standard authority for over 100 years and still possesses value today. It may be of interest to know that after the death of Hevelius in 1687, the copperplate of his map was made into a teapot!

From the observations of his friend Grimaldi, the celebrated Jesuit astronomer Riccioli, of Bologna, constructed a map the merits of which were at first not appreciated. Wiser in his generation than Hevelius, he boldly recast the lunar nomenclature, naming the rings and walled-plains after celebrated astronomers, philosophers, mathematicians and theologians. Needless to say, this flattering system prevailed, only ten of the names given by Hevelius surviving. Riccioli, whose map was published in 1651, termed the grey areas 'seas', the smaller patches 'marshes', but his use of the name 'terræ' for the bright portions has not been followed. Both Hevelius and Riccioli show the 'libratory regions', that is, those portions of the lunar surface alternately carried out of or brought into view as distinct from that portion always visible from our terrestrial standpoint.

The celebrated Italian astronomer, Cassini, was another early worker, and drew up a map 20 inches in diameter, containing more detail than that of Hevelius, the positions being obtained by actual measurement. This map is very rare; only two copies of the large original are known, one being in the library of the Royal Astronomical Society, London, although we possess reduced copies of this work. It seems to have been the fashion of those days to get rid of the copperplates from which the copies were produced, for after the death of Cassini, the printing plate was sold to a boilermaker. Whether this, like that of Hevelius, ended up as a teapot we do not know.

The first really accurate map of the Moon was constructed by the justly celebrated Tobias Mayer of Göttingen who, recognizing the want of an exact and detailed chart of the Moon, determined to complete such a chart in twenty-five sections. This project was never realized, but after his death, a small map, only 8 inches in diameter, was found among his papers and was published thirteen years after his decease. This chart, carefully shaded and shadowed, has always been regarded as a beautiful work of art, and remained the only accurate map until the great chart of Beer and Mädler was published in 1837.

After Mayer, selenography was advanced by the labours of Schröter, who commenced his observations with the aid of reflecting telescopes made by Sir William Herschel. Later, a great reflector of 19 inches aperture was added to his equipment, which unfortunately was deficient in any micrometrical accessories. With these instruments Schröter observed at Lilienthal, in Hanover, until the area was invaded by the French who, mistaking the brasswork of his telescopes for gold, pillaged the place and set the observatory on fire.

Having no true micrometer, Schröter determined the heights of peaks and the diameters of the ringed-plains by what he called his 'projection machine'. This was a mere board carried at right angles to the telescope tube and upon which the image seen by one eye could be brought into coincidence with the ruled squares, just as the telescopic view seen by one eye can be brought into coincidence with the ordinary view seen with the other eye. This method, although rough, is capable of considerable accuracy, and Schröter made many measures. His drawings (which have been closely examined by the Authors) are less valuable than they might have been owing to the indifferent definition of the mirror of his reflector as judged by present-day standards. These drawings, in his work, *Selenotopographische Fragmente*, in two volumes, 1791 and 1802, are well executed and are compiled with skill and arranged with care. Before obtaining the necessary materials he was occupied with 'changes' ascribed to the lunar atmosphere, traces of which he considered as established by the prolongation of the fine line of the cusps when the Moon was in crescent phase. A serious fault in Schröter's drawings is the lack of proportion; this prevents their use in the determination of possible physical changes in comparison with drawings of to-day.

While Schröter was thus occupied in selenographical studies, Sir William Herschel measured the heights of several lunar mountains, using an aperture of 4 inches on one of his reflectors. He also considered that at least one of the craters was in active eruption as it presented a bright star-like point when on the unilluminated portion of the disk. This crater, called Aristarchus, is frequently visible under such conditions, when it merely receives the reflected light of the Earth. It has since been established that its remarkable brilliancy when on the dark side is not due to eruption but to the capacity of the walls for reflecting light. These observations of Sir William Herschel were made at Bath. It is, however, possible that at least one of the appearances noted by Herschel was due to a 'flare', that is to say, a meteorite striking the surface. After all, it is not surprising that detail can occasionally be seen on the unilluminated portion. So much light is sometimes reflected from the surrounding sunlit cliffs or walls that Dr. W. H. Steavenson, using a shaded eyepiece, has seen the central mountains of the craters Agrippa and Godin when the interior of the crater was filled with shadow, and even noted the short shadow cast by the central mountains owing to the light reflected on to them by the cliffs.

Far more accurate than Schröter was Lohrmann, a land surveyor of Dresden, who, with a telescope of $4\frac{1}{4}$ inches aperture, commenced observations with a view to the construction of a chart in twenty-five sections. Failing eyesight prevented the accomplishment of his design. Four sections only of this map were published, but he issued, in 1838, an excellent general map, $15\frac{1}{4}$ inches in diameter. The remaining sections of his larger map were completed and published by Schmidt in 1878. This chart compares favourably with that of Beer and Mädler.

From 1830 to 1837, Mädler, observing in his friend Beer's private observatory in the Berlin *Tiergarten*, completed a survey of the lunar disk, measuring the heights of over 1,000 elevations, and published a detailed map of 37 inches diameter, divided into quadrants. This *Mappa Selenographica* and the accompanying book *Der Mond*, remained the standard authority for many years. In addition to their great map, Beer and Mädler issued a smaller chart, very cheap and, for its size, full of detail, but naturally lacking in minuteness. An outline map, based on Mädler's, was drawn up by Webb as an illustration in his classic *Celestial Objects for Common Telescopes*.

In their selenographical work, Beer and Mädler used a refracting telescope of only $3\frac{3}{4}$ inches aperture, a suggestive point for those who decry small instruments. While it is doubtless true, as Goodacre remarks, that this small aperture prevented greater accuracy in their measures of the positions of the various objects, the work actually accomplished is a remarkable tribute to their diligent perseverance, though Neison

1838 ~

contends that their limited aperture did not permit the detection of small illuminated surfaces, such as mountain peaks under the first or last rays of sunlight, so that in this matter Schröter must be considered a better authority by virtue of his superior aperture.

Beer and Mädler considered that the Moon has arrived at its terminal condition so far as the surface features are concerned; they did not deny the possibility of a greatly attenuated atmosphere, or of slight changes, but their own researches were against these probabilities. Owing to the conventional nature of their representation of lunar details, especially regarding the more minute features in their great map, it cannot be safely employed as an authority for the establishment of change. Mädler's work may be considered as completing the first period of selenographical history. Its immediate result was the stifling of further investigations, as it was concluded that the Moon's surface was a mere volcanic waste, without atmosphere or water, a world of eternal silence, without change, a sort of celestial museum case on which it was hopeless to look for traces of life in any form. This still appears to be the 'official' view.

The charts and drawings produced by the labours of the selenographers mentioned were not the only lunar activities. Several globes of our satellite were constructed, some of singular beauty, that of Russell in particular. Webb mentions another made by Sir Christopher Wren at the command of Charles II. On globes, the actual forms of the various features were depicted, while all maps show the appearance as we see it. Thus the well-known Mare Crisium (Sea of Crises) appears on the maps, through foreshortening, as decidedly oval from north to south; its true form is elliptical from east to west, and is so shown on a globe.

After more than thirty years of assiduous observation with the aid of the refracting telescope of the Athens Observatory, having an aperture of 7 inches, Schmidt published, in 1874, his great map of the Moon, in twenty-five sections on a scale of 75 inches to the Moon's diameter; a remarkable achievement in pre-photographic days. This wonderful map was published by the Prussian Government and was, for many years, regarded as the finest of its kind. It is a remarkable tribute to the accuracy of Schmidt to notice how well his map agrees, even with regard to minute features, when compared with the latest and the best of lunar photographs. He did not, however, make many measures of positions, although he made numerous height measurements, but adopted the positions of Lohrmann and Mädler. Schmidt's map remained until 1910, the most accurate in existence; its minuteness may be gauged from the fact that nearly 33,000 crater-like objects are depicted, as well as numerous hills, mountain ranges, clefts, valleys and other features.

In the same year that Schmidt's map appeared, a new book on the Moon was issued. This was *The Moon* of Nasmyth and Carpenter, with its beautiful plates, reproductions of photographs of plaster models of portions of the surface made by Nasmyth. In this work we are introduced to the volcanic theory of the origin of surface formations and also the theory of the cosmical origin of the Moon itself from the vast diffuse nebulous mass, an adaptation of the Nebular Theory of Laplace, to the formation of a compact, molten globe is presented.

What may be regarded as an English translation of Mädler's *Der Mond*, with additions and modifications, and accompanied by a map, in twenty-two sections on a scale of 24 inches to the Moon's diameter, was published by Neison in 1876. Neison, who was quite a young man when this classical work appeared, observed with a refractor of 6 inches in aperture and a reflector of $9\frac{1}{4}$ inches. His map shows less details in the mountains but more clefts than does that of Mädler, and while certain minute features were omitted (principally peaks on crater walls), it contains on the whole more detail than even the *Mappa Selenographical* of Mädler, though it is of necessity less detailed than that of Schmidt. Neison's *Moon* is still indispensable to all lunar students.

The British Association for the Advancement of Science, in an endeavour to stimulate lunar research, formed a committee in 1874, under the direction of a zealous selenographer, W. R. Birt, with a view to the construction of a detailed map of 200 inches diameter. After slight progress, the death of Birt, who was Secretary of the then active Selenographical Society, and the retirement of the Editor, Neison, caused the scheme to lapse, and the Society itself ceased to function after 1882.

The next advance in selenography was conducted by the Liverpool Astronomical Society, under the directorship of an extremely able man, T. G. Elger (afterwards the first director of the Lunar Section of the British Astronomical Association, founded in 1890). Elger, who died in 1897, published a small volume on the Moon, with a map 18 inches in diameter. A new edition of this map was prepared by Wilkins in 1950 and published, like the previous work, by George Philip and Son, London. Many of Elger's realistic drawings, with appropriate descriptions, will be found in popular books of that period, such as those of Flammarion, and the three Memoirs of the British Astronomical Association Lunar Section issued by Elger; the six issued later by Goodacre and the two recently published by Wilkins are a mine of information essential to every student of the lunar surface.

Meanwhile continental observers were active and the names of Klein of Cologne, and Krieger of Trieste, one of the most accurate of draughtsmen, must receive special mention. Krieger's work, drawn upon enlarged photographs, appeared in two elaborate volumes. In some of these drawings Krieger greatly exceeds anything done previously, and they are most valuable contributions to lunar science.

The greatest of French selenographers was Gaudibert, who drew up a somewhat crowded map in conjunction with Flammarion. Using a moderate-sized reflector, he added numbers of clefts and made numerous detailed and fine drawings, remarkable for their accuracy. In the department devoted to accurate measurement of the positions of formations, much work was also done, by Saunder in England, and Franz and König in Germany. These measures remain the foundation of any map pretending to accuracy.

Based on Saunder, the map of Walter Goodacre (second Director of the British Astronomical Association Lunar Section), on a scale of 60 inches to the Moon's diameter and published in 1910, in twenty-five sections, was the first great modern map, and reached a high standard of excellence. The original map was 77 inches in diameter and was reproduced in his book, *The Moon*, 1931, and marked the beginning of a new epoch in selenographical research.

In 1924 two lunar maps appeared, a 60-inch map by Wilkins and the Pictorial Chart of Karel Andĕl of Prague, a beautiful work containing much fine detail. The aspect of hill and hollow was enhanced by delicate shading and the skilful introduction of shadow, making this map one of the most striking yet produced.

In 1932 Wilkins published his 200-inch map, in quadrants and also as a reduced reproduction on one sheet, 30 inches in diameter. Then, in 1946, appeared the 300-inch map, which was again revised, and half redrawn for the publication of the 3rd edition in 1951. This chart is reproduced, on a reduced scale, in the present work.

In the early years of the present century, continental work was represented by the researches of Fauth, a German observer. After some earlier charts and a book, *The Moon in Modern Astronomy*, 1906, he issued, just before the war, a book, *Unser Mond* ('Our Moon'), which contains a summary of existing knowledge up to that time. He mentions a large map, 11 feet in diameter, which was lost during the late war, 1939–45, but a few sectional and special parts of this map were published. Fauth's charts frequently differ from all other representations; his 'Darwin', for example, bears no resemblance to the delineations of British observers (such as Barker and C. F. O. Smith); also he was most egoistic, a sad failing. The late Dr. Karl Müller, of Vienna, a capable selenographer and a very delightful man, had a map under construction, based upon the accurate measures of König, but this chart was never completed, owing to his death in 1942.

Detailed study of selected regions has attracted many observers, chiefly amateurs, the only professional astronomer who has undertaken serious lunar work in recent years being the late Professor W. H. Pickering, the distinguished American observer. He observed at Mandeville, in Jamaica. As a result of critical study of minute features the existence of variability was established which the Professor attributed to the existence of hoar frost and some form of life, possibly of vegetal origin.

Among the zealous amateurs conducting lunar observations, mention must be made of E. F. Emley; R. Barker; L. F. Ball; C. F. O. Smith; B. Burrell; D. W. G. Arthur; K. Abineri in Britain, and Prof. W. H. Haas; Dr. S. R. B. Cooke; D. Barcroft; E. J. Reese; E. E. Hare and other observers in the U.S.A. Recently, and especially since the end of the war, observation has stridden forward with observations in many countries. Mention must also be made of the fine measures of the late Dr. S. M. Green, A. Neate, and the late Dr. Young of Birmingham, who made a catalogue of the diameters of lunar formations.

Professor W. H. Pickering also compiled a complete photographic atlas, the plates being taken at the focus of a 12-inch specially constructed objective. Each region was photographed under five different angles of illumination, but on too small a scale for the recording of minute features. They possess great value, notwithstanding, especially in the limb regions. Lunar photography, closely connected with maps and charts, may be

21

traced in successive stages, from the early attempts of Draper, Dancer and De La Rue, to the very successful negatives of Rutherfurd in New York. Many fine examples of negatives were obtained at the focus of the great Lick telescope, and still finer ones with the Yerkes refractor. The latter contain features so fine as to tax the powers of a 6-inch telescope.

The finest photographic atlas is the beautiful production of the Paris Observatory, made by Loewy and Puiseux. The large-scale positives in particular are most valuable, although often enlarged too much for clarity. Many details have been culled from these photographs by Goodacre and Wilkins. But the climax of celestial photography, as applied to the Moon, is the magnificent series obtained by the aid of the 60-inch and 100-inch reflectors at the Mt. Wilson Observatory. For special reasons, however, even these fine results have been surpassed by the wonderful photographs obtained at the Pic-du-Midi Observatory, in France, by B. Lyot and A. Dollfus. Dr. Lyot took an active interest in the study of planetary and lunar detail, and his knowledge of minute features was manifest when Wilkins visited the Meudon Observatory in 1951. Some of these choice photographs appear in these pages.

Large apertures are essential for fine and detailed negatives, but pleasing results can be obtained with smaller apertures, which, if reflectors, can be taken at the principal focus. Refracting telescopes require a correction for chromatic aberration, as the visual and photographic foci do not coincide as they do in reflectors. This is usually secured by the use of a colour screen. The late H. G. Tomkins secured several fine photographs with the aid of a 24-inch Cassegrain reflector, a form of instrument particularly adapted for such research. This has been confirmed by the recent work, chiefly on the limb regions, by E. A. Whitaker of Greenwich Observatory, using the 36-inch 'Yapp' reflector there.

The photographs obtained by the Mount Wilson and Pic-du-Midi observers are not only invaluable to lunar cartographers (the fine detail on the Mount Wilson photographs was found, by Goodacre, to tax the powers of his 10-inch refractor), but will prove of the greatest importance for the detection of physical changes, if compared with negatives of similar area taken in the future.

In the past every author of a lunar chart has added or omitted names or lettered the more minute features according to fancy and inclination. No rigid system had been followed, although the system introduced by Langrenus, of naming the ring-mountains after personalities has now become established. Lunar nomenclature was placed upon a definite classification by a committee appointed by the International Astronomical Union, in 1932. The decisions, up to that time, were incorporated in a catalogue of 672 named lunar formations, with numerous minor features, and by the publication of a corresponding map, in sections, the inner portions of which were drawn by the late Mr. W. H. Wesley, the remainder by Miss Mary Blagg and Dr. Karl Müller. It is to be hoped that future selenographers will adopt this list, new names being given only to objects not already recognized.

There is indeed a great need for standardization of lunar nomenclature. Recently, for instance, G. P. Kuiper, in his photographic atlas, has altered some of the long-accepted names and has even omitted some, such as the Palus Nebularum. Meanwhile, the new names given to objects on the far side of the Moon, given by Soviet astronomers following their successful photography with Lunik III, have been generally accepted—and rightly so.

THE LUNAR SURFACE DETAILS

The lunar surface is rough and rocky, the largest and most prominent features being the great dark plains, called 'seas' by the early selenographers. They are visible to the naked eye, and collectively form the dim outline of the face of 'The Man in the Moon'. A small telescope reveals the chief characteristics of our satellite, the ring-mountains, mountain ranges, bright-ray systems and the plains.

The lunar formations have been classified as follows:

The great and, by comparison, level surfaces called 'Seas' (*Maria*), the smaller but similar features known as 'Marshes' (*Paludes*), 'Bays' and 'Gulfs' (*Sinus*); the bright plains far less conspicuous and not especially named; the mountain ranges, isolated hills, uplands and peaks; the valleys, gorges and clefts; the systems of bright rays and bright areas, while the great mass of the ringed structures have been divided into walled-plains, mountain-rings, ringed-plains, crater-plains, craters, craterlets, cratercones, craterpits, obscure rings and depressions.

The great plains are level and undisturbed compared with the mountainous regions and, in small instruments, appear quite smooth. With the aid of powerful instruments these broad expanses are seen to be very uneven, abounding in gentle slopes and considerable landswells; in other parts, the entire surface is covered with minute asperities, visible under a low angle of illumination. The convexity of the lunar globe is prominently displayed when the terminator crosses the broad expanses of the larger *Maria*; frequently the terminator presents an uneven appearance lingering over the depressions and advancing on the elevated regions. Many of the plains exhibit signs of subsidence, especially around the margins where clefts and long ridges frequently form concentric arcs with the mountain border. Isolated hills, often of almost Alpine contour, rise abruptly here and there; craters and ringed-plains are scattered over the surface, while such ringed-plains as happen to be situated on the borders generally exhibit signs of erosion in the past. In many instances, partially overwhelmed by the once-fluid or plastic material of the 'sea', they show signs of the overwhelming of the portions of the walls which face the 'sea'.

While the majority of the *Maria* communicate with each other, such as the Maria Serenitatis and Tranquillitatis, some, like the Maria Crisium and Humboldtianum, are completely surrounded by a lofty mountain border, abounding in high peaks, the ranges in general presenting a precipitous face on the seaward side and a gentle slope on the other. The Mare Humorum and the Mare Nectaris are well, but not completely, bordered.

23

The feet of the massive cliffs afford numerous instances of vast landslips; the resulting débris occasionally extends for many miles, as may be well seen along the face of the Apennine Mountains. These mountains form the south-west margin of the Mare Imbrium.

Some selenographers have regarded the surfaces of the *Maria* as the original crust of the Moon, but against this hypothesis may be advanced the obvious fact that the present surface overlies a still earlier surface, its existence being revealed by the numerous 'ghost rings', occasionally mere outlines, but once as prominent as those now existing. Also, if the *Maria* represent the original plastic surface, we would expect them to form portions of the same sphere; this, however, is not the case, the Mare Crisium, for example, being slightly depressed, while the Maria Serenitatis and Tranquillitatis are separated by a broad slope, indicating a difference of level.

In general of a greyish tint, some of the plains exhibit distinct though faint varieties of colour, greenish hues appearing under high illumination. Mare Serenitatis and Mare Crisium are prominent examples, the latter frequently appearing of a light greenish tint on which is superimposed a network of delicate light streaks. Some are evidently the relics of ancient rings.

The plains vary in size, from the vast Oceanus Procellarum with ill-defined borders, and covering an area of two million square miles, to the Mare Humboldtianum and the still smaller Maria Veris and Parvum. These are little larger than the greater walled-plains. As we see them, the 'seas' collectively occupy about one-half of the disk, and predominate in the Northern Hemisphere. Practically the whole of the north-eastern portion, and a considerable part of the south-eastern portion, is occupied by Oceanus Procellarum. In the north-west are Maria Crisium, Serenitatis and Humboldtianum, and in the south-west Maria Fœcunditatis and Nectaris. On or close to the limb are the Maria Australe, Smythii, Humboldtianum, Marginis, Parvum, and, on the south-east, the Mare Orientalis.

The superficial character of the dark surface material forming the 'seas' is clearly marked, in certain regions, by the existence of large numbers of bright spots, evidently the higher portions of an extensive stratum overlaid by the darker matter. In some cases this may be meteoric dust, but more generally volcanic ash ejected from neighbouring ringed-plains. The region to the south-west of the great ring-plain Copernicus is of this character; other examples will be found near Aristarchus and on the central portion of Mare Humorum.

While most of the plains are level (neglecting the curvature of the globe and various surface irregularities), the Mare Nectaris, in the south-west quadrant, is evidently concave in section, the low central portion being surrounded by concentric circles of ridges, rising in altitude towards the margin. These successive arcs probably resulted from the erosive action of a sea of lava, the fluctuating levels being frozen surfaces of waves originating in the once-molten 'sea'.

In the past some authorities, among them the late R. A. Proctor, have regarded the lunar 'seas' as seas in reality, beds of long since dried-up oceans. This theory assumes the past existence of both atmosphere and water, now assumed to have either dissipated into space or absorbed into the interior of the globe. The great difficulty with regard to this theory arises from the present almost complete absence of appreciable atmosphere. The general consensus of opinion inclines towards the idea that the Moon never possessed an atmosphere of sufficient density to permit the existence of large sheets of water as would be required to form lunar seas.

With the *Maria* must be grouped the smaller dark areas called Lakes and Marshes. These are often mere extensions of the greater plains, or, as in the case of the Palus Putredinis and the Palus Nebularum, are portions of them, distinguished by a difference in tint and, to some extent, divided off by ridges and hillocks. The most remarkable of these smaller areas is probably Palus Somnii, which adjoins the Mare Crisium on the south-east and, by its golden-brown colour (variable according to R. Barker), marking its limits under all illuminations. Its surface is scarified by hillocks and small craters, while the brilliant crater-ring Proclus marks its north-west edge.

Around the margins of the *Maria* there exist well-marked bays, of which by far the finest example is the magnificent Sinus Iridum, forming a great bay on the north-east border of the Mare Imbrium. This grand object is practically a semicircle, bordered by lofty cliffs, a mountain range, and is considered by some observers as the relic of a once completely enclosed area. But while the ring-plains on the borders of the 'seas' commonly show the effects of erosive action, traces of the once prominent seaward wall can always be found, as in Fracastorius, Letronne, Doppelmayer and Posidonius. Sinus Iridum exhibits nothing of this sort, even when viewed under the most suitable conditions of illumination, and it is probable that it never was a complete ring.

Far less conspicuous than the dark plains are the bright ones, of which a good example extends westwards from Cleomedes. More elevated than the *Maria*, the bright areas form more or less level tablelands, on the surfaces of which stand isolated rings of considerable size, as well as mountains and ridges. Spurr terms the bright mountainous regions 'lunarite' and the mare material 'lunabase'.

The walled-plains comprise the largest of the peculiar features collectively termed the 'lunar craters'. In many respects they resemble the smaller *Maria* and it is frequently difficult to determine the line of demarcation. Mare Humboldtianum might well have been included among the walled-plains, while such walled-plains as Grimaldi and Bailly could have been included among the 'seas'.

In general, the walled-plains may be described as approximately circular areas, enclosed by massive mountain borders, rarely continuous but exhibiting gaps; traversed by valleys and disturbed by subsequent eruptions and landslips. Some of the walled-plains, such as Ptolemæus, have their interiors on the general level of the surrounding surface; others, like Clavius, have greatly depressed floors, and though the mountainous border rises above the interior to a considerable height, in some cases, it is not elevated above the outside level. In size they vary from 180 miles in diameter, in the case of *320 km* Bailly, to 60 miles in such formations as Pitatus and Plato. They are more numerous in the south-east and south-west quadrants, and frequently lie in meridional chains, as may be seen in the groups of Ptolemæus, Alphonsus and Arzachel, or Furnerius, Petavius, Vendelinus and Langrenus.

The inner slopes of the walled-plains are, generally, of moderate inclination, abounding in rocky masses and landslides, with little gulfs and bays separated by promontories or headlands. The floor is usually remarkably level, occasionally convex, and frequently exhibits signs of subsequent disturbance, in the form of craters, hills or even mountains and, as in the case of Posidonius, the remains of an inner ring concentric, or nearly so, with the rampart. Some, like Ptolemæus and Albategnius, contain a number of shallow, saucer-like depressions, visible only under a low angle of illumination, evidently the remains of ancient craters. There are also large numbers of craterlets, often in chains, which craterlets are scattered over the surface. Clefts, or cracks, frequently prolong these craterlet-chains, or may traverse the interiors, sometimes cutting through the rampart, as is well illustrated by the ringed-plain Gassendi on the northern shore of Mare Humorum.

In the case of the more undisturbed examples, such as Schickard, the floor exhibits strong differences in tint, the darker patches being often apparently variable in outline and intensity. These variations can be traced in Schickard, Grimaldi, Riccioli and Stöfler.

Ruined Rings

Deslandres.

Closely allied to the true walled-plains are certain well-marked circular areas with low boundaries, but in dimensions often exceeding all but the largest walled-plains. One example, known as Hörbiger, will be found east of Walter, forming an almost circular area slightly depressed below the level of the adjoining Mare Nubium. On its southern border is the partially destroyed ring of Lexell; near its eastern edge is the crater called Hell; while the whole surface is pitted with innumerable craterlets and craterpits. Another of these areas will be found to the north of the above and is partially traversed, from north to south, by a remarkable fault in the surface, known as the 'Straight Wall'. This is about 800 feet in height above the surface on the east, but level, or almost so, with that on the west.

Ghost Rings

Smaller than the above, but as closely allied to the walled-plains, are the mountain-rings, encircled by low walls, rarely exceeding a couple of hundred feet in height. The great ring to the north of Flamsteed is a well-known example; another adjoins Plato on the south and was called 'Newton' by Schröter. South of Encke is a larger mountain-ring, some sections of the wall attaining a very considerable altitude. Oceanus Procellarum and Mare Imbrium abound in objects of this type, but they will also be found in the interiors of some of the walled-plains. A well-marked ring of this nature occupies the greater portion of the northern portion of Catharina.

Smaller and more numerous than the walled-plains are the ring-plains, with circular continuous walls, crowned at intervals by peaks and with steeper slopes; the interior walls often divided by terraces, the exterior broad and rugged, and the whole generally surrounded by a mass of partly concentric and partly radial ridges. A mountain group often occupies the centre of the floor, as in the cases of Bullialdus, Copernicus and Aristillus; occasionally this is replaced by a crater. An example of this is the ringed-plain Hesiodus, to which we may add Posidonius and Furnerius. This central mountain sometimes consists of a single conical peak, more often it is divided into several distinct masses; Copernicus, Gassendi, Theophilus, Petavius and Tycho are examples of rings containing multiple central peaks. The latter displays two distinct masses, the western being the inferior. On its summit is a small craterlet. Further examples of a crater on the summit of a central mountain are found in Alphonsus, Regiomontanus and Neper. Some central mountains are insignificant in comparison with the vast area of the crater; in others, a huge central mountain occupies the greater part of the floor. This is best illustrated by the ring-plain Alpetragius, which contains an enormous central mountain occupying most of the floor. On its summit Wilkins, with the great 33-inch Meudon refractor, discovered a minute pit.

While some central mountains stand high above the floor, others are lower; some show but traces of the peaks, while in several no traces remain, the floor being smooth. There can be little doubt that in cases where traces only of a central mountain remain, the mountain mass has either been melted down by erosive forces or partly concealed by the rising of liquid lava in the interior.

cf. Archimedes?

The most perfect of all lunar ringed-plains is doubtless the magnificent isolated ring of Copernicus, situated on a raised portion of the crust between the Mare Imbrium and Mare Nubium. The floor, 40 miles in diameter, contains a central mountain group split into seven peaks and surrounded by a continuous wall with an average height of 12,000 feet, surmounted by at least fifty peaks. The outer walls are of remarkable complexity; gigantic masses have slid down in vast landslips, and a mass of ridges partly concentric, partly radial, surrounds the great formation. As the surrounding ridges fine off to invisibility, rows of hillocks and vast numbers of minute craterlets and craterpits appear, while under a high angle of illumination, a system of bright rays appears. Vast numbers of craterlets can also be found around many other craters, including Theophilus, Aristoteles and Tycho.

The ringed-plains are generally considered as exhibiting clear evidence of volcanic origin in the central peak, and considered by Nasmyth as the actual vent over the original focus of eruption from which the first violent ejection of scoriæ forming the rampart took place. With declining activity, the volcanic forces caused the piling up of ejected matter immediately around the vent, thus forming the central peak. These peaks, however, are not always central; occasionally they are eccentric with the rampart, and this is difficult to reconcile with Nasmyth's volcanic theory. Another difficulty is introduced by the surrounding rampart often exhibiting an angular aspect by the walls standing at various angles to each other. Theophilus is a prominent example.

— no longer true

The crater-plains resemble the ringed-plains, but present clearer indications of their volcanic origin; the walls are lower, and the general aspect closely resembles the vast crater-plains still existing on the Earth.

Far more numerous than the foregoing are the craters, properly so-called. Ranging in diameter from 30 miles to less than 5, the craters have comparatively narrow walls, rising steeply from the surrounding country and falling as abruptly to the floor, the level of which is often much depressed. A small central peak can often be detected, though in the smaller specimens the minuteness of the central peaks makes them difficult to detect. Many of the craters have a newer aspect than their surroundings, and this is frequently enhanced by their brightness. Some of the craters stand on bright areas, possibly caused by material ejected from the crater. The craters are found on all parts of the lunar surface, on the plains, among the mountains, and even on the walls as well as the interiors of walled-plains and other ringed structures.

Craterlets are really small craters, and have no central peaks that can be detected. They appear in countless thousands. Some of the smaller examples will be found on the floors of such formations as Plato, Goldschmidt and Archimedes, and form excellent telescopic tests.

Cratercones are quite distinct from the preceding cavities, as they consist of steep conical hills with minute central orifices, and strongly resemble terrestrial volcanoes. Although Fauth denied the very existence of these features, they have been too well established for controversy; they abound in the neighbourhood of Stadius, between Eratosthenes and Copernicus, and there are two well-known specimens near Bailly. In the majority of cases the central orifices are so small that they are difficult to detect except in a giant telescope; those that can be seen appear to be of inverted conical or cup shape. In all cases, the floors of these objects stand high above the surrounding country, and whether central peaks exist it is quite impossible to determine.

Different from all classes are the craterpits, having no true walls, and very shallow. They exist in enormous numbers, and are visible only for a short time near sunrise or sunset. The south-west quadrant in particular swarms with these minute pits, the majority of which require considerable telescopic power for their detection. They are often of very irregular shape.

The obscure rings have already been mentioned in connection with the *Maria*. While the majority appear to be the remains of once-prominent craters, now worn down by erosion or covered by the once-liquid 'seas', it is not certain that all have resulted from these causes. It is possible that some at least are, so to speak, craters which never reached completion, as though the forces were spent before a well-marked cavity could be formed.

The depressions comprise a vast number of cavities, presenting the appearance of mere holes, often of very irregular shape, sometimes of considerable depth, but more often very shallow. The outer flanks of some of the larger ringed-plains are plastered with these 'blow-holes', a fine example being the outer glacis of the ring formerly known as Vendelinus C, but now called after C. F. O. Smith. The holes on this slope were noted by Elger and by Maw. Some of these slighter depressions are merely the space between adjacent ridges, but the true depressions probably represent either true blow-holes or the cavities formed by bodies striking the surface such as large masses ejected from neighbouring active vents or by meteorites.

The earnest student cannot but be struck by the remarkable tendency to circularity on the lunar surface. The *Maria* repeat the form of the craters, but although the ring-plains may have been formed by eruptive action, this will not explain the origin of such vast, yet approximately circular features as Maria Crisium or Serenitatis. Various theories advanced to account for the *Maria* and walled-plains will be elaborated further on.

Mountain ranges, so typical of the Earth, have their counterpart in the Moon, but to a secondary extent. On the Moon the craters are the predominating features, whereas on our own planet mountain ranges are the chief characteristic. Nevertheless, ranges exist, especially in the Moon's Northern Hemisphere, where they form the boundaries of the grey plains. Such are the Apennines, Caucasus and the Alps, bordering the Mare Imbrium, and the Hæmus Mountains forming the southern rampart of Mare Serenitatis.

The lunar Apennines are by far the most important range on the lunar surface, although higher peaks exist in the great Leibnitz Mountains, on the southern limb. The Apennines abound in high peaks and culminate in mighty cliffs rising abruptly from the dark Mare Imbrium. From this curved array of peaks the average altitude gradually falls in a gentle curve westwards to Mare Vaporum. The greatest extension of this hinterland is on the west where it joins the Hæmus range; on the south a broad band of hilly country joins the range to the mountainous region around Pallas and Bode. The highest peak of the Apennines is Huygens, which attains an altitude of over 18,000 feet above the plain. Just below its summit is a craterlet.

The lunar Caucasus and Alps, while of lesser extent, attain considerable altitudes; the highest peak of the former range reaches 19,000 feet. Mt. Blanc, in the Alps, rises, according to the best measures, 12,000 feet above the plain at its base.

The Hercynian Mountains, on the north-east near Otto Struve, also attain a similar or slightly greater altitude.

The Taurus Mountains, to the west of Mare Serenitatis, form a wild mountainous region rather than a true range; and although difficult of measurement, contain many lofty peaks, some rising at least 10,000 feet.

Other minor ranges exist in this hemisphere, including some unnamed on the limb itself, as well as isolated mountains, of which Pico, on the open plain to the south of Plato, is a well-known example. This bright mountain mass exhibits three peaks, the highest attaining 8,000 feet; at its base are some minute craterpits. There are several other peaks in the immediate neighbourhood but of lesser altitude. Of these, Piton, isolated on the plain south of the Alps, is remarkable for its brilliancy under certain conditions of illumination, Piton is really composed of two mountains close together; on the summit of one of them is a craterlet.

The general line of these isolated peaks is continued eastwards by the bright range of the Teneriffe Mountains and the Straight Range. Near the western headland of Sinus Iridum, Laplace, are peaks in the Jura Mountains, which equal, and possibly surpass, the loftiest heights of the Apennines, but it is very difficult to measure their altitudes accurately.

The mountain ranges of the Southern Hemisphere are less numerous than the Northern, the most important being the great range of the Leibnitz Mountains, often presented in profile on the limb. Stretching in a mighty arc from a point considerably to the west of the Pole, thence to the equatorial region on the east, are the gigantic ranges of the Leibnitz, Dörfel, Rook, D'Alembert and the Cordillera mountains; the first two ranges contain many peaks approaching 20,000 feet in altitude and, in one or two instances, 30,000 feet, according to Neison. It is probable that these ranges consist, in part, of great rings seen in profile, and the general direction is continued further to the north by isolated mountains, the most striking of which is a bright table-like elevation on the limb to the east of Riccioli.

With the exception of the mountain ranges on the limb, the Southern Hemisphere presents few prominent examples. The principal range is the Altai Mountains, which form a bright line of cliffs tending north-east from the ringed-plain Piccolomini, and thus defining an arc concentric with the margin of Mare Nectaris. The steep face of the Altai range faces westward and causes this range to cast little shadow at sunrise, the whole forming a bright line shortly before Full. Under evening illumination, when the direction of illumination is reversed, the general contour and the crowning peaks are revealed by their shadows prominently cast on the smooth plain below. The range attains considerable height immediately after leaving Piccolomini, but the loftiest peak, which rises over 13,000 feet, will be found towards the centre of the range, the total length of which is nearly 250 miles.

The Altai range terminates on the north, and to the east of Catharina, in what appear to be two ring-plains, the interiors of which have been nearly filled up with lava.

The Pyrenees form a mountainous region defining the western border of Mare Nectaris, and present many points of similarity to the Taurus mountains in the Northern Hemisphere. Except for the Riphæns in the Mare Nubium, a small scattered group of slight elevation, the highest only rising 3,000 feet, and the Percy Mountains containing a bright mountain arm extending from the east wall of the beautiful ringed-plain Gassendi, there are few other ranges of importance in the Southern Hemisphere.

Many portions of the lunar surface may be described as uplands, elevated regions containing numerous little peaks arranged without any approach to uniformity. Of such nature are the western border of Mare Humorum, the southern highlands of Mare Crisium and the borders of Mare Tranquillitatis.

With the mountainous regions must be mentioned the mountain ridges, common on the great plains, and also on the brighter portions, where they may be found connecting one formation with another or running down the centres of the larger rings, such as Bouvard and Riccioli. This is a common feature of the large rings near the limb. On the great plains they frequently run for great distances, connecting distant craters or hillocks and throwing out branches, and occasionally intrude within the ring of a crater formation, as in Arago and Mädler. These narrow rocky banks seldom exceed a couple of hundred feet in height, and are crowned here and there by isolated hills. Occasionally they form arcs of circles, doubtless indicative of buried rings.

The best known and most prominent of these mountain ridges is the great serpentine ridge extending along the western part of Mare Serenitatis, from a point to the north of Plinius to the east of Posidonius. This immense ridge consists of detached ridges of considerable height, united by shorter and much lower branches. East of Posidonius, the high ridge divides into two lower ridges, roughly at right angles with each other, which, with lower ridges to the north, enclose a square area some 50 miles across. Another prominent ridge runs southwards from the wall of Theophilus.

Mare Nubium and Mare Tranquillitatis also furnish numerous examples of contorted ridges, some approaching the altitude of the serpentine ridge in Mare Serenitatis. All the plains show ridges. The most prominent ridge in Mare Crisium is concentric with the eastern border. Again in Maria Nubium and Nectaris there are veritable networks of ridges, while some of the longest and narrowest streak across Oceanus Procellarum.

The lunar surface furnishes many instances of valleys, ranging from such vast trough-like objects as the Alpine valley and the even greater valley south west of Rheita, to the numerous and comparatively shallow winding dales to be found to the rear of the great mountain ranges. Concentric with the western shore of Mare Humorum are three prominent ridges, also three valleys, which, from their length and somewhat narrow nature, resemble gigantic clefts.

Of the true valleys, the three most prominent examples are the great gorge cutting through the massive Alpine range, the gorge west of Herschel, and the valley near Rheita. The Alpine valley presents, in small telescopes, the appearance of an elongated V-shaped trough, filled with black shadow for some time after sunrise or before sunset. The bottom is remarkably flat, and is traversed by a delicate cleft; on either side, the bordering mountains rise steeply. The gorge west of Herschel is of somewhat similar nature, with precipitous sides, but the Rheita valley has gently sloping banks and is, in part, formed of the remains of ancient rings. Another wide and shallow valley in the same region is that of Reichenbach; while among numerous other examples, those winding through the lofty mountains forming the southern coast-line of Mare Crisium deserve special mention, as also does the great valley-cleft near Herodotus. There is also a remarkable valley to the south-west of the ring of Vitruvius, which resembles a bowl at sunset.

As already stated, valleys range from those easily seen, through intermediate grades, to delicate winding gorges some of which might have been included among the lunar clefts.

The true clefts, once termed 'rills', of which nearly two thousand are now known, great numbers having been discovered in the past ten years, are of the nature of chasms or cracks in the surface, rarely exceeding a mile in width but frequently extending for scores or even hundreds of miles. Sometimes straight, but more often winding and twisting, they intersect each other and occasionally cut through hills or crater walls. They may begin and terminate on the open plain and often exhibit interruptions, with occasional enlargements or duplicity. A hill or mountain sometimes apparently causes a break, but the cleft frequently reappears beyond, as Webb remarks, 'as though carried through by a tunnel'. A common situation is the margin of one of the great plains, close to the surrounding mountain range. The interiors of the ring-plains often contain systems of clefts, as in the case of Gassendi, where over forty have been detected; or, as in the case of Petavius, a wide and deep cleft may run from the central mountains over the floor and cut through the surrounding walls.

The region to the north-west of Sinus Medii is traversed by a network of clefts, many originating at a point to the west of the small crater Triesnecker and connecting with a great cleft that passes through the smaller crater Hyginus. Fine clefts also connect the Hyginus cleft with the longer and deeper specimen associated with Aria-dæus on the west; this triple system of clefts forms the most complicated cleft system on the Moon.

Many clefts begin as exceedingly delicate cracks, gradually becoming wider and deeper, until they either join the parent cleft or themselves become the principal and only chasm. Some are narrow and deep, commonly appearing as fine lines of black shadow; others are wider and evidently shallow, since the bright line of the bottom can frequently be seen. Here and there masses have become detached from the sides and, falling inwards, have partially filled up the opening; in other situations they are seen to consist of rows of minute craterlets or pits which, after continuing as such for many miles, open out into the usual cleft form. A well-known example is the long crater-cleft to the north-west of Copernicus.

The earlier observers discovered but few of these interesting features, the first being the well-known and prominent example near Herodotus which was discovered by Schröter. Lohrmann, Mädler and Schmidt added to their number, while later Brenner, Elger and Goodacre found still more. The advantages of a large aperture for the detection of hitherto unknown clefts and other delicate lunar detail will be evident from the experience of the Authors. Although Wilkins has found 'new' clefts with his 15¼-inch reflecting telescope, such occasions are rare; but every time a giant telescope has been employed (the Meudon 33-inch refractor, the Cambridge 25-inch refractor or Dr. Steavenson's 30-inch reflector), 'new' clefts have invariably been found, even in regions which were supposed to have been thoroughly explored by other observers and with instruments of moderate aperture but of high optical quality.

A good instrument and a clear atmosphere are required to observe successfully such clefts as have already been charted. Great instruments are necessary for the finest specimens, as is evident from our remarks above.

Many clefts become deeper as they narrow towards their ends; the widest portion is not always the deepest but more often than not the more shallow. While the majority are invisible when far from the terminator some, including the Hyginus cleft, are visible under high illumination, appearing then as bright lines. The general direction of a cleft is frequently prolonged by rows of hillocks or craterlet-chains, and some have been seen prolonged over the terminator, probably due to the partial illumination of the surface there.

Many clefts appear to be chasms with sharp edges; others are bordered by raised banks. The latter is well illustrated by the crater-ring Petavius, where the great cleft traversing the floor has raised banks of such a prominent character as to be clearly seen in a 2-inch refractor. Other and far more delicate clefts exist within Petavius, which present sharp edges without any surface disturbance.

The actual depth of clefts is in general unknown, and estimates range from 10 miles, proposed by Nasmyth, to 200 yards, considered as near the truth by Elger and Neison. The first is obviously a gross over-estimate, and in all probability the depth of the great majority of clefts rarely exceeds half a mile, and in many instances is not more than 100 yards. Even if the clefts originally did attain a great depth, it would exceed probability for the chasm to remain open save to a moderate depth below the surface.

The most remarkable and mysterious of all lunar features are the systems of bright rays, radiating from certain crater-rings as centres, and stretching for long distances across the disk. Their bright-line appearance is best seen under high illumination. Although some of the rays can be traced when near the terminator, and have then sometimes been seen as dark bands by Thornton, they are only to be seen in their greatest perfection at Full Moon; that is, when the solar light falls directly upon the lunar disk as seen from the Earth. Under these conditions no shadows are visible, save close to one or other of the poles, as they are concealed by the heights which cast them. Although no shadows are visible at Full Moon, with the above exception, they nevertheless exist, for the actual angle of illumination varies greatly. At the central regions the sun appears high in the lunar sky; near the limb, on the other hand, the sun would appear close to the horizon to anyone situated there. Hence shadows would be seen by a lunar inhabitant of these regions, even although at the same time none are visible from the Earth. Some of the longest rays extend for such vast distances that their actual illumination varies greatly, yet presenting their most perfect aspect when no shadows appear. The actual bodies, whatever their nature, which collectively form the rays, must therefore be of such a shape as always to appear symmetrical to the observer, and this condition is fulfilled only by one regular solid—the sphere. It thus appears that whatever their origin or constituent material, whether the particles be inches or yards in diameter, their form must be spherical.

The most extensive and conspicuous of all the ray-systems is that grouped around Tycho as a centre. Hundreds of rays radiate from this ring-plain, stretching for great distances, one apparently crossing Mare Serenitatis on the dark background of which it is very conspicuous. Two other prominent rays from Tycho, one extending to Fracastorius and the other near to Bullialdus, attract the attention of the most casual observer. Under the best conditions, and under any illumination, they cast no shadows, thus clearly revealing that the rays are mere surface markings, of no appreciable height, and possessing remarkable reflective ability. The rays of Tycho do not reach the rampart of the crater, but are separated from it by a dark zone, which surrounds the ring-plain. Neither do the rays radiate from the geometrical centre, but from several foci, one to the west of the central mountains, another near the south-east wall; while several rays start at a tangent to the walls.

Under good conditions the rays are seen to consist of a series of dots and dashes, so arranged that as one begins to fade out another commences, and so the sequence is preserved. They are not continuous bands as far as brilliancy is concerned, but no real break occurs, as the continuity can be traced, if faintly, throughout their length. Whether the rays cross mountains, craters or the plains, they still preserve their individuality, so that the material of which they are composed appears to have been deposited on mountains and depressions alike. It is, however, possible that the ray material is not a mere surface deposit, but incorporated in the crust itself. In support of this it may be mentioned that the rays can be traced rising up the sides of some walled-plains which happen to lie in their paths. On this hypothesis they would appear to be of the nature of trap dykes.

One of the greatest difficulties regarding the rays is their enormous length. It is doubtless true, as Pickering remarks, that the individual rays are short, the entire structure being made up of a series of these, but this does not remove the difficulty attending the length of the combination of the streaks.

The Tycho rays are evidently related, not to Tycho itself, but to the region of which the crater is nearly the centre. Many writers have considered Tycho as the centre or even the source of the ray system, but it appears more probable that the rays originated before Tycho was formed. In that region, sudden and intense activity occurred, resulting in the formation of the rays, and also flooding the immediate surroundings; after which the ring-plain was built up, its somewhat eccentric position probably being due to a shifting of the focus of eruption.

Nasmyth considered the rays to be the result of cracking of the crust, the star form being due to the concentrated internal pressure and illustrated this idea by the similar cracking of a glass globe, the hollow interior being filled with water to which heat was applied; just, as on his hypothesis, the Moon then consisted of a thin shell, enclosing a molten interior. Immediately these cracks were formed, Nasmyth supposed they were filled with very fluid lava which, even if it overflowed, would settle at such a gentle angle as to render shadows imperceptible. Proctor inclined to this theory, while Pickering and Fauth favoured the idea of some powder, considered by Pickering as pumice, and by Fauth (following his fantastic glacial theory) as neve or ice particles; in either case rapidly conveyed and spread all around by currents in a once-existing lunar atmosphere.

The late H. G. Tomkins advanced the theory that the rays might be caused by saline deposits, and pointed to the existence of long lines of such deposits in India which, invisible at sunrise, rapidly dry in the solar heat, when they become brilliantly white. Mr. Tomkins said: 'It seems to ooze from any damp place in the regions where it is found, and dries in the sun bright white. It passes over elevations and depressions, like the rays in the Moon without any upset in formation, and often takes peculiar forms.' (Sixth Report of the B.A.A. Lunar Section.)

This very ingenious theory by an able and earnest student of the Moon is open to twin objections: the enormous length of the rays, and the assumed existence of both water and atmosphere in the past, while the conformation of the Tycho rays does not fit in well with the saline idea, although the Copernican ray system seems better suited.

Whatever the nature of the Tycho rays, whether they are surface deposits or penetrate the crust, they do not obliterate anything and they appear to be, if not transparent, at least translucent. Both the ice theory of Fauth and the saline hypothesis of Tomkins fulfil this requirement, but both assume the existence of water on the Moon at the present time; this, according to the Kinetic Theory, we have no right to assume.

It appears to us that a volcanic origin is more probable, and that the material of which the rays are composed is of a volcanic nature; in all probability a volcanic glass, of similar nature to the Pele's Hair so abundantly produced by the volcanoes of the Hawaiian Islands where the lavas are very fluid. This 'hair' is very light, and commonly appears as long strands, easily transported by slight air currents to great distances around the great pit from the lava of which it is formed. Not only do the Hawaiian volcanoes present strong resemblances to some of the lunar ringed-plains, but there are many indications that the lunar rays were of a very fluid nature.

While the Tycho rays are the most conspicuous and extensive, many other systems exist, of which those related to Copernicus and Kepler are the most important. The Copernican rays differ from those of Tycho; they originate from the ring itself and are neither as long nor as straight as those of the greater system, and they are not as centrally arranged. They are also far more numerous in the vicinity of the ringed-plain, which shines as a white patch under high illumination, in strong distinction to the dusky zone surrounding Tycho. The rims of Copernicus, Kepler and Aristarchus appear, at Full, brighter than the rays themselves. The rays from these formations cross the plains, while those associated with Tycho have a considerable extent of mountainous surface to traverse before reaching the plains, and, as Goodacre remarks, the rays are always fainter when crossing the plains than when projected on the mountains.

The Copernican, Keplerian and Aristarchan rays mingle and cross each other, forming a confused pattern impossible to draw and only correctly represented by photographs. They also appear to vary their positions and width as the angle of illumination varies.

Many minor ray systems also exist, some of limited extent, as well as isolated 'splashes' and white spots of similar nature, often the sites of minute craters. Of these minor systems that of Proclus is perhaps the most remarkable; the fan-shaped rays emanating from this crater-ring cross the dark surface of Mare Crisium and appear lighter in texture than any of the more extensive systems, while Proclus itself is one of the most brilliant regions on the Moon. It should also be noted that rays can be seen coming over the limb and evidently diverging from foci (craters?) on the further hemisphere. (See the special chart.)

From a consideration of all facts pertaining to the rays, we incline to the theory that the rays are of volcanic origin, the product of activity at certain definite foci, and that the material of which they are composed was ejected from the foci and from cracks in the crust formed by the eruption; that they are composed of volcanic glass of a similar nature to that so abundantly produced at the fused lava-pit of Kilauea in Hawaii; that the actual particles are of spherical shape, either hollow or solid and that they were deposited around the vent by the spreading of gases rushing from the focus without the necessity of a lunar atmosphere. At the same time we do not regard the true Tycho rays as being indicated by the apparent length as shown on photographs. The very long rays are due to comparatively short radiations from Tycho, and later reinforced by eruptions from smaller craters, or even pits, which were formed on a common line of weakness.

CHANGES ON THE MOON

One of the principal charms of scientific research is the detection and study of variations and changes; this is especially the case when dealing with celestial bodies. From its proximity to the Earth the Moon is the only such body on which actual details of variations with respect to small objects can be observed. Even with the best telescopes, changes can only be suspected; for proof, reference has to be made to drawings, charts or sketches of reasonable accuracy, or to the numerous lunar photographs. In this light we must consider the probability, or at least the possibility, of changes on the Moon.

The early maps must be discarded, as all they affirm is the certainty that the broad, coarse features have not altered from the days when men first observed the Moon with telescopic aid. There have been no grand convulsions since the first lunar maps. Passing from the broad to the more minute details, we find ourselves at a loss for materials upon which to base our decisions. Even the map of Schmidt cannot safely be relied upon as regards the more minute features among which changes might reasonably be expected; all lunar maps have errors of commission and omission, while even photographs only represent objects under a particular angle of illumination, and the appearance of lunar detail changes greatly during the course of the lunar day.

With the exception of Nasmyth, who contended that the Moon arrived at its terminal condition ages, if not millions of years ago, and Fauth (who, however, admitted variations), all selenographers have recorded certain appearances which they have considered to be indicative of change. Schröter was one of the first to record changes, which he ascribed to the effects of a lunar atmosphere. The most important of Schröter's designs considered as an authority for settling a disputed question relating to alleged changes, is his only drawing of that portion of Mare Serenitatis on which the crater Linné stands.

Beer and Mädler, and also Lohrmann, described and drew Linné in the form of a deep, distinct crater. In 1866, Schmidt announced that this description no longer applied, and that instead of a crater all that could be seen was a whitish patch. At the present time, Linné consists of a low dome in a white nimbus, and surmounted by a deep, minute pit; this was the appearance as described by F. H. Thornton in 1951, with his 18-inch reflector, and fully confirmed by the Authors in 1952 and 1953 with the Meudon 33-inch. There seems no doubt that there was a radical alteration some time between 1842 and 1866, but it is also possible that changes have continued since then, since up to the time of Thornton's announcement in 1951 it was generally believed that the modern Linné consisted of a depression, not a dome at all. Unfortunately Schröter's early drawing was made merely to show the bright streaks crossing the Mare Serenitatis, and other details are merely roughed in, so that there are two objects shown either of which might be Linné—and Bessel itself, which has never been suspected of change, is similarly shown. The white area round Linné exhibits variations in size during a lunation, and also during lunar eclipses. These variations were investigated by Professor E. E. Barnard with the superb refractors of the Lick and Yerkes Observatories; and in a letter to Wilkins shortly before his lamented death, Barnard gave it as his opinion that the changes were real and undoubted. Professor Pickering came independently to a similar conclusion.

Whatever may be said with regard to the alleged change respecting the depression Hyginus N (N stands for Nova), advanced by Klein and mentioned in the text, there can be no doubt that variations are exhibited by several formations including Plato, Grimaldi, Schickard, Eratosthenes, Messier, Aristarchus and other objects.

The late Professor W. H. Pickering, observing in the tropical skies of Jamaica, recorded variations in all the above-mentioned objects, attributing the variations on the floor of Plato to volcanic action. He described the floor of Plato as one of the most continuously active volcanic regions on the Moon. In Grimaldi he detected a greenish hue; the variations in Messier and its companion, named after him—Pickering—to hoar frost, while in Eratosthenes, certain moving spots and streaks or a dark tint, he attributed to some form of plant life. Whether we admit his explanation or prefer another, the fact of apparent variations has been definitely established. Prof. Pickering also observed cloud-like features along the face of the Apennine mountains, and within Conon, together with what looked like vapour from craterlets near Herodotus.

We have ourselves observed apparent changes in many objects. Within Plato we failed to detect a craterlet shown by such a prominent observer as Dr. W. H. Steavenson, with the 28-inch refractor of Greenwich Observatory, when we observed the floor with the still greater refractor of the Meudon Observatory. A few hours later an American observer, Mr. T. A. Cragg, failed to see any detail whatever on the floor with a 12-inch telescope. This looks very much like some obscuring matter slowly covering the floor from the east, and already obscuring the extreme eastern part when we observed at Meudon.

The most recent case of reported change concerns the crater Alphonsus, where activity was recorded on 3rd November 1958 by N. A. Kozyrev. There can be no doubt that a disturbance of some sort did take place at that time, which proves that the Moon is not so inert as many astronomers had previously believed.

Changes of various descriptions are evidently in progress on the Moon, whether due to great alternations in the temperature between the lunar day and night, to volcanic action, the formation and subsequent melting of hoar frost (as supposed by Prof. Pickering), or to the existence of some lowly form of vegetal life peculiar to the Moon.

The lunar surface is open to the Sun's rays for a period equal to fourteen of our days, and then is exposed to the cold of space for an equal period. During the long day the rocky surface probably becomes exceedingly hot, especially in the equatorial regions. During the night, heat would rapidly radiate into space, the absence of appreciable atmosphere greatly accentuating this rapid drop in temperature.

Following several attempts to measure the amount of heat received from the Moon, Lord Rosse, using his smaller 3-foot reflector, determined the degree of heat and cold to which the lunar surface is exposed. The maximum equatorial temperature was estimated at 200° C., and the minimum night temperature at minus 75°C. With more sensitive apparatus the late Professor Langley conducted experiments from which he inferred that even at the middle of the long lunar day the temperature does not rise above the freezing point, while during the night it falls below minus 200° C. Prof. Very, of Allegheny, modified this by the conclusion that at sunrise the temperature is below freezing point and does not rise above it until the Sun has risen to an altitude of 15 degrees in the lunar sky. As the solar altitude increases, so does the temperature; and when the Sun is overhead, the rocky surface is as hot as boiling water, and continues to rise until the middle of the lunar afternoon, when the temperature reaches 350° F. Then follows a very rapid fall; the freezing point is again passed, and the temperature towards the end of the long lunar night approaches that of interstellar space, which is considered to approach minus 243° C.   *273°C. ?*

Lord Rosse used a thermopile and a delicate galvanometer. Recently, a thermocouple at the focus of the 100-inch Hooker reflector, at Mt. Wilson, has been employed in the investigation of this matter by Pettit and Nicholson. They found that the spot which has the Sun in its zenith is heated to 134° C. Their measures were for such a spot near the centre of the disk at Full. The temperature of the night surface was found to be minus 153° C. Wilkins conducted some experiments in 1942, using a thermocouple at the focus of a 6-inch reflector. During the progress of the total lunar eclipse on August 26th, in that year, he found a rapid fall in temperature when only the penumbra was on the disk; the advent of the true shadow caused the reflected heat to drop so sharply as to become inappreciable with the imperfect apparatus employed. A great fall in temperature accompanies the penumbral phase, and in all probability the temperature drops fully 50 per cent when half-immersed and fully 80 per cent when the edge of the umbra reaches a lunar formation.

In 1949 Piddington and Minnett, using a 4-foot diameter metal-mirror reflector, focused radio waves reflected from the Moon into a sensitive receiver, and deduced temperature values based on the observed intensities. Their results appear to indicate that the maximum temperature is reached three days after Full, the total heat received from the Moon being considered. This result shows clearly that the radio waves penetrate slightly below the lunar surface so that the measured temperature is really that of a layer a centimetre or so below the actual surface.

In view of the conflicting results obtained by eminent observers, a word must be said of the Glacial Theory, first advanced by a Norwegian, Ericson, in 1885, and subsequently advocated by others, especially the late S. E. Peal, a tea-planter in Ceylon and an amateur astronomer. This theory assumes that the surface of the Moon resembles, only in a more marked degree, that of the summits of our highest mountains and is covered with a thick layer of ice. The surface of this icy mantle is exposed to the intense cold of space.

This theory is based on the non-existence of any appreciable atmosphere, but does not explain how such a mass of water could be formed or retained by the Moon. The telescopic appearance of the lunar surface is very different from that of an icy mantle. Moreover, it is incorrect to speak of the 'intense cold of space'; space is vacuum, and can thus have no temperature at all. It is therefore generally considered that there is no foundation to support this idea, and it is rejected by astronomers and also seleno-graphers, excepting Fauth, its chief exponent. (*Unser Mond*, 1936.)

Further, the surface features, if composed of ice, would eventually flatten out until all irregularities had disappeared, owing to the slow flowing of ice, which acts as a plastic.

The Moon is, in the words of Beer and Mädler, 'no copy of the Earth'; it is, in fact, totally different in surface features, temperature, surface gravity and length of day. The lunar geology has generally been ascribed to volcanic action, analogous to, but more intense than, that of the Earth. The low surface gravity, only one-sixth of that prevailing on our planet, has been considered an important factor in the formation of the vast crater-rings, since this in conjunction with the absence of aerial friction would enable scoriæ and other volcanic products to be projected to much greater distances than on the Earth. In 1910 the American, Professor Wood of New York, found what he re-garded as evidence of sulphur deposits near Aristarchus from an examination of photo-graphs taken with ultra-violet light, and sulphur is a well-known volcanic product.

The typical lunar 'crater' is a fundamentally different structure to the terrestrial type, since the majority of terrestrial volcanoes are of conical shape with comparatively small craters on their summits or flanks. The lunar craters are vast and very shallow depres-sions, the surrounding walls often being mere rings in comparison with the enclosed cavity. There are, however, certain terrestrial districts strongly resembling the lunar formations, such as the Solfatara and other semi-active volcanoes near Naples, the Hawaiian craters, a crater-ring in Mauritius, another in Africa, and the rings within which stand some of our finest volcanic mountains, such as Teneriffe. The arrangement of the lunar craters in pairs, the manner in which one intrudes upon another, the chains of walled-plains, often of diminishing size in a regular sequence, the craterlet-rows which radiate from rings, such as Tycho and Theophilus, the cratercones and the numerous small, bright craters situated at the centre of a bright area, are all explainable on a volcanic basis, and this theory applies more readily than any other hypothesis.

There are other theories as to the origin of the lunar features. Of these the impact theory has the greatest number of advocates. This theory considers the various features as due to meteors striking the surface and producing craters similar to some on ou globe. The largest crater on the Earth which was undoubtedly caused by meteoric im pact, so far as is known, is the Chubb crater in a very inhospitable region of Northern Canada. The best known of terrestrial meteoric craters is that of Coon Butte, in Arizona. This is about a mile in diameter, and its rim is raised 150 feet above the surrounding country and 500 feet above the floor, which is thus much depressed. Meteors can, and have, produced shallow depressions of considerable size on our own planet and, probably on the Moon also, but the vast numbers of meteors necessary to produce the lunar craters and the arrangement of these craters does not suggest a meteoric origin for the majority. The Moon to-day, practically bereft of any atmosphere, is constantly bombarded by meteoric missiles, but we can trace no evidence of the smallest physical change through their agency. The meteoric theory was first propounded by Gruithuisen and taken up by R. A. Proctor, and, recently, by R. B. Baldwin in his book, *The Face of the Moon*, 1949.

Dr. See considered cosmical dust to have played a great part in the production of the present surfaces of the *Maria* and the various partially filled up ringed-plains. He considered their filled-up appearance as due to the quantity of cosmical dust which has fallen into their interiors. Goodacre truly remarks that the results of this ceaseless fall of dust appear to be insignificant, and it is obvious that all parts of the Moon should equally exhibit signs of this dusty blanketing. As a matter of fact, the greater part of the lunar surface presents a freshness and sharpness inconsistent with any appreciable subsequent deposit of dust.

There is a remote possibility that the *Maria* may have been formed by the impact of large meteors, but it is certain that the origin of the vast majority of the lunar cavities cannot be so explained, and the volcanic theory seems to correctly apply, especially if we substitute erosive for explosive action in many cases.

The glacial theory assumes the formations to be composed of ice, but this idea is generally rejected. To assert, as Fauth did, that the rocky core of our satellite is covered by a layer of ice 200 miles thick is to labour an already overloaded and absurd hypothesis.

The origin of the various lunar features can never be established with certainty so long as men are confined to the Earth. Only when the first space-ships take off for the Moon, and we are able to view the surface at close quarters and actually analyse the lunar crust, will this question be finally settled.

The destructive effects exhibited around the margins of the 'seas' and, to a lesser extent, on their surfaces, the often partly destroyed nature of the ring-plains situated on the 'coast-lines' and the ghostly nature of the overwhelmed or buried rings, all testify to some erosive action. Green, in the *Selenographical Journal*, and Goodacre in his *Moon*, both consider that the existence of water in the past played a great part in the present weathered condition of certain formations. This, while not impossible, seems improbable, as it is very doubtful if the Moon ever possessed an atmosphere or water, especially to such an extent as to account for the appearances visible in our telescopes. Lava is not always dense; the lavas of Kilauea are almost as liquid as water, and even the Vesuvian lava is sometimes perfectly fluid at its source, before cooling effects have been in operation. Under the reduced gravitational attraction of the Moon, such thin lava might well spread to considerable distances.

Although the bright mountainous regions have an appearance of newness, and have been placed by some authorities in the final stages of the chronological order of appearance of the various classes of formations, the reverse is probably true, and they may date from an earlier epoch than the *Maria*. The partially submerged ringed-plains, such as Fracastorius, Letronne and Lexell, have obviously been, to some extent, sunk below the contiguous surface, thus presenting the clearest evidence of their earlier formation.

During the formation of the 'seas' by the outflow of lava from the interior of the Moon, the huge tides caused by the Earth's attraction must have caused fiery waves of great magnitude to beat continually on their margins, and must have melted down all but the most refractory rocks, thus producing vast and nearly level surfaces. After the molten surface had attained a plastic condition, further activity produced the rings and ringed-plains which we observe on the plains. If the Moon ever possessed an atmosphere, the attraction of the Earth would cause atmospheric tides, just as the Moon does in our own atmosphere. Appleton and Weekes, in 1939, established the existence of such aerial tides in the ionosphere. There may be a connection between these atmospheric tides and the relation between lunar phase and long-distance radio reception, established by P. A. Howell.

Other theories of the origin of the Moon itself and of its surface features have been propounded. The weakness of the celebrated Nebular Hypothesis of Laplace, advanced in 1796, was that the rings of matter he supposed to be left as the nucleus contracted could not condense into a single body owing to the looseness of the gravitational attraction. G. H. Darwin, the son of the famous naturalist, presented the theory that owing to the rapid rotation of the newly-formed Earth and the solar attraction, our then fluid planet assumed a dumb-bell shape. The smaller portion broke off under the strain and became the Moon. On this theory, the Moon is a thrown-off portion of the Earth itself. In this connection it should be mentioned that our satellite is unique so far as size is concerned. Other satellites are larger than the Moon, but are much smaller relatively to their primaries. The Earth and Moon indeed form a double planet rather than a system of planet and satellite.

Some people, Von Weizsäcker for example, have contended that the Moon never was part of the Earth. According to them the Sun passed through an interstellar cloud of gas and dust, and collected a gaseous envelope which condensed into planetary globes. The Moon was one of the smallest of these globes, and was eventually *captured* by the Earth. In any case, there is a definite limit from any planet within which a secondary globe cannot be formed or survive as a compact mass. Within this 'Roche's Limit' a globe would be broken up into fragments. This may be the explanation of the rings surrounding Saturn.

Boneff, of Bulgaria, has advanced the theory that the craters were caused by the tidal attraction of the Earth by sucking the once-molten matter in the interior of the

Moon through weak spots in the crust. The matter was, in effect, pumped out and solidified on exposure to the cold of space. On the other hand, Ruud has suggested a modification to the effect that the craters were formed by the crust contracting on the less-yielding interior, thus forcing matter through weak spots. On this theory the smaller features are to be regarded as formed before the larger. The great 'seas' would be the latest of all features. Yet another hypothesis was advanced by the French physicist, Fillias, who considers that the craters were caused by the expansion of the interior and not by the contraction of the crust. This resembles the expansion-on-solidification idea of Nasmyth.

The late R. L. T. Clarkson, F.R.A.S., of Ipswich, has postulated that the lunar 'seas' were once seas in reality and the numerous 'ghost' rings on their surfaces are buried under alluvial matter. Not only can the dark and sandy appearance of the floors of the 'seas' be readily explained if we assume the former existence of water, but with the certain existence of volcanic action in the past, other features. After stating that the cause of the great Alpine valley has always been a problem, he suggests that a volcanic or earthquake upheaval may have produced a fissure through the Alps and through this narrow defile the then existing water of the Mare Imbrium rushed, spreading and widening its bed as it reached the northern foothills of the Alps, finally spreading out on the north. This would explain the narrow defile through the Alps, the broader section further north and the great size of the whole.

As early as 1665, the famous Hooke suggested that the craters were, in reality, burst bubbles; the terraces, which are so common a feature of the lunar rings, being caused by fluctuations or pulsations. There may be some truth in this theory, so far as the smaller objects are concerned, and the numerous domes might be regarded as examples of bubbles which did not burst. These domes always appear dark under low illumination and their surfaces are frequently fissured, doubtless owing to internal pressure.

In 1917, D. P. Beard suggested that the Moon was once covered by an immense ocean and that the craters and other features are either limestone formations or coral atolls. He did not, however, go so far as to add palm trees or other manifestations of life on coral atolls!

There have not been wanting those who have denied the existence of any craters or mountains on the Moon at all. Herr Weisberger, of Vienna, declared the supposed craters to be merely storms and cyclones in the lunar atmosphere. Unfortunately for this idea, recent research has shown that any atmosphere the Moon may possess cannot exceed 1/10,000th that of the Earth. At a height of about 50 miles such an atmosphere would act as an effective shield against meteoric bombardment. It would indeed be as dense, if not more so, than that of the Earth, at a similar altitude.

Finally, from time to time, apparently sane people have gone even further than Weisberger and declared that the Moon, as a planet, does not exist. With a sublime disregard of gravitation or mass, and with particularly large bees buzzing in their bonnets, they have declared that our satellite is merely an empty shell, a hollow hemisphere or half-globe. In fact, all manner of fantastic ideas regarding the Moon have been, and still are, voiced, the loudness and vehemence of their presentation being only equalled by the depths of their advocates' ignorance.

They are hardly less imaginative than the seventeenth-century philosopher Descartes, who solemnly suggested that as soon as the craters received names, the spirits of those personages thus favoured took up residence in the craters bestowed upon them.

The most careful and reliable researches assure us that the condition of the lunar surface is comparable with that of what we are accustomed to regard as a vacuum, and that this has prevailed over great intervals of time. The Moon is too small to retain an atmosphere permanently; even Mercury, which is appreciably larger than the Moon, has an atmosphere which is only 1/350th that of the Earth's, according to the recent determination of Dollfus. In the absence of atmosphere we must reject oceans, coral atolls, storms, cyclones and, in short, all aqueous or meteorological agencies.

Goodacre considered that prior to the formation of the *Maria*, the Moon was covered with rings of which traces are left in the numerous ghost rings so common on the great plains. The very fact that any traces of these early formations can be found points to their formation being of very refractory rocks. Either they withstood, to some extent, the erosive action of the *Mare* matter, or the latter is of limited depth. It is possible that the erosive action lasted for only a brief period of time.

Owing to the peculiar relation existing between the rotation of the Moon on its axis and the period of revolution around the Earth, the same side is constantly presented towards us. The Moon's rotation being uniform while its revolution is variable, our satellite is sometimes in front of and sometimes behind its mean position. We thus periodically obtain a view of a zone beyond the limb at mean libration. At times we also obtain a view of regions beyond the poles, while, when the Moon is near the horizon, we are viewing her as from an eminence and can observe spots which are concealed as she approaches the meridian.

The effect of this swaying of the Moon, termed 'libration', is to extend our view of the lunar surface, so that instead of only seeing one-half we can see six-tenths of the entire surface, the remaining four-tenths being always concealed. There is no reason for supposing that what we may call the back of the Moon differs greatly from the side we see. The same characteristic features are found on the zones alternately carried out of or brought into view by libration, from which we conclude that the unseen portion also contains ringed-plains, mountains and 'seas'. Assuming that, as on the Earth, the plains on one side are balanced by a mountainous region on the other, it is possible to form a rough idea of the broad features of the averted hemisphere. We present a special map section of the libratory regions, centred on the back of the Moon.

It is reasonable to conclude that the Moon, at the present time is in a state of inertia and that the final stage has not yet been reached.

Considered as a satellite, the Moon is unique; it is the only satellite in the solar system the orbit of which is always concave to the Sun. Compared with the Earth's diameter of 7,927 miles, the lunar diameter of 2,160 miles seems very large. The largest satellites of Jupiter, Saturn and Neptune exceed the Moon in size; but compared with their primaries, these orbs are very small. The Moon's diameter is more than a quarter of that of the Earth; hence has arisen the idea that the Moon may not have been formed from the Earth but has always been a separated body. Professor Schwarz, of South Africa, suggested that the Moon and Mercury once formed a binary system, but the former separated by perturbations and was captured by the Earth.

To ourselves, whether the Moon was formed by matter thrown off from the Earth or captured during the course of ages, the study of its surface details is of absorbing interest to all who possess an astronomical telescope. Even the modest binocular is capable of revealing the broad features of our neighbouring world; a telescope of only 1½-inch aperture will show the principal craters and other objects. With instruments of from 2- to 3-inch aperture many a delightful evening may be spent in the study of the Moon; a 3-inch refractor readily reveals the Triesnecker cleft system. Such an aperture will allow the earnest student to detect and depict many hitherto unrecorded features, especially in the difficult limb regions. A 6½-inch reflector permits the study of quite minute objects; the work accomplished by the late A. Stanley Williams is sufficient indication of the value of such an instrument in the hands of a capable observer. Elger and Arthur Mee employed 8½-inch Calver reflectors; Haas, Reese and Barcroft have done much work with 6-inch instruments; R. Barker uses a 12½-inch reflector which is also the size employed by Moore. In instruments of such aperture an effect of relief will often be noted; we can actually see the hills sticking up towards us and the silvery disk is spread out like a map. For minute features and for work of the highest accuracy, very large apertures are required; the finest views of the lunar surface that the Authors have ever enjoyed were obtained with the great 33-inch refractor of the Meudon Observatory.

Selenography in the past has been almost entirely the province of amateurs; the selenography of the future would appear to lie in the careful and minute study of selected regions by keen observers using powerful instruments, or measuring lunar photographs, and making the most of every favourable opportunity for research.

The formation of the International Lunar Society in 1956 represents a most important advance in Selenography as it correlates the work of lunar observers all over the world. Important papers published in its Journal include an account by Dr. Leon H. Stuart, of Tulsa, Oklahoma, of what seems to have been a photo-visual observation of an impact of a large meteorite on the moon, 15 November 1953; a paper on the luminescence of the lunar surface by ultra violet radiation from the sun during lunar eclipses, noted by Professor Cimino of Naples; the relationship among the catamenial cycle, epilepsy and lunar phase by Dr. Fresa of Naples and the first part of a catalogue of lunar domes observed by Patrick Moore and P. J. Cattermole.

THE PRESENT CONDITION OF THE MOON

Whether the present condition of the Moon is final or a passing phase may be sum marized as follows:

The Moon, for all practical purposes, may be considered as an airless globe, its surface existing in an almost perfect vacuum. The surface is primarily a desert, probably due to the joint action of volcanic forces and meteoric bombardment. There are considerable areas of volcanic sand, intermingled with meteoric dust. Owing to the almost complete absence of air, meteoric masses would commonly reach the surface intact, the energy of their velocity being there converted into heat. On Earth, meteors are usually dissipated into dust before they can reach the surface; on the Moon, such dissolution must be regarded as altogether exceptional, unless there exists a rare atmosphere which, at great heights, acts as a shield. The very fact that the lunar features are not concealed to any great extent, the remarkable whiteness of many formations proves that they, at any rate, are not covered by a layer of dust, and these facts may be held to favour the idea of a rarefied lunar atmosphere.

Dr. Harlow Shapley of Harvard College Observatory proposes that the Moon may possess a very thin atmosphere of argon and other chemically inert heavy gases, released by the radioactive decay of a potassium isotope in the lunar rocks brought to the surface by meteoritic bombardment. Most of the argon thus produced could be retained by the Moon. It would appear that a lunar atmosphere formed in this way would eventually reduce the intensity of meteoritic bombardment of the surface.

The lunar surface is exposed to interplanetary space without the shield of atmosphere, hence the surface is continually bombarded by undiluted radiation from the Sun and outer space. All wavelengths reach the rocky and rough crust; they are not filtered out as with ourselves. Electrons ejected from the Sun, and cosmic rays, strike portions of the surface, which may act as a deflector of free electrons, while the surface in other places may consist of material which emits electrons under the influence of light or electronic bombardment. This may be the explanation of the fluorescent appearances noted, from time to time, in connection with various formations, especially Aristarchus. These luminous appearances are quite distinct from the purely optical metamorphosis of such objects.

Lunar life, of any kind, must be capable of withstanding not only a wide range of direct solar radiation, but also great extremes of temperature, especially in low latitudes, where variations are most pronounced. It must also be capable of flourishing in the absence of free atmospheric oxygen or, probably, even carbon-dioxide gas. Some observers have suggested that gases, of unknown composition, are occasionally ejected from cracks or sub-lunarian cavities beneath the surface. The outer layers of the crust may well be of a spongy nature. We may not agree with the vegetation or insects suggested by Professor W. H. Pickering as being the true explanation of the moving spots within the crater Eratosthenes, but we have to explain how these spots apparently move in the contrary direction to that in which shades or shadows would do. It is not impossible that on the Moon there may exist, or have once existed, some form of life peculiar to the Moon and totally unlike anything ever known on the Earth. There may be, although it is very unlikely, fossils in the lunar crust.

Those who deny the existence of variations on the Moon are opposed to the experience of the great selenographers of the past and the present time. Selenography must be founded on observation, not on preconceived and often erroneous conceptions; let us be observers first and theorists afterwards.

CLASSIFICATION OF LUNAR DETAIL

This book is intended primarily for observers. The maps are the largest and the most detailed yet compiled. As perfection is not yet achieved, errors of commission and omission may be found here and there. The maps are based on actual observation, including the use of some of the finest telescopes in the world. They combine the results of forty years' observation on the part of the senior Author.

Every endeavour has been made to render this work supplementary to other books and not a mere repetition of already recorded observations. We have tried to present the most detailed maps and the most accurate text, so that the work may act as a reliable guide in the observatory as well as in the study, combining the selenography of the past with the new selenography of the present.

Whether the reader possesses a small telescope or a finely-appointed observatory, he will find the Moon a celestial object of absorbing interest; a sphere where instruments of all apertures can usefully be employed for the detection of hitherto unrecorded detail, especially near the limb. Only keen observers deserve to enjoy the wonderful intricacy of detail on the silvery disk of that most beautiful of orbs—the Moon.

THE INTERNATIONAL LUNAR SOCIETY

Astronomy is an international science, and the Moon is naturally one of the main objects of study. It was felt that observers in different countries were not sufficiently in touch, and to remedy this an International Lunar Society was formed in 1956. This represents an important advance in selenography, as it correlates the work of lunar observers all over the world. The Permanent Secretary is A. Paluzie-Borrell (Spain), and the General Secretary G. D. Roth (Germany); the first President elected was H. P. Wilkins (Britain) with W. H. Haas (United States) as Vice-President. The Society now publishes a six-monthly Journal which includes results of work carried out by lunar observers in many countries, and Quarterly Bulletins of items of topical interest. Fellowship of the I.L.S. now exceeds 400.

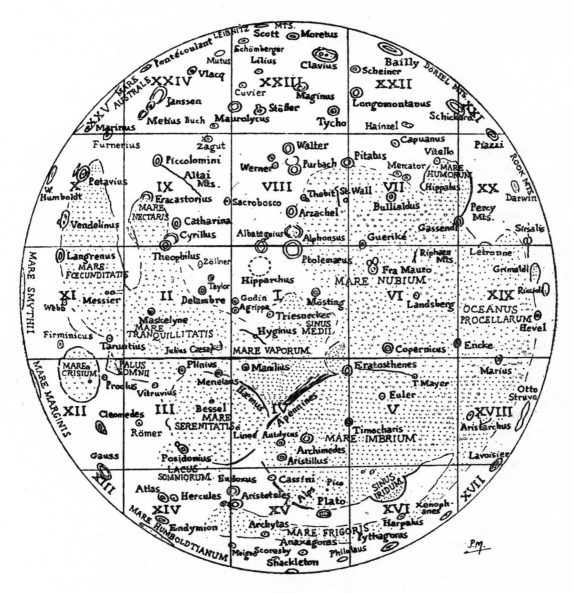

KEY MAP

This small-scale map will be found useful as a guide to the sections of the large Map given throughout the book. Only the main features of the Moon's disk are shown; reference to the Key will, however, give the Section numbers of any important formation.

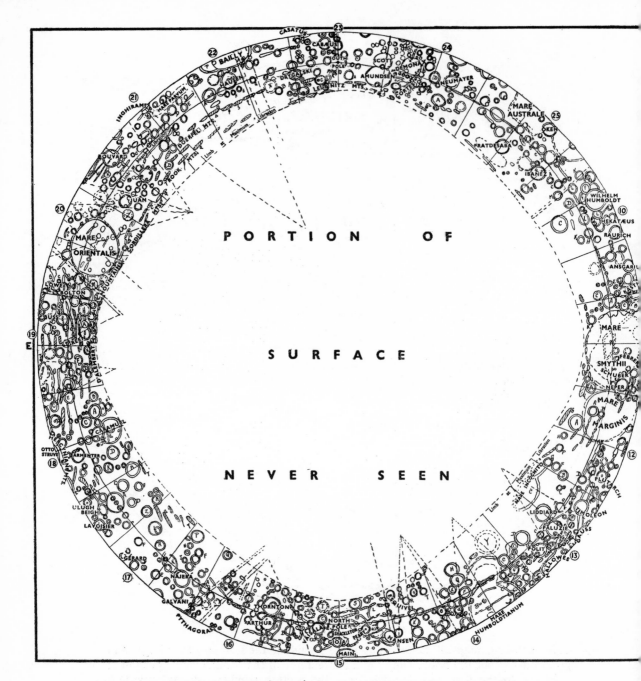

CHARTS OF THE LIMB REGIONS ON STEREOGRAPHIC PROJECTION

Owing to the effects of libration, more than 50 per cent of the Moon's disk can be seen at one time or another. The formations at the limit of visibility are of course extremely foreshortened, and normal maps give no idea of their real shape. This special chart is, therefore, more truly representative of these features.

It is also possible to detect bright rays coming over the limb from the far side of the Moon, and the positions of several 'ray-craters' permanently invisible to us have been inferred with fair accuracy.

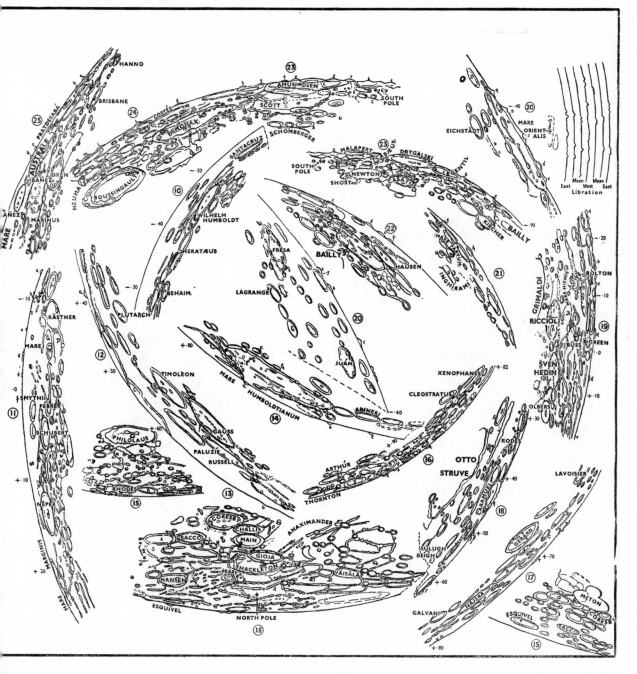

CHARTS OF THE LIBRATORY REGIONS

The main sections of the Map, as given throughout the book, are naturally drawn for conditions of mean libration. This means that some features which are beyond the limb at mean libration cannot be shown. These special charts are drawn for conditions of maximum libration in the regions concerned.

The figures given in circles beside each section indicate the relevant section of the main map, to which reference can be made.

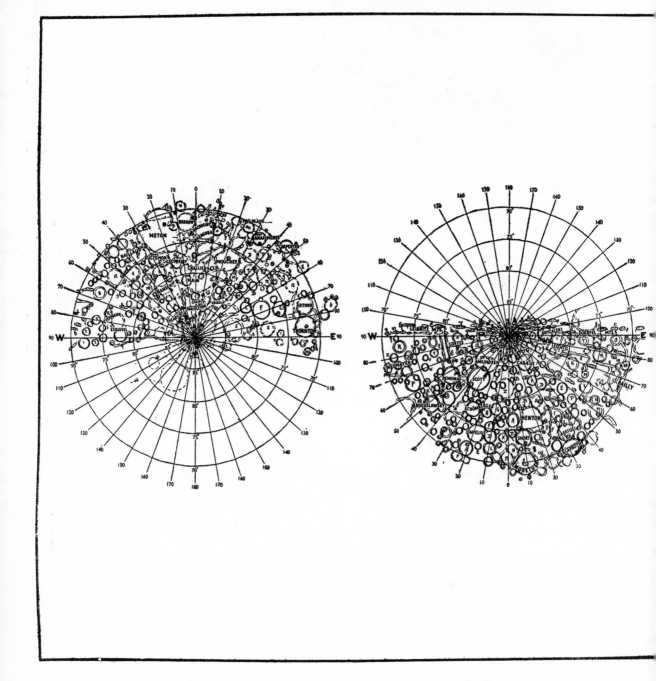

NORTH AND SOUTH POLAR PROJECTION CHARTS

The extreme regions of the disk, near the Poles, are not easy to observe or to represent on ordinary charts. It is therefore an advantage to show them on a special map. The North Polar chart (left) has been drawn mainly from observations made by the Authors; the South Polar chart (right) from the work of K. W. Abineri, D. W. G. Arthur and the Authors.

I

This section includes a region around the centre of the disk, and is bisected by the first meridian and the Equator. It is crowded with formations of all kinds, including the two small dark plains Sinus Medii and Sinus Æstuum. The most important of the large walled plains is Ptolemæus; other noteworthy objects are Herschel and Mösting.

The great cleft associated with Hyginus will be found in this section, and also the very complex cleft system near Triesnecker.

There are also several fine examples of partially ruined formations, among which may be mentioned Réaumur, Schröter and Murchison, while the vast but imperfectly bordered Hipparchus is a splendid example of how a once-magnificent formation can be ruined by erosive forces.

The fine ringed plain Albategnius is partly shown. Like Ptolemæus, it contains several shallow, saucer-like depressions on its interior.

All the coarser details on the map are visible in small telescopes, but the finer features, such as the smaller clefts and minute craterlets, require larger apertures for their detection.

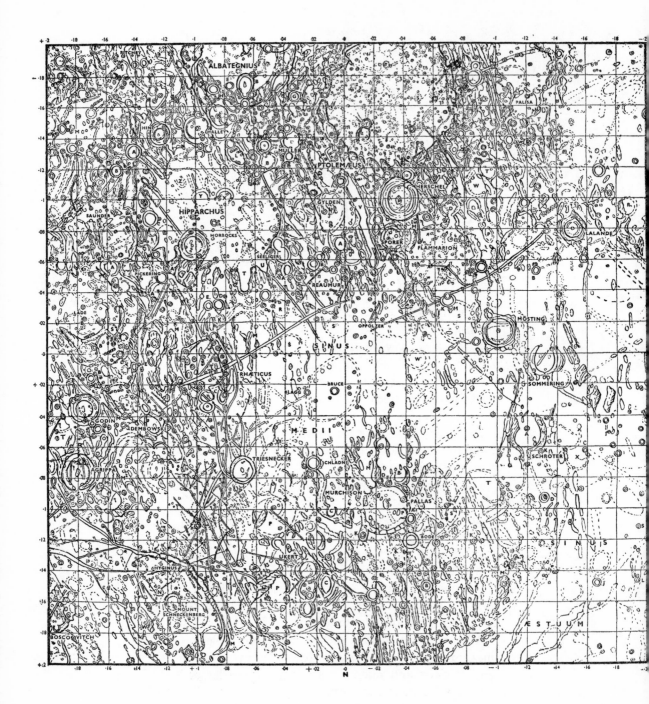

I

AGRIPPA, +181 +073 [Bithynian astronomer, *circa* A.D. 92]. A ring, 28 miles in diameter, with bright, terraced walls rising 8,000 feet on the east and 7,000 feet on the west; on the south is a peak, Beta. The walls are linear on the east, with evidences of land-slips both inside and outside. The interior contains a large central mountain with a cleft on either side; there is also a craterlet close to the inner south slope, an elongated depres-sion on the north, to the west of which is a gap. On the north, beyond a rocky spur, are two craters from the eastern of which originates the Hyginus Cleft with another, 19, at right angles. West is a large, low ring, F, traversed by a cleft extending to Godin, while on the east is an isolated mountain mass, on the site of an ancient ring, B, of which the eastern portion alone remains. A bright crater, E, crowns the summit. The floor of this ring contains several craterlets, hillocks, a crater and obscure rings.

ALBATEGNIUS, +067 −197 [Arabian astronomer, A.D. 850-929]. A great walled-plain, 80 miles in diameter, with very broad, complex walls abounding in depressions, divided by immense terraces and crowned by peaks from 10,000 to 14,000 feet in altitude. The central mountain bears craterlets on its flanks; abutting on the west is a low ring, K. On the north wall is a large crater, B, with a central peak, a crater on the south-east rim, another on the north, the common wall having disappeared; adjoining this is a crater-row on the west. On the south-east portion of Albategnius is a large ring, formerly A, now Klein, with a central peak, the highest portion of a longitudinal ridge, craterlets, hillocks, and also craters on its rim. There are other craters to the east.

The north wall, both east and west of the crater B, contains several craters, of which Alter, H, G, M and N are the most prominent. Adjoining N, and on the floor of Albategnius, are two buried rings, saucer-like depressions, *h, g*, with others, *f* and *l*, to the south. These depressions are similar to those found on the floor of Ptolemæus. In addition to these features, there are many craterlets, all delicate objects. Under low illumination several low, meridional ridges can be detected; under these conditions the floor is very dark. The inner west slopes are very broad, and abound in rocky masses, with two craters near the crest; beyond the outer slope is a long valley, V.

ALTER, +033 −164 [Contemporary American astronomer]. This crater was formerly known as Albategnius G, and is described with Albategnius.

BLAGG, +026 +021 [English selenographer, 1858-1944]. A small crater in the Sinus Medii, west of Bruce.

BODE, —042 +117 [German astronomer, 1747-1826]. A ring 11 miles in diameter, and conspicuous at Full. On the interior, which lies 5,000 feet below the crest, is a ridge extending to the wall. East, beyond a low ring, is the bright crater, B, with others on the south, while on the north are numerous craterlets, a low ring open on the south and several parallel ridges with valleys, while to the south-east is a crater, D, from which a valley runs to the wall of Pallas; a very shallow valley joins this, originating from the wall of Bode. Between Bode and D and B is an obscure ring, open on the south and containing at least three craterlets, while between B and D are the remains of an old ring. South-east of D are two ancient depressions with fragmentary walls. North of Bode, which is the centre of a minor ray system, is a large oval depression, to the west of which is a marked extension of the Apennine hinterland, the most prominent object being the crater A, with a low ring, S, on the north-west. Through S runs a cleft, the southern portion of which expands into craters, X, Y and Z; while the northern portion is flanked by a craterlet-row on the east.

BOSCOVICH, +188 +170 [Italian physicist, 1711-87]. A dark and imperfect ringed-plain, the floor being subject to variations in tint. The wall is wanting on the south-west, contains two partial enclosures, E and F, on the north, and is massive on the south, where the promontory facing west resembles the head of a horse and includes a crater, D. The interior is traversed by a cleft which cuts through on the south; there are also some delicate craterlets. East of Boscovich is a large, ancient enclosure, F, with openings both north and south. On the north extremity of the western fragment are two craters, A and B. Between F and Boscovich is a plain containing many objects, including two craters, several ancient rings of which S is the largest, and some ridges. North is a large obscure enclosure, P, on the rim of which are craterlets, while the interior contains a few craterpits only detectable in powerful telescopes.

BRUCE, +007 +020 [American woman benefactor to science, 1816-1900]. A small crater, close to the centre of the disk under conditions of mean libration, and in the centre of a large, obscure ring within the Sinus Medii. On the east are two craterlets, and there is another on the north-north-west. On the west rim of the large, obscure ring is a smaller crater, Blagg. There are some very minute hillocks and pits in the neighbourhood.

CHLADNI, +020 +070 [German physicist, 1756-1827]. A deep, well-formed crater at the south end of the western rampart of Murchison, and thus east of Triesnecker and on the north border of the Sinus Medii. Close outside the west wall is a craterlet and, on the north the bright crater B, with other but more shallow depressions nearby.

DEMBOWSKI, +126 +048 [Italian astronomer, 1815-81]. A depression on the east of Godin, the slightly depressed interior containing a craterlet and a hill. To the south is the crater A, with a feeble central peak, while on the south-west is a craterlet. The surroundings include many hills, none of any height; craterlets, and ridges. On the east is a short cleft, with another further east, and a ridge between.

FLAMMARION, —070 —052 [Great French astronomer, 1842-1925]. A rather dark plain, roughly enclosed, the walls being much broken and, in places, reduced to mere fragments. In the centre is a very low ring, *a*, with another, *b*, on the north-east; there are also at least twenty craterlets scattered over the surface. On the northern border is the crater K, with a small crater on the crest of its south wall; from K a cleft runs towards Lalande. To the east of K this cleft throws off a short branch cleft, which runs to the centre of Flammarion. Another cleft runs from the craterlet I, near the south border, through a pass in the south-west wall, and then along the outer west glacis of Herschel. On the east wall is the bright crater A.

GODIN, +176 +033 [French explorer and mathematician, 1704-60]. This fine ringed-plain is 27 miles in diameter and departs markedly from a circular shape especially on the outside. The inner slopes are terraced. The floor contains a central hill, with a smaller elevation on the west, and a craterpit close to the foot of the inner east slope. With the 33-inch Meudon refractor, on 21 April 1953, Moore found the remains of a ruined ring on the floor, east of the central elevation. On the inner E slope there is also a low ridge, or it may be a landslip from the walls above. On the crest of the south wall is a distinct crater and there are two others on the north wall. At the foot of the outer south-east slope are two small craters while, on the north-west is the fine, bright-rimmed crater, A, and the remains of an ancient ring, T, which is crossed by a cleft. A valley runs alongside the south rim of T. On the east of Godin is another ancient ring.

GYLDÉN, +003 —092 [Finnish astronomer, 1841-96]. A peculiar depression on the western side of the great gorge to the west of Herschel, with a low rim, except on the east where it is tolerably lofty and borders the gorge. The interior contains a crater near the centre, three craterlets, of which two are close together on the northern portion, and a mound of some altitude. There are also some other irregularities.

HALLEY, +101 —141 [English Astronomer-Royal, 1656-1742]. A bright and very distinct crater 21 miles in diameter, the largest of the rings on this portion of the border of Hipparchus. The walls are broad and terraced on the inner slopes, and are continuous except on the north-east, where a pass places the floors of Halley and Hipparchus into communication with each other. The walls are highest on the east, where they rise 7,500 feet above the interior. Close to the crest of the rampart, on the north-east, is a crater. On the depressed floor is a nearly central craterlet, and there are others on the south-east and also on the north. East of Halley is a ring of no appreciable altitude, but containing several hills, all very low, and at least one crater. A wide valley runs from the south wall to the surface west of the walled-plain Albategnius. Adjoining the outer north wall of Halley, and thus on the interior of Hipparchus, are two curved ridges, probably the remains of once-complete rings now reduced to mere fragments. Many objects around exhibit evidences of erosion as for example the ring J, which adjoins the large ring to the east of Halley and is included among the formations on Hipparchus. This ring contains at least nine craterlets, as shown on the map.

HERSCHEL, —036 —099 [Great Hanoverian astronomer, 1738-1822]. This fine ringed-plain is 28 miles in diameter, and is easily found as it lies on the northern border of Ptolemæus. The inner slopes are terraced while on the floor is a large central mountain bearing a summit crater. Outside the massive rampart, on the north, is the ring Herschel A, now called Spörer, which presents clear indications of having been partly filled up with lava. It has broken walls and contains several craterlets, and was first drawn in detail by Maw, in the second Memoir of the Lunar Section of the British Astronomical Association. East of it is a curved mountain ridge, M, separated from Spörer by a space of 5 miles. North are two little craters and a large imperfect ring, opening into the Sinus Medii. West of Herschel is a great gorge, tapering at either end and 80 miles in length. Neison describes a central ridge in Spörer. We have found some hills and craterpits on the floor.

HIND, +127 —138 [English civil engineer and astronomer, 1823-95]. A circular crater 16 miles in diameter, on the border of Hipparchus, with beautiful walls terraced down to the floor, on which is a ridge and a craterlet on the north. There are craterlets on the inner north and south slopes, and the interior lies 10,000 feet below the crest of the east wall, but is lower on the west. To the north-west is a ray-surrounded crater, A, from which two deep valleys cut through the wall of Hipparchus. Beyond A is a smaller crater, B. There is a deep little crater on the north-east crest of Hind, easily seen and filled with shadow at sunrise or sunset.

HIPPARCHUS, +085 —090 [Greek astronomer, *circa* 140 B.C.]. This is one of the largest ringed formations on the entire lunar surface, but is rarely seen as a connected whole save under low illumination. One hundred miles across, the great mountain-ringed enclosure is in a ruinous condition, and the walls are very broken and disconnected, consisting of mountain masses separated by valleys, on a smaller scale but similar to the southern coast-line of the Mare Crisium. Very imperfect on the north, the walls are highest on the west, where they rise about 4,000 feet above the interior, which seems to be at the same level as the outer surface. On the vast interior are numerous objects; of these, the most prominent are two large rings, with very low walls and also imperfect, being open on the north. These rings, X and Y on the map, are connected to the walls by low ridges. There are numerous craterlets and some craters on the north, also several shallow saucer-like depressions, chiefly on the eastern portion. On the western side is a cleft, and there is another which originates from a depression on the north-east. The conspicuous crater, C, near the south-east wall, is surrounded by depressions, while there is a crater-row from the south wall to the elliptical depression on the west wall of Ptolemæus. The largest crater associated with Hipparchus is:

HORROCKS, +102 —069 [English astronomer, 1619-41]. Eighteen miles in diameter and over 8,000 feet deep on the east. On the outer slopes are landslips, and there is a craterlet on the crest of the south wall. Another will be found on the north-east. Horrocks contains a central hill, and some lower elevations. From the wall a cleft runs across Hipparchus to the south-west. At the foot of the inner slopes are some minute craterlets. On the north are several isolated and somewhat lofty mountain masses and the crater A, with the larger, B, now called E. C. Pickering. Further north are two parallel clefts. To the east of Horrocks, the border of Hipparchus is very irregular, with some deep bays, of which T and U are the most prominent.

HYGINUS, +109 +135 [Spanish astronomer, *circa* A.D. 100]. In itself this is a large craterpit, some 4 miles in diameter, with a very low rim missed by Webb; but its interest is on account of the great cleft which passes through it and which is easily seen in a small telescope. On the northern rim is a smaller depression, missed by Mädler, but shown by Lohrmann. The great cleft begins on the west, at a small craterlet to the north of Agrippa, and soon throws off a branch; furthermore, a delicate cleft runs to the Ariadæus cleft. Near the junction of the main cleft and this branch, on the south, is a prominent mountain mass, M. The cleft becomes broader and deeper, passes over four craters and enters Hyginus. Here it is bordered by raised banks visible as fine lines of light when the interior of Hyginus is in shadow, and is so shown by Schmidt. Webb noted that the east portion was lower than the west, so that these lines sometimes appear imperfect amid the shadow. Within Hyginus and south of the cleft, Wilkins, with a 12½-inch reflector found 8 June 1935, a minute hillock. The cleft bends towards the north, and presents a jagged outline, possibly mere enlargements, though they may be the remains of craters; it ends, on the north-east, in a wide valley. This valley leads to the Mare Vaporum. Several minute craterlets and delicate branches, mere cracks, can be detected along its course.

Although, in small instruments and with low powers, the Hyginus cleft appears continuous, more powerful instruments reveal its true disjointed nature, owing to the crater-like enlargements along its course.

The environs of Hyginus are of great interest, and include all manner of objects. Fine clefts run from the south rim through a slightly concave dark spot, 8 miles in diameter, while to the east of the mountain mass, M, is a large dark spot within which Goodacre found two bright objects, possibly cratercones. Professor W. H. Haas of Las Cruces, New Mexico, U.S.A., has found a winding cleft from this dusky area to the straight clefts to the west of Triesnecker. This is the spot mentioned by Webb (*Celestial Objects*), as large near quadratures, covering two ranges of hills and the vale between. He did not mention the clefts found by Haas, but they have been confirmed by McLeod and photographed by Latimer Wilson of Nashville, Tenn., U.S.A.

North of Hyginus and connected by a wide but shallow valley is a curious spiral mountain (Schneckenberg). This has broad low walls and the interior is depressed only about 700 feet. Schmidt and Goodacre drew a central craterlet, but Brenner and Fauth many more. Wilkins found two craterlets and a hill on the interior, all difficult objects. Krieger, in his *Mond Atlas*, Vol. I, Pl. 8, depicts the interior as filled with shadow except for a central strip, on which is a pit. Another drawing, under a higher angle of illumination, shows two pits, from the more northerly of which a branching cleft runs north-east. Krieger also found other delicate clefts, confirmed in part by Fauth and Klein. For the positions of these clefts reference should be made to the map and to the beautiful photograph which was taken at the Pic-du-Midi Observatory by Dr. Lyot.

In 1878 Dr. Klein announced the appearance of a 'new' crater in this region and which became known as Hyginus N. (Nova). The short-lived Selenographical Society was then in activity, and several drawings of this region appeared in its Journal. Of these drawings those by Neison, N. E. Green and McCance are of particular value as representations of the aspect of this region seventy-four years ago. The alleged 'new' crater, N, is depicted as a depression rather than a true crater and, under low illumination, appears rimless. A short distance to the south-west of N a second and smaller depression, N1, was detected, the two depressions being connected by a dark band. On occasion N was seen as large as, but rather more diffused than, Hyginus itself. Close to and just west of N is a mountain ridge, shown by Mädler and Lohrmann as a hill; and the crater-like aspect of N, soon after sunrise, appears to be, in part, due to the shadow of this ridge. Towards sunset, when the shadows are thrown westwards, the crater-like appearance is much less marked, thus clearly proving that the appearance of this region, like many others, is dependent upon the direction of the solar illumination. Dr. Klein's contention that N was a new feature has not been proved, despite the fact that both N and N1 were omitted from the charts of the earlier observers. It is probable that it was merely another instance of the overlooking of comparatively easily-seen detail.

Recent observations have shown that the present appearance of this region is well represented by the drawings of Neison, Green and McCance, indicating that no major change has taken place since attention was especially directed towards it.

In addition to Schneckenberg and N, there are several craters and, on the north, some mountain ridges, rising in places as much as 700 feet, and arranged roughly in parallel chains in a general south-south-west to north-north-east direction.

A very remarkable sketch of this region by Herr Brenner, 10 June 1894, 8h. 15m.—11h. M.E.T., 7-inch O.G., and published in the third Memoir of the B.A.A. Lunar Section, depicts many objects not confirmed by other observers. While no trace of N1 appears, a black spot, with a diameter one quarter that of N, is shown north-east of N and claimed by Brenner as a new formation. Immediately to the north of N is a small hill, and running alongside its north flank a cleft, double near the hill and traversing two dark spots near its west end. These spots were subsequently seen as craterlets. To the south-east of N is a crater apparently situated on a cleft, which runs into the wide valley from Hyginus; and this crater, which Wilkins has confirmed, was afterwards seen by Herr Brenner larger than the depression N. The objects depicted by Herr Brenner have not yet been inserted on maps, pending confirmation.

LADE, +172 −020 [German selenographer, 1817-1904]. A large partial formation to the south of Godin; of the former wall only the northern portion now remains. On the

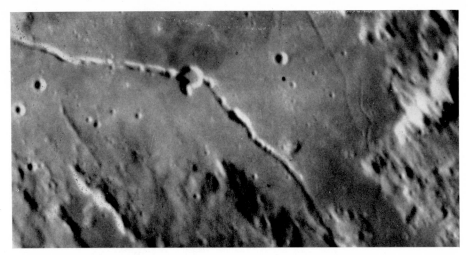

1a. Hyginus, showing the Great Cleft

1b. Ptolemæus, showing the delicate interior features

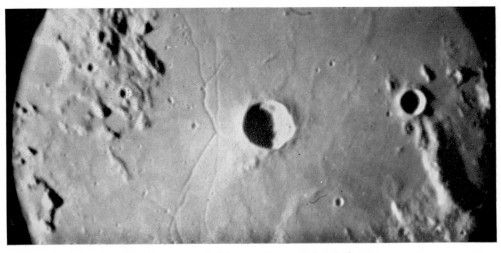

1c. Triesnecker, with portions of the cleft system
(All three photographs taken at the Pic du Midi Observatory)

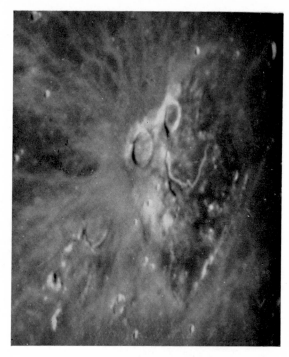

2a. Aristarchus, Herodotus and the Serpentine
Valley. Photograph by E. A. Whitaker, Greenwich Observatory

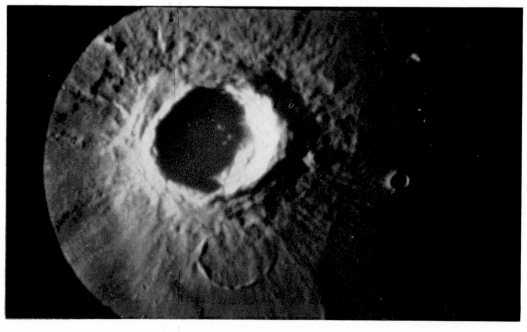

2b. Aristillus. Photograph taken at the Pic du Midi Observatory

interior is a nearly central crater, while on the north-east is the fine crater A; and along the north floor, close to the wall, a craterlet-row. The west wall ends in a sharp promontory. To the south of the crater A are isolated hills, the site of an ancient ring. On the east, beyond a valley, is another fragment of the wall, while on the outer north is a crater, B. On the north-east is a crater, C, and some craterlet-rows, together with many obscure rings.

LALANDE, —149 —078 [French astronomer, 1732-1807]. This formation has a wall 4,500 feet in height, with a mountain mass on the outer west slope. On the floor is a small central hill and the remains of a once-complete inner ring, also a landslip on the inner east. On the summit of the central hill is a depression. Outside on the south-west is a long valley which can be traced as far as the wall of Alphonsus, a distance of 130 miles. Ancient rings lie to the north-west, and on the north-east is a partial ring, P.

LYOT, —014 —148 [Great French astronomer, 1897-1952]. This crater was formerly known as Ptolemæus A, and is described with Ptolemæus.

MEDII, SINUS, 000 +025. 'Central Bay'. A small, dark plain in the centre of the disk, with an area of about 13,000 sq. miles. All around its margins are the relics of rings now reduced by erosion. Pettit and Nicholson found that the temperature of this region, at Full Moon, was 400 degrees Kelvin.

MÖSTING, —102 —012 [Danish statesman, 1759-1843]. A well-marked crater, the walls rising 7,000 feet above the depressed interior but only 1,600 feet above the outer surface. On the floor is a low central hill. To the north-west is a large ancient ring, of which only isolated fragments now remain. To the south-south-west is the brilliant crater A, one of the standard points. A is a ray centre, and its position, as found by Franz from Schlüter's observations with the Königsberg heliometer, is: longitude —5 degrees, 10 minutes, 19 seconds, plus or minus 7·9 seconds; latitude —3 degrees, 11 minutes, 24 seconds, plus or minus 5·5 seconds. The corresponding rectangular co-ordinates are —0900, —0556.

South-east is another crater, B, with a smaller on the south, while on the east is a remarkable group of hills and a craterlet. The interior of A is white and smooth.

MÜLLER, +035 —133 [German selenographer, 1866-1942]. A peculiar and interesting formation to the west of Ptolemæus, with a low central hill and two lower elevations, also a craterlet on the interior. To the north-west are numerous craterlets. On the south wall are two craters from which a very remarkable crater-row runs east-north-east. This row consists of five complete and two incomplete craters. On the outer north is a prominent crater, while on the walls and all around are many craterlets; also a craterlet-row on the north and several craterlets on the eastern rim.

MURCHISON, 000 +090 [Scottish geologist, 1792-1871]. This ring, 35 miles in diameter, has low, bright walls on the west, but the eastern portion is now some distance to the east as though it had drifted away. On the extremity of the west wall is the crater

Chladni, and north of it the wall is broken by another crater. On the floor is a crater-let under the west wall and some hills on the south. To the south-east is a shallow ring, in connection with which Professor Holden, with the 36-inch Lick refractor, 1891, found a cratercone on the south-west rim and a craterlet on the south-east flank.

OPPOLZER, —006 —026 [Austrian astronomer and physician, 1841-86]. This is a ruined formation immediately north-east and adjoining Réaumur. The walls have been reduced to mere fragments, and on the interior are five craterlets, a hill, and a short cleft close to the eastern wall. On the outer north a cleft begins, and can be traced across the interior of Flammarion to a crater west of Lalande.

PALISA —125 —165 [Austrian astronomer, 1848-1925]. An obscure ring, to the east of Ptolemæus, with very low ramparts reduced to mere ridges in places, and with some craterlets on the interior. On the west is a long valley, and south a large ancient ring crossed by a cleft with craterlets in its course. East is a ring with a lofty east wall.

PALLAS, —029 +095 [German explorer, 1741-1811]. A fine example of a ruined ring, 30 miles in diameter. The walls are pierced by numerous passes, especially on the west; on the south they are low, and here the broad slopes are prolonged south and, bending round, partly enclose a partial ring, B. The inner slopes of Pallas are bright and broad, while on the interior is a central mountain, also some hills and ridges on the north. On the north-east crest is a bright crater. The north wall is divided by narrow valleys, and where it joins Murchison is a high mountain mass with a craterlet near the peak. On a spur from the north wall is a crater, K.

PICKERING, E. C. +122 —050 [American astronomer, 1846-1919]. This crater lies close to Horrocks, and is described under that heading.

PTOLEMÆUS, —048 —158 [Greek astronomer, *circa* A.D. 130]. A great walled-plain, over 90 miles in diameter, and very favourably placed for observation near the centre of the disk, with complex and, in part, discontinuous walls, divided by valleys and passes into separate mountain masses, with numerous spurs and projections on to the interior. These form little bays around the margin. The southern rampart separates it from Alphonsus, and is especially broken up by passes, while a prominent pass also exists in the north wall. Through a pass in the south wall a cleft passes, and crosses the interior on the eastern side. The walls contain many craters, the outer slopes in particular; on the west wall is the conspicuous crater H, and just north of it the lofty peak Ptolemæus Eta, which rises over 9,000 feet above the interior, the highest portion of the entire rampart.

The interior of this magnificent formation is a very dark grey when near the ter-minator, and numerous ridges, not exceeding 100 feet in height, can then be seen; but under high illumination it is much lighter, and appears comparatively smooth, with a marked darker area on the north-east.

The principal object on the interior is the great cratercone, formerly known as A but

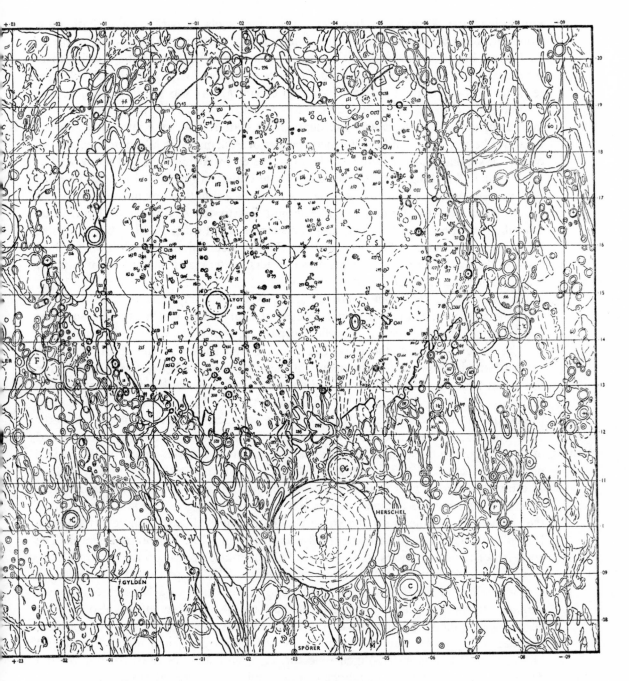

PTOLEMÆUS

This special chart of Ptolemæus has been based on the best available photographs,
particularly that taken at the Pic du Midi, as well as on visual observations.

now called Lyot, 4·5 miles in diameter, with bright walls, in part steep, a gentle outer slope and remarkably white under high illumination. A central peak was once suspected by Bridger but it is certain that it does not exist. Neate has shown the interior to be bowl-shaped, while Wilkins searched for a central peak, with the 33-inch Meudon refractor, but could find no trace of such an object. Moore was similarly unsuccessful.

Immediately to the north of Lyot is a low-rimmed object, a, the largest and the best marked of many shallow, saucer-like depressions scattered over the interior. Filling up the space between Lyot and the northern border of Ptolemæus, in addition to a, are two objects of similar nature, b and c, the first discovered by Arthur Mee and the second by W. H. Maw. All three depressions have minute craterlets on their rims. Of the other shallow depressions, which vary greatly in size, some are not by any means easy to see, except when near the terminator. The largest lies to the south-east of Lyot. After Lyot the largest crater is D, to the east. This crater is not quite circular, but elongated from north to south. It lies between two shallow depressions. In addition to these features there are over one hundred smaller craters, craterlets or pits on the interior, the majority of which are very delicate objects.

Saunder found that some were so small as to be completely concealed by the micrometer thread. Many stand on the edges of light streaks which can be seen under high illumination, and form a complicated pattern, somewhat variable in intensity.

The crater Lyot and the peak Eta (η), are well shown in the chart of Tobias Mayer, but our knowledge of the details of the interior is chiefly due to the activities of the Lunar Section of the British Astronomical Association. In the third Memoir was published a chart by Elger, then the Director, depicting the salient features. The great formation was afterwards carefully examined by Saunder, whose chart, published in the sixth Memoir, contains about sixty craters in addition to the shallow depressions and other objects. The most remarkable of the latter are two craterlet-chains on the eastern portion, one of which develops into a distinct cleft which, after following the contour of the wall, enters a pass in the north-east rampart. The other craterlet-chain is very short and the craterlets diminish in size, the whole being directed towards the centre of the interior. These objects are shown on the chart published by Goodacre in the eighth Memoir, the details of which were chiefly derived from a Mt. Wilson photograph. The great majority of the objects on the chart of Saunder also appear on that of Goodacre, as well as many objects not detected by Saunder. Wilkins published a much more elaborate chart in the B.A.A. Journal for April 1949, based to a large extent upon a magnificent photograph taken by Lyot at the Pic-du-Midi Observatory, also showing all the objects shown by Saunder and Goodacre whose existence had been established, together with features shown on the Mt. Wilson photograph, and others from direct observation with Wilkins' 15¼-inch reflector. A careful study of the Lyot photograph first revealed some craterlet or hillock chains running on to the interior from the north wall.

The special section of the map shows all features whose existence may be regarded as established.

Schmidt shows about seven depressions, Mädler four; of the craters, Schmidt shows nearly all of the more conspicuous ones, including 11, opposite a gap in the east wall. No. 4, near the foot of the west wall, and 23, near the border of Alphonsus, are also shown. The crater 6, in Elger's chart, was not seen by Saunder, but it appears on the Mt. Wilson and Lyot photographs. It was first seen by Dr. Sheldon, 25 January 1893. No. 14 was discovered by Maw, while Nos. 24 to 29 were detected by Elger, Mee, Brown and Paterson respectively, and are not shown on the maps of Mädler or Schmidt. Crater 2 was discovered by Maw, who also fixed the positions of many of the craters, although the greater part of the triangulation was conducted by Saunder. For our special chart Wilkins fixed the positions of all the objects shown, and found that some of the earlier measures were inaccurate. The charts mentioned should be in the possession of all earnest students of this great formation, one of the most interesting of all lunar objects.

RÉAUMUR, +013 −040 [French physicist, 1683-1757]. A fine example of a ruined ring, 30 miles in diameter, with very fragmentary walls, especially on the north-east. What remains of the west wall is divided by fine valleys or ravines, and there are craters on the south. On the floor are craterlets and a cleft on the west; another cleft on the north can be traced across the Sinus Medii. Outside the west wall is a cleft. On the southern exterior is a double crater from which a cleft runs north-west, with another running west towards Hipparchus. There is also a larger crater, A, and a crater-chain. Dr. S. M. Green found a delicate craterlet-chain on the floor of Réaumur.

RHÆTICUS, +084 000 [German mathematician, 1514-76]. An irregular formation, with broad and broken walls rising at the highest peak to 5,000 feet. On the north are two intruding rings; of these the more southerly is open on the south. The ring to the north has a central hill, and from it a cleft runs northwards to Triesnecker. Another cleft tends east to a ridge projecting from the wall of Rhæticus. A coarse valley runs from the south wall, and there is a coarse valley-cleft partly crossing the interior from east to west. Outside the wall this cleft is resumed, and can be traced to Réaumur. Near the west inner wall it throws off a branch cleft, which crosses the central ridge within the formation. Passing this ridge, the cleft runs to the south-east inner slope, where there is a crater-row. On the inner slopes are some craterlets; others are also to be found on the floor. On the outer south are some partial rings, while from the north outer slope several clefts begin and form part of the Triesnecker system. There is also a cleft outside the east wall, which follows its contour and joins the Triesnecker system.

RITCHEY, +143 −192 [American optician, 1864-1918]. A peculiar object to the west of Albategnius, with two large craters on what remains of its north rampart. The south wall is almost straight, and the formation approximates to a square. From Ritchey a series of rings runs to Hind. On the west are many hills and craters.

SAUNDER, +151 −074 [English selenographer, 1852-1912]. A large but low ring to the west of Hipparchus, with a deep crater, N, on the south-east wall, here broken. On the interior are ridges, hills and some craterlets. On the north is the crater A, with its walls broken on the south and the north. To the east of A is another crater, while on both the west and east are crater-chains. To the south is a high mountain ridge, on the west of which is a crater-chain.

SCHNECKENBERG, MOUNT, +109 +160. This curious spiral mountain lies near Hyginus, and is described under that heading.

SCHRÖTER, −118 +047 [German selenographer, 1745-1816]. A ruined formation, 20 miles in diameter, with the wall wanting on the south, and also open on the north. The remainder of the rampart is low. South of the centre is a crater, A, from which Professor W. H. Pickering suspected an ejection of steam. The north wall has mountain spurs on either side of the gap. Outside and to the north is a crater, D, also some low ridges on either side of a long, shallow valley. This object was considered artificial by Gruithuisen, but was shown by Webb and others to be a natural feature. Dr. S. M. Green found a short winding cleft running south from the crater D.

SEELIGER, +053 −039 [Austrian astronomer, 1849-1924]. A double ring on the north-east wall of Hipparchus, with a crater, A, on the north. To the north-west is the deep bay, U, in the rampart of Hipparchus. From a low ring on the north-west a cleft runs towards the centre of the disk.

SINUS ÆSTUUM, −140 +210. Bay of Billows ('Seething Bay'). A plain to the south-west of Eratosthenes, remarkably smooth, but containing some very low ridges and a few craterlets. Of these craterlets, J and L are the most distinct, followed by H and G.

SÖMMERING, −130 +004 [German surgeon, 1755-1830]. Another ruined ring, 17 miles in diameter, with a gap in its south wall, and low on the north. The western portion of the wall rises 4,000 feet above the dark interior, on which are three mounds. To the west are hills, while on the east an ancient ring abuts against the rampart. Further east are some mountain masses, none of much height.

SPÖRER, −030 −074 [German astronomer, 1822-95]. This used to be known as Herschel A, and is described under that heading.

TRIESNECKER, +063 +073 [Austrian astronomer, 1745-1817]. A crater, over 14 miles in diameter, with a wall highest on the west; this portion overshadows the lower eastern part at sunrise, so that the formation then resembles a breached crater. This is caused by a fault. On the floor is a central hill, to the south of which is a low mound. There is also a low ridge under the east inner wall. The inner slopes are terraced. On the east are some low ridges, and large but shallow rings, also valleys. On the outer north slopes are hills, and a fault which has disturbed the surface in a very obvious manner. Faint light streaks radiate from the ring, visible under high illumination, the majority tending northwards and crossing a number of very low depressions, *a*, *b*, *c* and *d*, on the northern side of a long, low ridge. Triesnecker is the crater associated with what is undoubtedly one of the most remarkable cleft systems on the Moon.

THE TRIESNECKER CLEFTS

Lohrmann shows no clefts in his sections, but draws a long cleft to the east, seen in part by Neison, 20 August 1878, but not since detected.

This interesting and complex cleft system requires instruments of considerable aperture and optical excellence to be seen in its entirety, but the chief members can be detected with a good 3-inch refractor. Existing representations differ greatly in the positions and numbers of the finer members, many of which are too delicate to appear on even the finest photographs. Of these photographs the best is that by Dr. Lyot, reproduced in this book.

To the west of Triesnecker is a spot, considered by some observers as a craterlet, from which the clefts radiate. Two easily seen clefts run south towards the wall of Rhæticus. The more westerly divides on the south, one member crossing the eastern cleft. Here also are some delicate craterlets. Returning to the spot west of Triesnecker, two clefts run north, really continuations of those on the south. One runs north-north-west towards the crater A, but divides before reaching this object; of its branches one, running south-west, passes through two craterlets and ends at a mountain mass. North of this is a shorter cleft, which passes through two pits. East of A are two long clefts, which run for a long way to the north. This region is traversed by numerous fine clefts, some connecting with the great Hyginus cleft. One cleft curves convex to the east and crosses the chief clefts ending, on the west, at a small mountain. Between this mountain and Triesnecker is a crater, B, from which two fine clefts run north. The whole system is far too complex for mere description, and reference should be made to the map and photographs.

UKERT, +024 +134 [German historian, 1780-1851]. A crater about 14 miles in diameter, with bright walls on which is a craterlet on the south-west. There is a spur from the south wall, beyond which are two hills and several parallel ridges and rings; also a large obscure ring, P. On the north is a depression, A, with craters inside; and on its north a second ring, B, with terraced walls. To the west is a remarkable mountain ridge, enclosing an obscure ring, B. Some branches of the great Hyginus cleft run to its western side, and one of the clefts of the Triesnecker system cuts through its northern portion. On 21 April 1952, Moore, using the 33-inch Meudon refractor, found a delicate cleft running to the north-west wall of Ukert. East of Ukert is a crater, C, on the south of which is a valley which passes through some crater-like enlargements as far as the crater Bode A. This crater has a craterlet on its outer north slope, from which a long cleft runs north to the hinterland of the Apennine mountains. Where the valley reaches A is a low ring, L, with one craterlet and two hills on its interior. A strong mountain ridge, M, lies on the south-west of A, and there are numerous hills and craters around. Most of the hills tend north and south, with craterlet-chains between some of them, the whole forming a complicated hilly region omitted by Goodacre but full of interesting detail and difficult to draw. The cleft running north from Bode A divides on the far north, and the branch reaches the hills of the western Apennines.

II

This section is naturally divided into two portions
that on the south being occupied by many formations of which Theophilus, Capella, Isidorus and
Delambre predominate, while the northern part is
largely occupied by the broad expanse of the Mare
Tranquillitatis, one of the darkest of the lunar 'seas'.
On its east are some ruined formations of which
Julius Cæsar is a well-known example; here are
some long clefts connected with the Sabine-Ritter
group and the great Ariadæus cleft. The Mare contains numerous ridges, some of which form portions
of circles and evidently represent once-prominent
formations now apparently overwhelmed by the
material forming the surface of the plain. Some peculiar domes will also be found, two near Arago being
striking objects even in small telescopes.

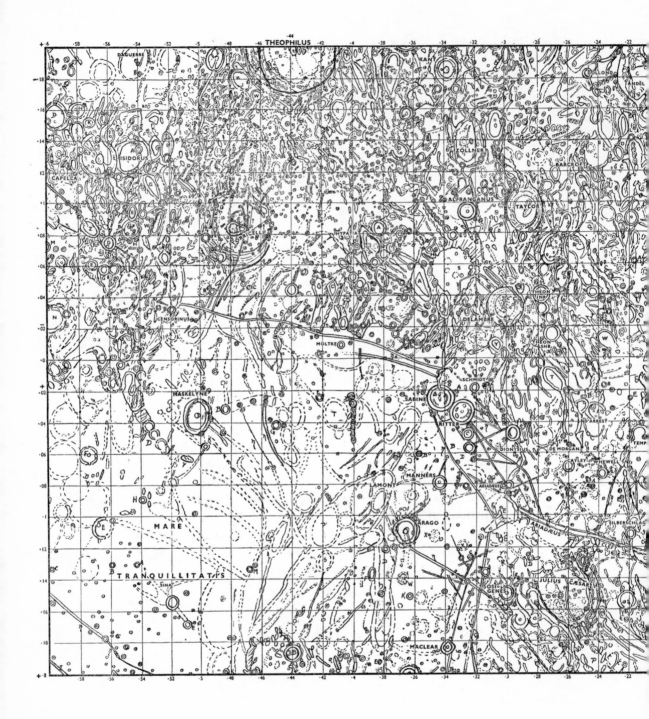

II

ALFRAGANUS, +324 −094 [Arab astronomer, *circa* A.D. 840]. A small crater, 12 miles in diameter and the centre of a minor ray system. It has a central hill and is very brilliant at Full, hence easily found under high illumination. North is a ring, B, from which a crater-chain runs south-west. On the south is a low ring with a central hill and craterlets on its walls. To the north also is a peculiar, nearly circular formation, with wide walls, cut by narrow ravines and with little craters in places and a large ring, B, on its north where also is a narrow pass opening eventually into the Mare Tranquillitatis, south of Sabine. The interior of this ring is smooth except for a few mounds and a craterlet on the north portion.

ANDĔL, +211 −182 [Czech astronomer, 1884-1947]. A large but low-rimmed ring containing hills, ridges and a few craterlets. The south wall is broken by a crater while from the west wall a crater-row runs to Dollond. On the rather broad south wall are two large and well-formed rings while the surroundings contain many ridges and depressions; the north-east wall is cut through by passes.

ARAGO, +363 +107 [French astronomer, 1786-1853]. A distinct crater, 18 miles in diameter with walls of no great height and not circular. On the interior is a small central mountain connected by a ridge to the north wall. On the north crest is a small crater while there are at least five peaks on the east rampart, none of any great altitude. On the surface on the west is a very remarkable, complex system of ridges enclosing the relic of a once-prominent ring about 50 miles in diameter while on the east and also on the north are large but low domes. These two domes are easily seen in a small telescope. From the north wall a cleft can be traced towards Sosigenes. Diggles found, 10 September 1933, three craterlets to the south of Arago. In 1954 Moore detected summit pits on 3 of the most prominent domes: one of these pits has been seen by H. G. Allen as a distinct craterlet (1954 June 7).

ARIADÆUS, +297 +080 [Macedonian king, died 317 B.C.]. A bright little crater, 9 miles in diameter, with a smaller crater in contact on the north-west. This Fauth shows as overlapping. Just to the north are two smaller craters. On the north is an ancient ring of which the south-west wall has disappeared, probably because of erosion by the material now forming the surface of the Mare. On the east are two ruined rings with another but less marked example on the south. This is little more than a curved ridge. From the east wall of the old ring to the north of Ariadæus there begins a great valley-cleft, discovered by Schröter in 1792 and easily seen in small instruments except at Full, when it is difficult to detect. The total length is over 150 miles, and soon after leaving Ariadæus it receives a branch from the south; there is also a short cleft which runs to the north-east wall. The great cleft then cuts through the old ring north of the crater B, is interrupted by a mountain, cuts through another and continues to the mountain arm to the north of Silberschlag. This portion is double, with the ends overlapping, as noted by Webb. Lohrmann traced it through all the hills, though greatly narrowed by the highest. The mountain arm here forms the border of an ancient and imperfect ring; after traversing this the cleft tends to the north-east and again divides into three portions, of which one connects it with the great cleft of Hyginus (see Section I). West of the crater Ariadæus, R. Barker and the Rev. W. F. A. Ellison have traced a continuation through the Mare beyond Manners, but this is very difficult to detect. Wilkins found, 25 April 1939, a delicate cleft to the east of Silberschlag and connected with the great cleft.

BARCROFT, +236 −136 [contemporary American selenographer]. A ring, formerly known as Dollond B, to the north of Dollond and south-east of Taylor. The walls are breached on the south-east while on the floor is a faint central mound and a low ring. On the west wall are craters while on the north-east is another partial ring, C, and the deep crater, D; to the north-west are rings, craterlets and mountain ridges.

CAPELLA, +567 −133 [Carthaginian lawyer, *circa* A.D. 450]. A fine ringed-plain over 30 miles in diameter with broad though low and terraced walls broken by a crater on the south, and here there is also a pass from which a valley runs towards the Mare Nectaris. On the north wall is a crater which has a break on the north-east, opening into confluent craters. On the interior of Capella is a large central hill bearing a distinct summit crater, and a ridge crossing the floor from the south-west to the north-east. On the west of this ridge is a fine cleft, while on the east is a lower ridge; there are also some low hills on the north. D. W. G. Arthur found a craterlet on the inner south-east and a crater-cleft to the south from a double crater on the west. Schmidt shows some crater-chains on both the west and the east of the central mountain. On the outer west and south-west are some obscure rings while to the south are mountain spurs and craters. The low ring on the west has craters on its walls.

CAYLEY, +260 +069 [English mathematician, 1821-95]. A bright crater 9 miles in diameter with a twin craterlet on the south wall. A very low ring abuts on the west. From this ring a cleft runs to Ariadæus.

CENSORINUS, +540 −007 [Latin grammarian and mathematician, *circa* A.D. 238]. This is a very brilliant crater 3 miles in diameter situated on a bright area. On the west is a larger crater, and east, a long cleft running to the mountain ridge south of Sabine. West is a large enclosure, F, with craters on the south and a craterlet-chain to a smaller enclosure, A, to the north. East of this is a mountain ridge running to Censorinus. North-east is a small, isolated mountain, Beta, and several craterlets. At times Censorinus is one of the brightest objects on the Moon.

DAGUERRE, +545 −200 [French photographic pioneer, 1789-1851]. A low ring, the walls being mere ridges, to the west of Mädler and thus on the border of the Mare Nectaris. There is a crater-row on the east rim. On the interior are two craterlets in the centre; also a crater, B, on the northern portion.

D'ARREST, +257 +040 [German astronomer, 1822-75]. An imperfect crater to the south of Whewell, with a break in the east wall. On the interior is a crater, A, touching the inner south-west slope, also some small hills. To the south-west is another ring, on the edge of a large imperfect ring of which the northern rampart is wanting.

DELAMBRE, +298 −033 [French astronomer, 1749-1822]. A great ringed plain, 32 miles in diameter, with terraced walls rising 7,600 feet on the east but 15,000 feet on the west. On the north wall is a crater, and there is another on the south-east. On the inner east is a landslip, with another on the north-east. There is a bright craterlet on the inner south-west, and others elsewhere. The central mountain has a summit craterlet, and to the east of it is a small ravine. Dr. S. M. Green shows a crater close to the south wall, noted by Goodacre, also a fissure extending from the centre towards but not reaching the south walls, found by Elger and confirmed by Goodacre. Goodacre shows no detail except the central mountain and the crater on the south. Green found some low ridges on the western portion of the interior, and a curved ridge-like object on the inner north slope, which Wilkins has seen as the more northerly of two very low-rimmed rings. The ridges on the western portion have also been confirmed. In addition Wilkins has noted two isolated hillocks on the eastern portion between the central mountain and the foot of the walls, also a curved valley-cleft traversing the inner north-east slope, ending in a minute craterlet. To the south, on the outer surface, is a mountain mass with a depression on the west. North-east is an ancient ring, and on the plain to the north the remains of two old rings. Of these only the south walls now remain. On the south-west is a large, smooth enclosure, S, with very broad inner slopes traversed by narrow valleys. On the floor is a bent cleft on the north-east, as shown on the map; also some very low mounds.

DE MORGAN, +257 +058 [English mathematician, 1806-71]. A bright crater, 5 miles in diameter. On the south is an irregular enclosure, from the north-west of which a wide, shallow but rugged valley runs towards Delambre.

DIONYSIUS, +297 +048 [Saint, A.D. 9-120]. A bright crater, 12 miles in diameter, and light-encompassed. On the outer west slope is a craterlet-chain, while two clefts run from the wall, one to Ritter. On the floor is a narrow ridge concentric with the west wall, either a landslip or the fragment of an ancient ring. Thornton has found a ridge traversing the crater centrally from north to north. The surface to the north contains many hillocks. In 1950, Thornton, using his 18-inch reflector, found a dark band running to the inner north wall of Dionysius, and this is particularly interesting because, unlike many other bands in craters, it is not placed directly opposite the rising Sun, and cannot therefore be due to any trick of the light. It has been confirmed by Moore.

DOLLOND, +246 −182 [English optician, 1706-61]. Another bright crater, 6 miles in diameter. On the east is a large, low ring with a broken east wall, while to the north is Anděl. To the north-east are several partially enclosed rings and craters, the most prominent being Barcroft. A crater-chain on the north runs to the west wall of Anděl.

HYPATIA, +381 −070 [Egyptian female mathematician, died A.D. 415]. A remarkable formation, distinctly triangular and 30 miles in diameter. The walls rise 7,000 feet on the east, while there is a deep crater, A, on the south-east wall. On the west there are gaps in the wall, which is also low on the north. On the floor is some faint detail, including a hill. To the north-west is a great rocky mass, and on the north-east a mass of craters of which F and K are the deepest. To the west are isolated hills running north and south. On the north is a ring, F, containing a central crater.

ISIDORUS, +543 −140 [Spanish bishop, A.D. 570-636]. This crater lies on the east of Capella, which has intruded on to the floor. It is 30 miles in diameter, with terraced walls. The interior contains a large crater, A, near the east wall, and also a craterlet on the north. On the outer south is a ring with the southern portion of its rampart wanting, and close by is a mountain mass. To the north is a large low ring, with others, and a crater, D. On the east is a circle of isolated hills, evidently the remains of a once-perfect crater. On the north-east is a crater, G, and due north many craters of which E and C are the most prominent. The latter is really three confluent depressions, the dividing walls having disappeared. D. W. G. Arthur has found a pass in the east wall, and another to the north, with a craterlet.

JULIUS CÆSAR, +257 +156 [Great Roman soldier, 102-44 B.C.]. A large but imperfect formation open on the west. There is a large crater at the end of the east wall, and another on the north. On the broad outer west slope are three confluent craters, while the inner slopes are terraced, especially on the east. The floor gradually darkens towards the north, where it is almost as dark as Plato or Grimaldi. Dotted over the interior are low hills, one nearly central, and several craterlets. Fauth shows a cleft traversing the floor from the south wall, while Wilkins found a winding cleft traversing the dark area on the north and dying out on the interior. On the south-east are many craterlets, and also a crater-chain. There is a craterpit on the summit of the central mound. The dark area on the northern portion is bluish in the lunar morning, according to Haas.

KANT, +340 −184 [Great German philosopher, 1724-1804]. A well-formed crater, very deep, with a double rampart, according to Schmidt. The inner walls are finely terraced, while the interior contains a large central mountain connected by ridges to the north wall. There is a craterlet on the south rim, and there are two craters on the outer north, with a valley, V, between them. To the north-west is a lofty mountain mass, very prominent under low illumination, and rising 14,000 feet. It has an old ring on its south-west, which region contains many craterlets. To the south of this ancient ring is another, while north-west of the great mountain mass is a ring, C, with a central hill and many minute craterlets and ancient rings scattered around. Trouvelot, 4 January 1873, found a mist-like appearance inside Kant, obscuring the known detail for some time.

LAMONT, +392 +090 [Scottish astronomer, 1805-79]. A low and imperfect ring to the south-west of Arago. On the south is another imperfect ring with two craterlets on its south rim.

MACLEAR, +338 +183 [Irish astronomer, 1794-1879]. This formation is decidedly polygonal, with low walls and a dark floor on which is a low central hill. From the north wall a cleft runs to the crater Plinius A, and another cleft from the north wall runs to Sosigenes A. On the east is a fine, long cleft, which probably joins that running north-east from Sabine. This cleft has a total length of 200 miles, and is interrupted by Sosigenes A.

MÄDLER, +487 −191 [Great German selenographer, 1794-1897]. An elliptical crater 20 miles in diameter, with walls rising 6,000 feet on the east but only 3,000 feet on the west. A ridge cuts through the north wall, and traverses the floor to a central hill. To the north of Mädler, this ridge forms the western side of an ancient ring. In addition to the ridge and central hill, there are some low ridges on the interior, which is also shaded in a peculiar manner. On the west are four old rings, crossed by light streaks and low ridges, and also containing many tiny craterlets first seen in 1953 by Moore with the 25-inch Newall refractor at Cambridge. To the south are some delicate craterlet chains, and some low ridges running into the Mare Nectaris.[1]

MANNERS, +341 +080 [English naval officer, 1800-70]. A bright crater, 10 miles in diameter, with a small central hill. On the south-west is a brilliant crater, B, containing a central hill, while further west is the smaller crater, C, close to which is a ridge from Lamont towards Sabine.

MASKELYNE, +500 +038 [Astronomer Royal, 1732-1811]. This crater is 19 miles in diameter, and has a terraced inner slope and a depressed floor, also a crater on the east wall. On the interior is a low central hill, while to the east are ancient rings and a cleft from three small craters. To the north-west are three partial rings, and on the east is the crater, B, from which a shallow valley runs east. From this valley two clefts can be traced towards the north.

MOLTKE, +410 −010 [German military officer, 1800-91]. A small crater near the border of the Mare Tranquillitatis and due north of Hypatia. On the south is a long cleft from Censorinus as far as the mountain arm to the south of Sabine. On the north-east is another but shorter cleft, while crater-chains exist both on the north and south.

RITTER, +329 +035 [German geographer, 1779-1859]. A fine crater, one of a pair of twin objects, the other being Sabine. It is 19 miles in diameter, and has narrow walls, finely terraced and rising 4,000 feet above the floor, on which is a central hill and a cleft

[1] Name omitted from map.

concentric with the east wall. The floor is uneven, and contains two craterlets on the south, also a swelling near the foot of the inner north wall. On the outer north are two craters, while Wilkins has seen two craters in contact on the northern portion of the floor and a depression to the south-east of the central hill. There is also a hill on the western portion. From the north-east wall three clefts tend to the north-east, and are crossed by another from the crater B to Dionysius, but not easily seen.

SABINE, +343 +024 [English astronomer and explorer, 1788-1883]. The companion crater to Ritter, 18 miles in diameter, with narrow but continuous walls and a low central hill. There are two slight breaks in the north-west crest, and a larger break on the north-east. On the south crest is a peak, and from this a ridge runs south. West of this ridge are two parallel clefts along the border of the Mare. The more southerly of these clefts may be traced to Censorinus. To the north of the central hill is a shallow ring, while on the outer west is a chain of low-rimmed craters.

SCHMIDT, +322 +017 [Great German selenographer, 1825-84]. A small but bright crater, 8 miles in diameter, to the south of Ritter. On the east is a small bright area, and on the north are two craterlets in contact, from which a cleft runs north-east to Dionysius. On the south are many low hills.

SILBERSCHLAG, +216 +108 [German astronomer, 1721-91]. A bright crater, 8 miles in diameter, on a strong mountain arm, which, on the south, is the relic of an ancient ring crossed by a cleft and joining another cleft running south. On the north the mountain arm also curves and encloses an ancient ring which is crossed by the great Ariadæus cleft.

SINAS, +518 +154 [Greek financier, 1810-76]. A small crater with a smaller on its north-east and others near on the south-west, as well as two craterlets, A and B.

SOSIGENES, +299 +151 [Greek astronomer, *circa* 46 B.C.]. A circular crater, 14 miles in diameter, with a central hill. On the south-west is the crater A on a long cleft, and connected to Sosigenes by a ridge. Closely under the west wall is a cleft. On the north is an ancient ring, containing a central mound.

TAYLOR, +285 —095 [English mathematician, 1685-1731]. An elliptical depression, 25 miles from north to south, and with walls broken on the north by a crater; others exist on the south. On the floor is a large central mountain, with a ring to the south of it. On the south-west is a mountain mass, while there is a low ring on the west with a smaller one on its north. On the north-west are two rings in a ruined state, and others lie further out. From the south wall a ridge with craters on its summit runs south-west to a large ring. To the west of this is a still larger ring, and some partial rings lie to the west.

TEMPEL, +206 +064 [German astronomer, 1821-89]. An imperfect ring south-east of Whewell, with broad slopes and a break on the north. On each segment either side of the break is a craterlet. Tempel stands on the rim of a large ancient ring crossed by a cleft. South is the relic of another old ring, of which the south wall is still rugged and lofty. South is a mountain mass, Delta, also some hills and small craters.

THEON JUNIOR, +273 −042 [Alexandrian astronomer, *circa* A.D. 380]. A crater, 10 miles in diameter. On the south-east is a low imperfect ring, with a hill on its interior and two craterlets. From a crater on the north wall of this ring a strong mountain arm runs north to just east of Theon Senior.

THEON SENIOR, +266 −014 [Greek astronomer, *circa* A.D. 100]. A bright and deep crater, 11 miles in diameter, to the east of Delambre, with a crater to its north and another nearer and on the edge of a shallow valley leading to a large low ring, on the broad north wall of which are other ruined rings, S. On the south are two rings, while on the north is a low ring, T.

THEOPHILUS, +435 −199 [Saint; Alexandrian bishop, died A.D. 412]. A magnificent ringed-plain, the leader of a grand group, the others being Cyrillus and Catharina. It is 65 miles in diameter, with a narrow crest made up of linear segments and continuous all around, rising, on the west, over 18,000 feet above the depressed floor. The inner slopes are broad and divided by rows of terraces with some craters, the largest being on the north-east. Scriven Bolton detected a minute pit, less than a mile in diameter, on the extreme western crest. This was confirmed by Moore in 1952 with the 25-inch 'Newall' refractor at the Cambridge University Observatory. The outer slopes are rugged, and contain grand landslips on the north-west; and the whole is surrounded by radiating ridges, valleys and rows of minute craterlets. From the outer north-west slope a short but very conspicuous ridge runs southwards, ending near Beaumont. Along its western side is a long but delicate cleft, on the east a chaos of rings and depressions. The inner slopes on the south-east exhibit great landslips; two in particular are very evident where the great formation intrudes upon Cyrillus. On the interior is a majestic multiple-peaked central mountain mass, split into two major and lower peaks with a crater-like depression on the north. The base of this mountain mass is, on the east, shaped like a horse-shoe, suggesting buried rings. At the foot of the slopes are many little craters, while on the floor are some cones and low ridges. One of these cones is very prominent on the north-eastern portion, and is the node of a system of light streaks, studied by Scriven Bolton and well seen under a high sun. The contour of the central mountain appears to change as the lunation proceeds, attributed by Prof. W. H. Pickering to the deposit and subsequent melting of snow deposits. Haas, Barcroft and other observers in America have also studied the appearances, and find that Pickering's drawings no longer represent the present sequence of apparent changes. In addition to well-formed craters, the inner slopes contain ruined enclosures, evidently the relics of former craters; on the inner north-east, just below the crest, is a crater-row, some components of which are in a very ruinous state. The crest is everywhere very lofty, and there are few peaks, the whole forming a spectacle far surpassing anything on the Earth. A fine photograph is that taken at the Yerkes Observatory, 12 October 1900. Owing to the brightness of its details, Theophilus can always be detected.

TORRICELLI, +475 —084 [Italian physicist, 1608-47]. A remarkable double ring, the larger component being on the west and 12 miles in diameter, with a slight break on the south. The smaller, eastern component is 5 miles in diameter, with the wall broken down at the point of contact with the larger ring, and with two minute craterlets at the point of junction on the south. Owing to this gap, Molesworth, Arthur and others have seen a ray of light, at sunrise, shining through the gap and on to the floor of the formation. Burrell and Thornton have seen a cleft traversing the floor of this object, shown, however, by Burrell as a craterpit-chain. The smaller ring also has a gap in its east wall, with a craterlet outside to the south, and the sunlight sometimes streams through this outer gap before passing through the inner and thence on to the floor. From the south wall, a long cleft is said to run to the east; Thornton and Moore have seen a ridge to the east of the smaller component. Two other, shorter and parallel clefts have been reported on the south, with another further east. Goodacre mentions the triple system of clefts on the south, but Thornton has failed to confirm this with his 18-inch reflector. To the west are two more clefts on the rim of a large and prominent ancient ring, traceable in its entirety but very low in places, Torricelli being situated on its interior but not centrally. This ring must once have been a most imposing object; now, the wall is especially low on the north, and here are some crater-chains. They run parallel to the cleft from the north wall of Torricelli. Several minute craterlets will be found scattered over the interior of this old ring.

Thornton, 3 March 1952, found variations in the shadow on the inner west, afterwards confirmed by Wilkins; also a bright band on the inner slope. There is a fault across the western part of the floor, while on the east Thornton has seen a cleft crossing the floor and then up the south wall, to end in a minute depression on the rim.

TRANQUILLITATIS, MARE, 'Sea of Tranquillity'. A great and dark Mare very prominent to the naked eye, while in the telescope it is dotted over with ridges, especially near Arago, where they present remarkable contortions; craters, ancient rings, craterlets and clefts. The latter are particularly well seen around the margins. This vast plain is obviously at a different level from the neighbouring Mare Serenitatis, the latter being at a lower level. The margins contain many little bays, and these are best seen on the north where two to the west of Julius Cæsar strike the eye.

WHEWELL, +237 +073 [English philosopher, 1794-1866]. A very bright crater, about 5 miles in diameter, first named by Birt. The open plain around is dotted with many craterpits; of these, three in a row on the south are easily seen, but the majority are very delicate objects and require powerful instruments. They average 500 yards in diameter, although some are over a mile.

In addition to the above features there is a craterpit in contact with the north wall of Whewell, and a craterpit on the east. From a mountain to the east a cleft can be traced running northwards, and crossing the interior of an ancient ring.

ZÖLLNER, +320 −140 [German astronomer, 1834-82]. A large enclosure with low but broad walls, situated between Kant and Taylor. There are some craters on the walls, while on the interior is a distinct crater on the eastern portion and a low-rimmed ring on its west, together with some ridges, none however of any magnitude. To the south-east is a smaller enclosure bearing evidences of the action, in former times, of erosive forces. On the outer south-west slope are some abnormal enclosures, and others along the west wall, while there is a crater on the outer north. From a peak on the rim of the large ring on the south-east a ridge runs to Taylor. North-west is a partial ring and a peak, Eta, and south-west is the great mountain, Kant Alpha, rising 14,000 feet and overshadowing this region under low illumination. C. F. O. Smith reported a plateau-like formation between Zöllner and Kant, but this has not been confirmed.

III

This section is largely occupied by the Mare Serenitatis, one of the most interesting of all the lunar
'seas'. The passage between it and the neighbouring
Mare Tranquillitatis is dominated by the prominent
crater Plinius, an imposing formation which presents
very different aspects under different illuminations,
and has been critically studied in recent times.

Several long clefts will be found around the margins of both the Mare Serenitatis and the Mare
Tranquillitatis, and others are associated with the
ringed plains Posidonius, Chacornac and Römer.
One of the most prominent mountain-ridges on the
Moon is that which winds its way across the western
portion of the Mare Serenitatis.

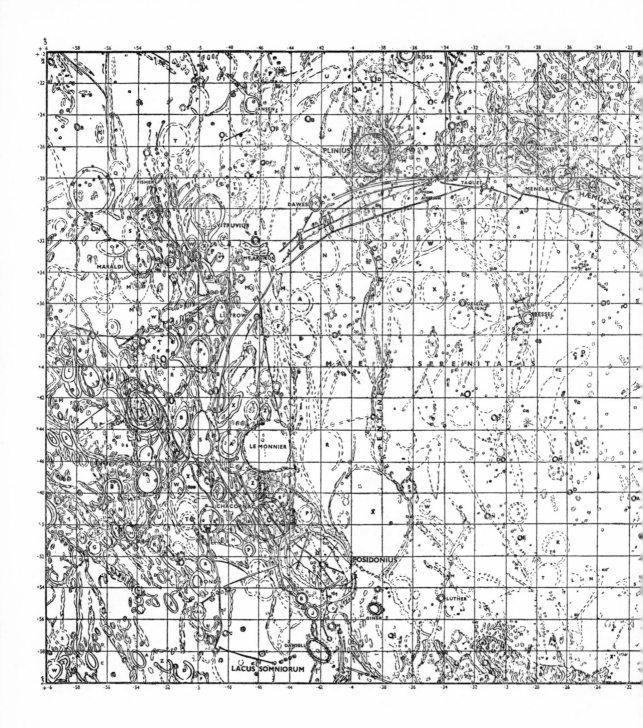

III

ACHERUSIA, PROMONTORIUM, +354 +288. A cape or promontory at the western end of the border of the Mare Serenitatis, and to the north-east of Plinius. It rises 4,850 feet above the plain. Three slightly diverging clefts run westwards towards Dawes, and there is another cleft running north-east to Taquet. This latter cleft gives off a branch, Eta 7, parallel with the first three clefts, and traceable nearly as far as Mt. Argæus.

ARGÆUS, MOUNT, +450 +355. A small mountain mass named by Webb, and remarkable for the long spire of shade which it casts at sunrise. It is divided by a ravine and rises, at the highest point, to 8,000 feet above the dark plain at its base. On the south L. F. Ball found two craters. On the north is an ancient ring crossed by a cleft, which probably connects with one of the valley-clefts connected with Plinius.

AUWERS, +284 +260 [German astronomer, 1838-1915]. A small crater to the south-west of Menelaus, in the hilly country bordering the Maria Tranquillitatis and Sereni-tatis. South is a peak, Alpha, and north-east are some depressions forming an interest-ing region; one of these depressions is a square enclosure. West is a bay of the Mare Tranquillitatis, also the bright little crater A, from which a long cleft runs southwards with a very short cleft on the south-east.

BESSEL, +286 +370 [German astronomer, 1784-1846]. This is the largest crater on the surface of the Mare Serenitatis, and, being isolated, is a prominent feature. About 12 miles in diameter, it is situated on the broad light streak which crosses the Mare. The walls rise sharply to 3,600 feet, with little peaks on the north and the south rims rising approximately 200 feet higher. The floor, which is depressed 2,000 feet, is rather dark and there is some faint detail, considered by Webb as a central mountain. This, how-ever, has rarely been seen as such. Moore was unable to find it on 21 April 1952, with the 33-inch Meudon refractor, though a low hill east of the centre was discovered. There is a minute craterlet on the inner west slope. Abutting on the south wall are the remains of an ancient ring, of which a ridge to the south forms the west wall. Fauth found two low hills on the north-west portion of the floor of Bessel. On the south-east is a small crater, E, with three craterlets on its east, while east are the craters G and F.

BOND, G. P., +501 +536 [American astronomer, 1826-65]. A formation 12 miles in diameter, with craters on both the north and the south rims, according to Neison, though these are omitted by Schmidt. On the south is a ring with a gap on the north; north is a large ancient ring, with another on the south-west. The wall of this latter ring is wanting on the south, and there are some craters on the east side of the remaining

F 81

wall. To the east of these objects a long cleft may be traced, while a finer cleft crosses the southern portion of the ancient ring. The cleft on the east has been found by Arthur to have some crater-like enlargements along its course.

CHACORNAC, +456 +497 [French astronomer, 1823-73]. A pentagonal formation about 30 miles in diameter, with a bright western wall and a deep crater south of which is a shallow, lava-filled ring. On the north are depressions, while a crater occupies a break in the north-west rampart. On the floor is a bright-walled crater, with a ridge on either side and two parallel clefts. On the north are chains of hills, and craterlets on the south. On the broad western glacis are large depressions. A valley from the floor runs along the western part of the neighbouring Posidonius. Wilkins has found the cleft on the western part of the floor to be, in part, a craterlet-chain and to traverse a low ring. This was confirmed by Moore on 19 April 1952, with the 33-inch Meudon refractor, and a third floor-cleft, not far from the west wall, was also discovered.

DANIELL, +422 +580 [English physicist, 1790-1845]. A very distinct crater, 19 miles in diameter, and connected by two clefts and ridges with Posidonius. On the north is a craterlet-chain, while on the east is a cleft which cuts through an ancient ring. The inner slope has a narrow valley running all round. On the north-west is the craterlet K, from which a cleft runs south-west, while on the east are mountain ridges and several other clefts.

DAWES, +424 +296 [English amateur astronomer, 1799-1868]. A fine crater, 14 miles in diameter, and standing on a bright area which marks the site of an ancient ring. There is a small central peak, according to Goodacre, but Thornton has failed to find this feature with his 18-inch reflector. Using his 12½-inch reflector, Moore, in 1952, suspected two dusky bands on the inner east wall, and in 1953 these were confirmed by the Authors, using the Meudon 33-inch. Thornton has detected a ring abutting on the inner west slope, and a delicate cleft crossing the interior from this ring to the south-east rim.

DESEILLIGNY, +328 +360 [French selenographer, 1868-1918]. A small crater to the west of Bessel, and thus on the surface of the Mare Serenitatis, presenting no remarkable features.

FISHER, +528 +280 [American astronomer, 1878-1949]. A crater, 9 miles in diameter, south-west of Vitruvius. To the north lie three craterlets and a larger, low-rimmed crater A, with a central hill; south is an ancient ring, T, and to the west the low-walled ring D, described with Vitruvius.

GINER +385 +553 [Contemporary Spanish astronomer]. A crater 10 miles in diameter, lying north-east of Posidonius, and described under that heading.

HÆMUS MOUNTAINS. A range of mountains forming the south-east border of the Mare Serenitatis, and abounding in little peaks rising from 4,000 to 8,000 feet.

Comparatively few valleys run between the mountains and on to the Mare, while the entire range is bright under moderate illumination.

HALL, +500 +555 [American astronomer, 1829-1907]. This is a ring on the western edge of the deep bay to the west of Posidonius, and possesses no remarkable features.

JANSEN, +466 +234 [Dutch optician, died 1619]. A crater 16 miles in diameter, with very low walls, rising only 300 feet above the dark floor, which is at the same level as the outer surface. On the floor is a crater to the south of the centre. All around are numerous curved ridges and old rings, especially on the south-west and the north, also small craters. South of Jansen is the crater B, a small crater of unusual shape. It tapers to the west, where its floor is occupied by a crater and associated with a large ruined ring, whose floor is slightly darker than the surrounding surface, and which is partly bounded, on the west, by a ridge. This ridge has its northern termination at a peak of some altitude.

KIRCHHOFF, +544 +504 [German physicist, 1824-87]. The larger of two craters, to the east of Newcomb, with a smooth floor and a minute craterlet on its south-east wall. West of it is a slightly smaller crater with craterlets on its floor. To the south-west is the old ring, N, opening into the ring B, on the south. North-east of Kirchhoff is an obscure ring, R, while on the north, are mountain ridges, outspurs of the Taurus range.

LE MONNIER, +455 +448 [French astronomer, 1715-99]. A fine example of a partial ring, as the portion of the rampart which faces the Mare Serenitatis has almost disappeared; only a few low mounds now remain. It thus appears as a bay on the border of the 'sea'. One of the remaining fragments of this former wall, on the south-east, rises 3,000 feet. On the interior Schmidt shows a craterlet, while Fauth shows three craterlets on the north wall, from which he also shows some clefts running north. On 26 September 1953, Moore had a very fine view of Le Monnier with Dr. W. H. Steavenson's 30-inch reflector at Cambridge University. The low east wall, while of negligible height, could be traced in its entirety; the floor, certainly one of the levellest areas on the whole Moon, was blank except for two indistinct white patches.

LITTROW, +486 +367 [German astronomer, 1781-1840]. A deep crater, 22 miles in diameter, with broad walls, especially on the east, but broken by a pass on the south. On the south-west crest are two craters, beyond which is a low ring. To the west is an ancient ring with its north wall breached, and with a crater on the inner north-west slope. Farther to the west is a larger, ancient ring. A crater-chain runs down the outer north slope of Littrow, while on the dark floor are two mounds and some other detail. To the east are a bright crater, a dark spot and some clefts.

LUTHER, +342 +547 [German astronomer, 1822-1900]. A small crater on the open plain to the west of Posidonius, and on the eastern rim of a large square enclosure formed by low ridges. On the south are two minute pits, and there are others on the west. The north wall is connected by a low ridge to a mountain mass, forming a promontory of the mountains bordering the Mare on the north.

MARALDI, +539 +332 [Italian-French astronomer, 1709-88]. A dark and low ring, open on the south and with low rings on either side of the site of the former south wall. Other low rings abound in the vicinity. There is a crater on the inner north wall, and beyond it a rounded hill. To the south-west is a crater, H, and north the still larger crater, K.

MENELAUS, +264 +280 [Greek geometer and astronomer, *circa* A.D. 100]. A very bright crater, 20 miles in diameter, with beautifully terraced walls rising 8,000 feet above the floor. The floor contains a mountain not quite centrally placed, from which a ridge runs to the inner south-east wall; this ridge forms part of the wall of a very old ring on the south-east floor. There are depressions in the south and east walls of Menelaus, giving the impression of dark 'bands' under high illumination. Menelaus lies on the boundary of the Mare Serenitatis, and dark Mare-material has flowed over the northern, though not the southern, floor.

East of Menelaus is a peculiar formation, F, consisting of a crater which intrudes upon an old, squarish formation with a dark interior. Between it and Menelaus are several short, parallel ridges, well seen by Moore, using the 33-inch Meudon refractor, on 20 April 1953.

Menelaus is brilliant at Full Moon, and is the origin of a light streak which crosses the Mare Serenitatis. In the midst of this streak is a cleft, which can be traced for 20 miles from Menelaus' north wall. South-west of Menelaus is the little crater, Auwers; to the east lie the Hæmus Mountains, with a long cleft parallel to the 'coast'. North-west of Menelaus, on the Mare, is a craterlet, A, and beyond it a low ring, P.

PLINIUS, +387 +265 [Roman historian, *circa* A.D. 23-79]. A fine crater, 30 miles in diameter, with almost circular walls, finely terraced and with crater-like depressions on the east. There is another depression on the north, and concentric rings on the west. Nielsen in 1882, found, with a telescope of 6½-inch aperture, two craters on the south-east crest connected by a cleft which winds along the inner east slope. R. Barker found 8 October 1933, a fine curved cleft commencing to the east of Jansen E and skirting the outer north glacis of Plinius, ending a little further to the east. All around are radial ridges, and there is a small mountain close to the north-east wall. Some craterlet-chains can be seen on the south. To the north are three parallel clefts; that nearest to Plinius is broad and, in part, a crater-chain. On the north-west this cleft is crossed by another running south. Barker noted a large craterlet under the west wall, a light patch on the east and some other detail. Schröter shows a mountain in the centre of the floor, Lohrmann a double mountain and Mädler central craters on low mounds. Schmidt described it as a reversed omega. Goodacre depicted these as two craters. Neison shows two central mountains, and Elger says that a little south of the centre are two crater-like objects with broken rims which assume different aspects under varying conditions of illumination. Goodacre remarked that the bright central mountain sometimes presents the appearance of a double crater. On the inner west is an oval crater, according to Goodacre, with a depression on its north. Haas mentions seeing the central craterlets at co-longitude 348° but apparently an ellipse at 355°. From 80° to 105° the central mountains appear as a solid mass of uniform brightness except for a small dull area in the centre. Under a high light Plinius resembles a wheel (Goodacre), but Martz, Roth and Haas find the 'spokes' to be composed of separate bright spots.

Wilkins has had little difficulty in seeing the double crater aspect, and this is manifest at sunrise. As the angle of illumination increases, the floor presents a confused array of light spots and streaks which it takes a good telescope to show clearly. Some way east-south-east of Plinius, in the foothills of the Hæmus Mountains, is a small crater, Plinius A, marking the northern end of a cleft. The floor of A is decidedly dark under high light. Outside the north-east wall of Plinius is a rounded mountain, B. Using the Meudon 33-inch O.G., Moore, on 20 April 1953, discovered that this has a minute summit craterlet. This was confirmed by Wilkins.

POSIDONIUS, +419 +526 [Greek philosopher, 135-51 B.C.]. A majestic ring, 62 miles in diameter, with low and narrow walls, rising at their highest point 6,000 feet above the light interior and broad on the west, but especially narrow on the east, where they rapidly thin and end in a distinct break. On the surface, to the outer east, are little hills. On the interior, which has a peculiar glittering aspect, are the remains of an inner ring, well marked on the west but wanting in parts on the north and fragmentary on the south-east. On the interior of Posidonius, apart from this ring, is a nearly central crater. A, with a rough circle of hills on its west, doubtless the relic of a once-perfect crater. There are smaller craters on the south, one of which Lamèch declared to be subject to occasional obscuration in a manner similar to what Schröter found in connection with the great crater A. On the northern portion are numerous hills, craterlets and a low ring. On the north wall is the deep crater, T, with smaller craters, B and D, to the south. On the southern portion of the floor is a fine cleft, running east to west and easily seen, while several other clefts exist; one to the crater A and some more delicate clefts intersecting on the west. Two clefts run northwards from A to a cleft tending east to west on the north, while a cleft cuts through the north wall and others divide the western rampart. To the south-east of Posidonius is a large, ancient ring, from the south-east of which a strong mountain ridge runs, in a somewhat serpentine fashion, southwards across the Mare Serenitatis. This ridge rises, in places, to 800 feet and is very easily seen in small instruments. Along the outer north-west glacis are low rings and beyond, among others, the crater Giner. It is of some interest that the crater A is shown on the map of Riccioli (1651). Tobias Mayer depicts a central mountain, as he also did in the case of Archimedes, probably owing to the small aperture of his telescope. He was, also probably, misled by the appearance under high illumination. The crater A was seen by Schröter and also Schmidt to be shadowless at times when it ought to have exhibited some.

Dr. R. W. Porter, using the 60-inch reflector of the Mt. Wilson Observatory, found, 11 July 1929, a rough circle of hills west of A, a cleft from north to south skirting the western side of A, which then bends west and passes between some hills on the south and ends at a portion of the inner ring. East of A was seen a long hill from which a cleft runs south to a minute craterlet. He also found a crater to the north-east of A, and five shallow clefts from the western part of the inner ring towards the rough circle of hills west of A. There was also a short branch cleft to the great cleft on the northern part of the interior, and many mounds or landswells. Of the craters connected with Posidonius, Arthur found that J has a hill on the south-west part of its floor and a ridge on the inner north and east. D. C. Brown, with a 10-inch telescope, found minute craterlets near Giner, which also contains two brilliant spots on its floor. He traced pits between Giner and Daniell.

Recently Neate has carefully mapped the outline of Posidonius but did not insert the details. Wilkins independently measured this crater, and there is good agreement with the work of Neate; the final form is shown on the map, to which reference should be made for the details connected with this great formation, one of the most important and interesting on the entire lunar surface.

RÖMER, +537 +429 [Danish astronomer, 1644-1710]. A fine crater, 35 miles in diameter, with broad, terraced walls rising 11,600 feet on both west and east. On the interior is a central hill bearing a summit craterlet, a craterlet to the north, a cleft and ridges. On the north is the crater A, with a central hill and walls rising 3,700 feet on the east but 6,000 feet on the west.[1] Römer overlaps an older ring, and has intruded on the north portion. Outside the south-east wall is a crater, D, from which a very long cleft runs northwards, with some branches at intervals. West is a large, low ring, P, with a hill, Delta, and a cleft running north-west from it. On the east, beyond D, is a large ring, R, one of many low rings in this region. On the north are also some craterlet chains.

ROSS, +363 +202 [English explorer, 1800-62]. A crater 18 miles in diameter, with a central peak and traces of terraces on the bright inner west slope. It is not quite circular, and there are two minute craterpits on the northern crest. There is a deflection of the south-east wall, and a short mountain spur tends from the south crest. To the north-west is the crater, B, on the edge of an ancient ring.

SERENITATIS, MARE, +285 +440. 'Sea of Serenity'. This beautiful and circular dark plain or 'sea' is about 430 miles in diameter, and is bordered by the Taurus Mountains on the west, the Caucasus on the north-east, the highlands of Posidonius on the north-west and the Hæmus Mountains on the south and east. The surface is lower than that of the Mare Tranquillitatis. In the past it was charted by Birt, and also by Johnson and Williams, whose chart shows approximately 200 craters and other details. There are clear indications of subsidence on a very considerable scale around the margins where also are some clefts. Of the numerous ridges on the plain the most prominent is the great serpentine ridge discovered by Schröter, which rises, in places, to 800 feet. This ridge was shown, in part, by Tobias Mayer, in 1775.

TAQUET, +315 +286 [Belgian mathematician, 1612-60]. A bright crater, 6 miles in

[1] Now called ATATURK after the founder of modern Turkey.

diameter, with a craterlet on the north and a long cleft. On the east is a hill, and a craterlet from which a fine cleft runs to the north-east. A narrow ridge, or 'razor edge', joins Taquet to the border of the Mare Serenitatis, and on this ridge Wilkins found a craterlet, with a short, previously unrecorded cleft on its east.

TAURUS MOUNTAINS, +580 +460. This is rather a hilly upland than a mountain range, and has many little peaks which rise, near Berzelius, to over 10,000 feet in altitude, though elsewhere they are much lower, few attaining 3,000 feet.

VITRUVIUS, +495 +303 [Roman architect and engineer, *circa* 100 B.C.]. This ring is 20 miles in diameter, with bright walls but a very dark floor on which is a low central peak. To the west is a centrally peaked crater, A, and, on the south, some crater-chains. On the north-west is a low ring, while on the south-west, beyond Fisher, is a large ancient ring, D, containing craterlets. In 1920, W. S. Franks reported that some of the peaks near Vitruvius were unusually bright at times, and varied considerably in brilliancy.

IV

Stretching across the central portion of this section is the majestic arc of the Apennine Mountains, the most important range within the disk, flanking the Mare Imbrium and separating this plain from the Mare Vaporum. In the midst of the Apennine highlands is the small crater Conon, containing some delicate detail, while, on the broad expanse of the Mare Imbrium is the striking crater-group of Archimedes, Aristillus and Autolycus. Archimedes, 50 miles in diameter, has a smooth interior on which are several minute craterlets; its massive walls and the hilly region to the south-west, the latter traversed by a remarkable system of clefts, renders this one of the most interesting of lunar regions. This section also includes Linné, drawn and described by Mädler and Lohrmann as a deep crater but found, in 1866, by Schmidt, to have lost that character and to have assumed the appearance of a white spot, conspicuous under high illumination owing to contrast with the dark surface of the Mare Serenitatis. An interesting example of a fragmentary crater, Wallace, lies on the surface of the Mare Imbrium, some distance to the east of Mt. Huygens, the highest peak in the Apennine Range. The Apennines terminate at Eratosthenes, which is, in part, shown on the map. In the upper left-hand portion is the crater Manilius, which is very brilliant at Full. It is the centre of a ray system, and eight bands radiate from it, according to Haas.

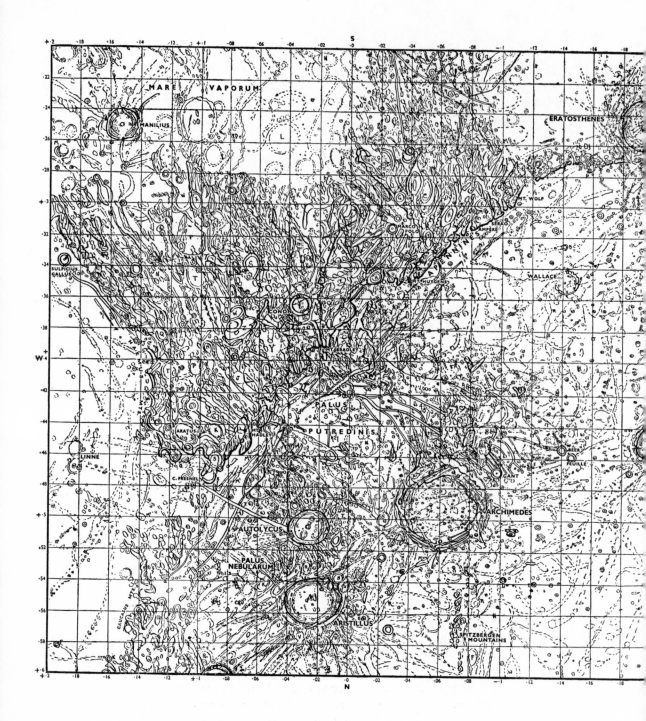

IV

AMPÈRE, —060 +335 [French physicist, 1775-1836]. A peak of the Apennine Mountains, south of the principal peak, Huygens, rising 10,600 feet above the Mare Imbrium. A valley lies between it and the next mountain mass, Delta, and this valley runs south-east to the crater K on the south flank of the crater. On the open plain to the north-east is a row of pits, and beyond these the mountain ridge M4. From the north tip of this ridge, a beautiful craterlet-chain runs north-east, half-way to Wallace.

APENNINE MOUNTAINS, —200 +280 to +090 +490. This is by far the most imposing of the lunar mountain ranges, and forms the south-western border of the Mare Imbrium. The elevated region is of triangular shape, with the Apennines forming the base; the portion which borders the Mare Serenitatis is known as the Hæmus Mountains (which see). The range rises gradually from the Mare Vaporum, the peaks becoming higher and culminating in the great cliffs flanking the Mare Imbrium. The most lofty peak is Huygens; not far from its summit is a bright craterlet nearly a mile in diameter. Haas found that after co-longitude 40° the craterlet is seen as a bright spot only, and that after 160° it becomes indistinguishable from the rest of Mt. Huygens, but at sunset again reveals its true nature. According to Schmidt, the peak rises 18,500 feet above the dark surface of the Mare. To the north is Mt. Bradley, 16,000 feet, on the curved ridge of which Pickering noted certain variable spots which he ascribed to clouds and snow deposits. The termination on the north is marked by several isolated peaks, and, on the main mass, the striking Mt. Hadley, 15,000 feet. To the south are several peaks attaining 16,000 feet. The range then narrows, and is broken by valleys into separate mountain masses, of which Wolff, of very triangular shape, rises 12,000 feet. To its east is another mountain rising 4,000 feet, and this is followed by a row of little peaks to the glacis of Eratosthenes.

On the hinterland are many lofty peaks, but very few craters, the principal being Aratus, Conon and Marco Polo. Narrow winding valleys can be traced running in a general south-western direction between the mountains; one of the most prominent will be found near Conon, and on its floor is a distinct bent cleft. On the Mare, are rocky spurs and hilly masses roughly concentric with the great range; also some long clefts.

ARATUS, +072 +400 [Greek poet, *circa* 315-245 B.C.]. A bright crater, 6 miles in diameter, near an irregular depression which formerly bore the name.[1] It is surrounded by lofty mountains; one on the north rises 10,000 feet, another on the north-west 14,000 feet, while on the west is a pair of small craters. In 1953, Moore, using the 33-inch Meudon refractor, found a hill on the eastern floor of Aratus. This is a very difficult object.

[1] The map follows the old nomenclature.

ARCHIMEDES, −060 +497 [Greek scientist, 287-212 B.C.]. The largest of the ringed-plains on the Mare Imbrium, with broad, very complex walls averaging 4,200 feet but bearing several towers, rising to a maximum height of 7,400 feet. The interior is remarkably smooth, and is about 50 miles across, depressed only about 650 feet below the outer surface. Here and there are what appear to be landslips which intrude upon the floor; these are especially marked on the west and south. The mirror-like surface is crossed, from east to west, by lighter streaks dividing it into four zones, easily seen under high illumination and containing several minute objects. The earlier observers depicted at least fifteen craterlets or pits, all very minute, the most conspicuous being on the east. Moore, with the great 33-inch refractor of the Meudon Observatory, 3 April 1952, noted ten objects on the floor, only four of which appeared as distinct craterlets. A light streak on the eastern part of the floor was also recorded. Near the centre is a very shallow, oval depression, 6 miles across. Krieger drew this as a flat crater-like depression. On the north-east are two other very shallow depressions with another on the south and a dark patch on the east. A remarkable chart by T. P. Gray, showing many of these features, was published in the *Selenographical Journal*, Vol. V, No. 59. Knott saw nine spots, Molesworth also nine.

One craterlet to the south-west of the centre is remarkably bright when it first emerges from the shadow at sunrise. There is a strong resemblance between Archimedes and Plato; both have smooth floors containing several delicate objects, but the interior of Archimedes is much lighter than that of Plato. On the south-east wall is a crater-chain, bordered by a hilly region, beyond which is the deep crater, Gant (Archimedes A), containing a central peak. From the south-west wall of Gant two clefts run south-west; on the east are several craters and craterlets. A chain of seven shallow and, in part, confluent rings, lies on the outer south glacis; at its western end is a small crater-chain, also a cleft. From this, extending south and south-west, is a disturbed region, covered with bright little mountains and including several curved ridges, evidently the relics of once complete rings. This region is traversed by a system of clefts, the majority of which run parallel to each other, all tending to the south-west and connecting with the long clefts running parallel to the main crest of the Apennines.

North of Archimedes is a bright isolated mountain and further north a group of peaks, while to the north-east is a double mountain mass, Z. Using the 33-inch Meudon refractor, in 1953, Moore found each of the pair of mountains to be crowned by a summit craterlet. Wilkins at once confirmed these interesting objects. Each craterlet is perfectly symmetrical on its mountain, and there can be no doubt that they are volcanic in origin.

ARISTILLUS, +018 +557 [Greek astronomer, *circa* 280 B.C.]. A grand and boldly marked crater, 35 miles in diameter, with walls beautifully terraced on the inner slopes, but marked on the outer slopes by deep ravines, conspicuous even in small instruments. The wall peaks rise 11,000 feet on the east and 9,000 feet on the west, above the floor, on which is a fine, triple-peaked central mountain and lower hills. The floor is depressed

3,000 feet below the outer surface. On the south crest are two little craters and, on the east, a peak. A mass of radiating ridges surrounds this great crater; these enclose portions of the surface and resemble obscure rings. The largest of these, and by far the most prominent, lies on the north, and contains a feeble central peak. On the south-west is another ancient ring, and beyond it a bright hill, also two shallow clefts. South-east is the deep little crater B, within an imperfect ring.

On the north-west inner slopes and extending over the rim is a dark band, which Pickering found to be composed of two streaks which are easier to divide outside the rim. They require good conditions and instruments for their detection. H. M. Johnson, in the U.S.A., has found some ridges crossing the course of the bands on the inner slopes. These bands are an excellent test for definition, and also resolution. Three dusky bands extend from the central mountain to the south and the east walls, discovered by Abineri in 1951 and confirmed by Moore. The north-east segment of the walls seems to appear strangely bright for a day or two just after Full Moon.

AUTOLYCUS, +022 +510 [Greek astronomer, *circa* 330 B.C.]. A similar but smaller companion to Aristillus, 24 miles in diameter, with wide, terraced walls, broken on the west by a deep little crater. The walls rise 9,000 feet above the depressed floor, on which is a chain of three craters; there is also a partial crater on the inner north-east, and the remains of two old rings between the centre and the east wall. A wide but shallow valley runs from the west wall but is rarely to be seen. On the south and the south-west are little groups of mountains, and some craters, while on the north are a craterlet-chain and some ridges. Under high illumination Autolycus is seen to be the centre of a small ray system, somewhat difficult to detect. Under a low sun the crater is seen to be surrounded by radiating ridges.

North-east is the pointed crater A; south are three mountains in a triangle, the largest being Beta, and there are many clefts associated with the hilly ground south of Archimedes. Of these clefts one runs to the ring, S, on the west of Archimedes; another runs south to the west of the mountain Beta. There is also a long cleft on the far west, which divides into three to the south-west of Autolycus. Further south is a peculiar star-shaped mountain, and between it and Autolycus are the remains of an old ring, full of craterlets, craterlet-chains and numerous delicate ridges.

BEER, −140 +455 [German selenographer, 1797-1850]. A crater 8 miles in diameter, with a slightly smaller companion, Feuillé, on the north-east. From the south-west wall a crater-chain runs to the hilly ground south of Archimedes. To the west are four shallow confluent craters and, on the south, a dome. Haas has suspected that Beer and its companion, Feuillé, undergo changes in aspect, similar to Messier and Pickering; this has been confirmed by Moore, who considers they are merely optical effects. Generally, the walls of Beer are a little brighter than those of Feuillé. A low ridge runs south for some 20 miles, ending in a hill. Moore found a minute craterlet some 15 miles to the north-west. Barcroft has noted dark spots in the interiors of both formations only visible under high illumination. There are several craterlet-chains in this area, and due south of Beer is a rounded hill, P, which Moore, using the 33-inch Meudon refractor, found to be crowned by a pit. This pit, seen also by Wilkins and by Madame Hermann a few minutes after its detection, is probably about the most difficult object recorded by the Authors at Meudon.

BRADLEY, MOUNT, +006 +396 [English Astronomer Royal, 1692-1762]. This lies close to Conon, and is described under that heading.

CAUCASUS MOUNTAINS, +090 +510 to +230 +655. A mountain range between the Maria Imbrium and Serenitatis, divided into distinct sections between which are numerous hillocks. The mountains are highest on the east; the loftiest peak to the east of Calippus rises nearly 20,000 feet. On the south are other peaks rising from 5,000 to 10,000 feet; they are still higher to the north-west of Calippus, where they attain 12,000 feet.

CONON, +032 +369 [Greek astronomer, *circa* 260 B.C.]. A not quite circular crater, 13 miles in diameter, in the midst of the Apennines, with walls lower on the south and the east, sometimes seen as gaps under low illumination. Just below the western crest is a pit. Mädler and Goodacre mention a central peak, the existence of which was denied by Pickering. He ascribed the appearance of such an elevation to the variable brightness of the floor. Vaughn and Thornton have seen some very low hills or mounds on the floor, while E. J. Reese has detected much detail in the form of delicate streaks, clefts, spots and mounds. There are also some dusky streaks on the inner east slopes. Pickering found many variations in the immediate surroundings and on the neighbouring ridge of Mt. Bradley. On the south is a partial depression from which a wide and easily seen valley winds southwards to the Mare Vaporum. Schmidt shows this as a crater-rill, Gaudibert a cleft from the south-west wall; between Conon and Mt. Bradley are clefts, hillocks, craterlets and valleys. Some of these objects were found by Pickering to be subject to variations, ascribed to snow deposits and clouds, partly confirmed by Martz.

Wilkins critically examined Conon on 3 April 1952, with the great 33-inch Meudon refractor. At that time about a third of the floor, on the western side, was in shadow. He was not able to confirm some of the details reported by Reese with a 6-inch reflector. The details clearly seen were: A small crater just within the south crest, a long and very low central ridge marked on the east, by a delicate line of shade; four lighter patches on the dusky floor, and two dusky bands running up the bright inner eastern slope. At the foot of the inner north slope were two most minute craterpits, so small as to be only just within the capacity of the giant telescope. It is thus clear that Pickering was wrong when he asserted that Conon possessed no central peak; it has a central elevation in the form of a short ridge.

ERATOSTHENES, −190 +250 [Greek geometer and astronomer, 276-196 B.C.]. This grand object, 38 miles in diameter, lies at the southern end of the Apennine range, and is a striking telescopic object under a low sun. Under high illumination, however,

Eratosthenes is exceedingly difficult to find, and its site is occupied by a confused array of dark and light areas.

The walls, which are linear in parts, rise 16,000 feet on the east above the floor, are finely terraced on the inner slopes, and have a very complex and intricate outer glacis. The floor is depressed 8,000 feet below the outer level, and contains a complex central mountain, with a crater-like depression in the middle. The western peak of the central mountain mass also contains a summit crater, discovered by Wilkins in 1953 and confirmed by Moore. The base of this mountain mass is serrated by what appears to be the remains of old rings. There are also some low hills, ridges and, under a high sun, dusky spots, especially on the south and the south-east. These spots vary in intensity and outline in a surprising manner, and were considered by Pickering as due to the growth of some form of vegetation. Haas, however, using an 18-inch refractor, found no trace of the complex pattern of 'canals' and 'oases' described and drawn by Pickering. The more prominent of these certainly exist and have been seen by both of the Authors.

On 30 January 1947, Harold Hill noted that the eastern component of the central mountain was free from shadow at a time when it should have been present. This may have been related to the obvious changes witnessed monthly in the aspect of the floor and inner slopes. At and near Full, Eratosthenes is difficult to detect, partly owing to the development of the Copernican ray system. The central peak is then bright, and white areas have made their appearance under the south-west and north walls. Ther s also, at this time, a large dark patch adjoining the white area on the north, while a still larger dark area is prominent on the south-east and this extends both within and without the crest.

To the north is a magnificent mountain arm, which rises 9,000 feet and is intersected by a cleft.

FEUILLÉ, −146 +459 [French astronomer, 1660-1732]. This crater was formerly known as Beer, A and has already been described under Beer.

FRESNEL, CAPE, +075 +483 [French physicist, 1788-1827]. A cape at the extreme northern end of the Apennine range, being the northern portion of an old ring. Near are two minor peaks, Gamma on the south and Beta on the north. The latter rises 8,500 feet above the surface of the Mare Imbrium.

GANT, −098 + 470 [contemporary American selenographer]. This crater was formerly known as Archimedes A, and is described under that heading.

HADLEY, MOUNT, +072 +452 [English physicist, 1682-1743]. A peak near the northern end of the Apennines, rising 15,143 feet, while on the south is another peak which rises fully 12,500 feet.

HUYGENS, MOUNT, −044 +345 [Dutch astronomer and optician, 1629-95]. This is the highest peak in the Apennine range, and rises 18,500 feet above the dark Mare

Imbrium. Near the peak is a craterlet. Schröter found the height to be 21,000 feet, but this was clearly an over-estimate.

IMBRIUM, MARE, −230 +520. The 'Sea of Rains'. This is the largest of the great dark areas which have received the name of 'seas'. Approximately circular, it measures 750 miles from east to west and 690 miles from north to south, with mountainous borders on the north, west and south, but merging into the vast Oceanus Procellarum on the east. The surface of this great plain varies greatly in tint, being lighter around Archimedes; and many light streaks, chiefly from Copernicus, run across the surface. There are also some small ray systems, and over 700 craters, craterlets and pits, according to Goodacre's count on one of the Mt. Wilson photographs. In addition, there are numerous craters, isolated mountains and old rings on the broad expanse. The largest of the ringed structures is Archimedes; the finest of the isolated mountains is Pico, with Piton a close rival. Many new measures of position have recently been undertaken by Arthur.

LINNÉ, +181 +465 [Swedish botanist, 1707-78]. This is one of the most interesting of all lunar objects. It was described by Lohrmann and also by Mädler as a crater, 5 miles in diameter, very deep and visible under all illuminations. Schmidt, in 1866, pointed out that this description no longer applied and that Linné, so far from being a deep crater, was in fact no crater at all but resembled a whitish cloud. Subsequently, Secchi and other observers detected a very shallow depression within the bright area; this depression contained a minute pit. Corder, a good observer, and afterwards Goodacre, described and drew Linné as a cratercone on the east rim of a shallow ring, while on the west was a little peak. Pickering concluded that the original Linné disappeared between 1843 and 1866; the shallow crater in its place, seen in 1867-8, had disappeared by 1897; the cratercone of Corder and Goodacre apparently varied in size as regards its central orifice. He also noted that the white area was invisible close to the terminator and, when first seen, coming out of the shadow, was at its maximum size. The diameter of this white area then decreased until shortly after local noon, when the diameter began to increase, but did not reach the original size when sunset arrived. These changes were ascribed by Pickering to the deposit and melting of hoar frost.

The alleged changes in Linné depend entirely upon the reliability of the statements of Lohrmann and Mädler in former times and those of Goodacre and Corder in latter. Schröter's solitary drawing of this area is inconclusive, since his drawing contains two spots near the position of Linné, one dark, thus suggestive of a depression filled with shadow, the other a white spot, such as Linné was declared to be by Schmidt. Both spots are so displaced on the drawing that it is impossible to decide which, if either, was meant for Linné; this is because Schröter's attention at the time was directed mainly to the bright rays crossing the Mare, and other details on his drawing are merely roughed in. Some observers have found Linné, that is to say the white area, to become enlarged after immersion in the umbra during lunar eclipses. A critical review of the matter shows a distinct possibility of a real change having taken place in this region. Whether

Linné was, in the time of the Master of Selenography, a crater, as asserted by Mädler, and whether this was converted into a whitish area, possibly owing to the original crater having been filled up with very fluid lava which overran the slopes and presented such a gentle gradient as to prevent any shadows being cast, whether afterwards Linné became a cratercone, as asserted by Corder and Goodacre, it appears possible that another change has recently taken place. It is very difficult to imagine Goodacre describing Linné as a cratercone on the edge of a very shallow depression if this was not the appearance presented in his telescope, an 18-inch reflector by Calver. To-day Linné is neither of these things. It is neither a white area nor a depression, but, according to Thornton, who has examined it with his 18-inch telescope, is a low mound on the summit of which is a deep pit, filled with shadow under low illumination. When the slight shadow cast by the mound has disappeared, owing to increasing solar altitude, the pit on its summit still holds shadow, although this eventually disappears. No other detail whatever can be detected except the white area which looks like some matter thrown out on all sides when the pit was formed. This description of Thornton's was fully and completely confirmed by the Authors, using the 33-inch Meudon refractor, in 1953.

South of this mysterious spot is a shallow ruined ring with a small peak on its east rim, while on the north are two domes, of which the larger and the more easterly has a peak to the east.

MANILIUS, +153 +250 [Roman poet, *circa* 100 B.C.]. This beautiful crater is 25 miles in diameter, and is very brilliant under a high sun, when it appears as the centre of a minor ray system, the members of which are rather faint and difficult to detect. The crater is not quite circular, but has linear portions on the south and the east. The crest is broken by a crater on the south, while on the north is a narrow pass. The inner slopes are very finely terraced, with a distinct ravine on the inner south. On the interior is a central mountain, which is connected to the south-east rampart by a ridge. Two dusky bands run from the centre to the east wall. Many radial ridges traverse the outer slopes, gradually decreasing in prominence until they sink into the plain. On the west is an ancient ring, of which fragments alone remain, the most prominent being a triangular mountain mass. This ring is 20 miles across. Some distance to the east is another ancient ring, but better preserved than usual, and considerably larger than Manilius. The western border is broad, though low, and contains a small crater on the south-west. Near the centre of the ancient ring are three little hills. A ridge at the foot of the inner walls completely encircles the floor of Manilius. Haas has noted eight radial and broad bands from the walls. An isolated mountain, 6,000 feet in altitude, is a prominent object on the plain to the north-west.

MARCO POLO, −054 +282 [Venetian traveller, 1254-1324]. A shallow and irregular depression, 10 miles in diameter, on the western side of a wide valley in the midst of the Apennine highlands, and with a feeble central hill. Being surrounded by lofty mountains, it is not well defined or easily seen, except for a short time near sunset. Neison declared that it had no raised rim, but this feature is perceptible under a low sun. In contact with the south rim is a slight depression, and on the south-west a small crater within the valley. Beyond the valley is a well-marked crater. The valley itself is well bordered, in places by steep cliffs, and there are hillock rows and ridges on the broad southern portion.

NEBULARUM, PALUS, +050 +630. 'Marsh of Mists'. This is really a portion of the Mare Imbrium to the west of Aristillus and Autolycus, and lighter in tint than the rest of the Mare. Its surface is covered with low ridges, hillocks, and craterlets; and there are some clefts on the south.

PUTREDINIS, PALUS, +010 +480. 'Marsh of Decay'. Another portion of the Mare Imbrium to the south-west of Archimedes, traversed by clefts from this great ringed-plain. Of these clefts over twenty-seven are shown on our map, together with numerous ridges, hills and craters.

SERAO, −108 +300 [Italian journalist, 1825-1911]. A low ring near Mt. Wolff in the Apennines, on the Mare Imbrium and at the south end of a ridge, M4. On the south and west are craterlets, and on the east is the crater, A. The I.A.U. Map makes Serao a peak in the Apennine range.

SPITZBERGEN, −075 +568. A series of bright little hills north of Archimedes. Moore (1948, with a 6-inch O.G.) noted that they lay on the western border of a large ring whose walls have been destroyed so that it can now be traced only by its slightly darker hue. This ring is crossed by a very shallow, groove-like valley.

SULPICIUS GALLUS, +191 +336 [Roman orator and scholar, circa 168 B.C.]. A bright crater 8 miles in diameter, with walls rising to 8,000 feet. The formation is, therefore, very deep for its size. In April 1953, Moore, with the Meudon 33-inch, confirmed a dusky band to the inner south-east wall first reported by Whitaker, and also observed a central hill. To the east of Sulpicius Gallus is a cleft; to the north-east, two craterlets and a hill. Sulpicius Gallus is conspicuous at Full Moon.

VAPORUM, MARE, +070 +240. 'Sea of Vapours'. A dark plain, south of the Apennine Mountains and near the centre of the disk. It is comparatively smooth, the highest of the ridges which cross its surface being only 2,800 feet. These ridges will be found near Hyginus. On the west are some very low ridges, while there are also low rings.

WALLACE, −143 +347 [English naturalist, 1823-1913]. This is an interesting example of a fragmentary crater, and lies in an excellent position on the Mare Imbrium, some distance to the north of Eratosthenes and east of Mt. Huygens, in the Apennines. It is well shown on one of the Mt. Wilson photographs.

The crater has obviously been partially filled in by the material of the Mare when this was in a fluid condition, with the result that the walls can still be traced, except on the west, where the relics of its former presence can only be seen when close to the terminator. Under high illumination it will be seen that the low walls are surmounted by five portions more elevated than the rest. The southern fragment, Beta, is stated by Neison (*The Moon*, p. 294), under the designation of Eratosthenes x, to rise 1,790 feet. Neither Neison, Schmidt or Goodacre show any detail in their maps, but Goodacre, in his chart of the Mare Imbrium, (B.A.A. Memoirs, 23.4), draws a craterpit on the south-eastern portion of the interior. On Wilkins' map, the three most elevated portions of the wall are marked Alpha, Beta and Gamma, the latter being the least elevated, while ten exceedingly minute specks are shown on the interior. One, nearly central, is obviously a craterpit; the remainder are probably of similar nature but require very favourable conditions and a good instrument to be seen at all. There are also several pits outside the ring, especially on the south. The eastern portion of the wall is curved in a normal manner, but the southern and northern portions exhibit a linear tendency. The extreme termination of the southern wall consists of a peculiar triangular projection running down to the level of the Mare, with the tip hooked towards the north. As a pre-Mare object, Wallace must have been an imposing structure; even in its present, almost submerged, condition it will repay study.

Moore, with the 33-inch Meudon refractor, found a short cleft from a minute pit running to the tip of the southern wall; on the northern headland he noted an elongated but small depression.

WOLFF, MOUNT, −130 +280 [German philosopher, 1679-1754]. A triangular mountain mass, in the Apennine range, rising 12,000 feet. To the north-east is Serao, and south the mountain, Eta, followed by Beta, the crater B and a cape. From this cape are three isolated hills: Gamma, Delta and Phi, at the extreme south-east end of the Apennines and north of Eratosthenes. West of Wolff is a low ring in a valley, and a mountain, Delta, followed by K and the heights of Ampère. South-west is a valley, with the mountain ridge, Beta, bordering it on the south, together with other mountain ridges, gradually decreasing in altitude to the bright little crater F.

V

This section is largely occupied by the broad expanse of the Mare Imbrium, and thus contains comparatively few formations. The upper portion of the map includes the Carpathian Mountains, which form a portion of the southern border of the Mare, and also the disturbed region immediately to the north of Copernicus. Between this region and Eratosthenes, which is partially shown, is one of the most curious of lunar regions, owing to the numerous craterlet and crater-chains, some of which eventually become distinct clefts.

The principal ringed structures are Timocharis, Pytheas, Euler, Diophantus and Delisle, all presenting features of interest. Several isolated mountains also exist, La Hire and Dyson being the most prominent, and are distinguished by their brilliancy, especially when near the terminator. A large number of minute craterlets, and other objects, are scattered over the plain, forming excellent telescopic tests.

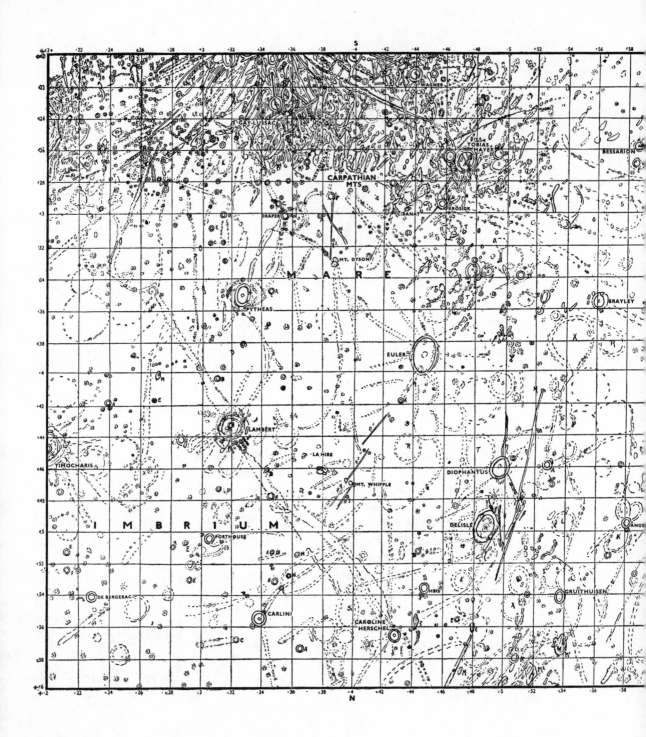

V

ÅNGSTRÖM, −576 +498 [Swedish physicist, 1814-74]. A small crater on the open plain to the east of Delisle, with a craterlet in contact with the outer north wall, and situated on the rim of an obscure ring, K. On the south are other obscure rings, marked by almost imperceptible ridges, and difficult to detect. On the south-east is a short cleft.

BANAT, CAPE, −424 +299. A promontory of the Carpathian Mountains to the north of the ringed-plain Gay-Lussac, with a craterlet on its east not far from the actual headland. A somewhat similar headland, also with a craterlet, lies on the east, beyond a small bay.

de BERGERAC, −231 +544 [French writer, 1620-55]. A small but tolerably conspicuous crater to the west of Carlini; there are many craterlets in the neighbourhood.

BESSARION, −585 +256 [Greek cardinal, 1369-1472]. A bright crater, 6 miles in diameter, and situated on a bright area. It has a small central hill. On the north is a smaller but brighter crater, now called Virgil. Bessarion and Virgil are surrounded by ridges, evidently the relic of a once-prominent ring. To the north-east are other bright, but small, craters; and on the south-west are some isolated hills. E. A. Whitaker found, 1951, a radial band to the south-east wall, confirmed by Moore. Moore also found a bright, circular area on the floor to the south of the band with the 33-inch Meudon refractor. There is a craterlet to the south, about $2\frac{1}{2}$ miles in diameter and of some depth.

BRAYLEY, −561 +356 [English scientist, 1801-70]. A bright crater, 10 miles in diameter, with a faint central hill and a low hill on the outer west. On the west is a bright crater, B, with some hills between it and Brayley. East are two small craters, C and E. Just outside the west wall are three little hills. The crater B stands on the rim of an obscure ring, with the bright little crater, D, to the south-west. Beyond D are several mountain masses; two low rings and a cleft, Eta, run from the peak Gamma, which rises 2,100 feet. The peak Delta rises 2,400 feet, and east of this mountain are hillocks and a craterlet on the rim of the old ring, T. North-west is the large but obscure ring, X, with the crater, R, on its east. Faint radial dark bands were traced to the north-east wall of Brayley by Whitaker in 1951, and these have been confirmed by Moore.

CARLINI, −339 +555 [Italian astronomer, 1783-1862]. A crater about 5 miles in diameter, the floor being depressed 2,000 feet below the outer level, and with a small central hill. On the northern part of the floor is a craterlet. On the south-east wall is another craterlet, and there is another on the outer north-west, while south are the

103

craterlets, R, H, N, M and K, with smaller pits and some low ridges. To the north-east is the bright crater, A, and north-west the smaller and less conspicuous crater C.

CARPATHIAN MOUNTAINS, —260 +270 to —540 +220. A range of mountains to the north of Copernicus, and extending for a distance of 225 miles. They form the southern border of the Mare Imbrium. The peaks M4 and M5 rise 2,600 feet and 5,000 feet respectively; while M10, near Krosigk, rises 7,000 feet, and M7 is little inferior. The entire range is very discontinuous, and consists of detached mountain masses. From a hill north-west of the crater C, on the south of Cape Banat, a fine cleft runs across the open plain, as shown on the map, and there is a shorter cleft from the mountain M5 to the west of the bright crater B. On the extreme west are several isolated mountains, that farthest to the west, M1, lying near the prominent crater-chain on the east of Eratosthenes.

DELISLE, —492 +500 [French astronomer, 1688-1768]. This prominent crater, 16 miles in diameter, has a break in the north wall and a central hill on the interior. To the south-east is a mountain mass with three peaks, from which a cleft runs northwards. On the north-east is a group of hills and also an ancient ring. D. C. Brown, of Manila, has found two low domes to the south of Delisle, not previously recorded.

DIOPHANTUS, —499 +463 [Greek mathematician, *circa* 350 A.D.]. This somewhat irregular crater is 13 miles in diameter, with a wall of varying height, highest on the west, and with a fault which has dislocated the north wall. On the floor is a central hill. To the east is a cleft, between which and the wall lies a fault which can be traced to the mountain on the south-east of Delisle. From the north-east wall a cleft runs to the mountain mass, Beta, while on the floor of the plain, to the north, is a minute but bright craterlet.

DRAPER, —353 +302 [English physicist, 1837-82]. A small crater on the Mare Imbrium and south of Pytheas. On the south is the smaller crater, C. Draper stands on the west edge of an obscure ring, N, which has craterlets on its very low wall. To the south-east is the crater, J, with two crossed clefts on its north.

DYSON, MOUNT, —378 +336 [Astronomer Royal, 1868-1939]. A bright, twin-peaked mountain, rising 900 feet above the plain. Just to the south-west a long cleft runs southwards to the crater J, and this cleft is crossed by another midway along its length. A ridge connects Dyson with Euler.

EULER, —447 +395 [Swiss mathematician, 1707-83]. A terraced crater, 19 miles in diameter, the interior being depressed 6,000 feet below the outer level. There is a slight break in the south wall, and a crater just below the north crest. On the floor is a central hill, and a partial ring on the south, while along the inner east slope are evidences of landslips. To the south-east are some isolated hills, evidently the highest portions of an ancient ring which has been largely filled up. Euler is the centre of a minor ray system. To the west are some low domes.

GAY-LUSSAC, —345 +240 [French physicist, 1778-1850]. A prominent crater, 15 miles in diameter, in the middle of the disturbed and hilly region to the north of Copernicus. The walls are low on the north, while on the east a segment has, apparently, slipped inwards. On the interior, which is traversed by two clefts, lie a central hill and three craterlets; also a craterlet west of the central hill. There is also a hill near the south wall, while a cleft-valley traverses the inner east slope, though this may really be a gap left by the landslip already mentioned. From the east wall a cleft runs south-east, crossing the numerous crater-chains and ridges radiating from Copernicus. On the south-west is the smaller and deeper crater, A, with an irregular west wall, a central craterlet and a cleft which can be traced far to the south, ending at a small crater.

The environs of Gay-Lussac are very hilly, and contain numerous depressions and craters, mostly shallow, together with craterlet-chains, commonly found on the low ground between the ridges.

Further west the hilly region ends, and is succeeded by a plain extending from Eratosthenes to Copernicus. This is traversed by a very complex system of crater-chains, one of the most prominent running north to south from the crater, M, which is a node for many such objects. This chain loses its crateriform character to the north, and then becomes a distinct cleft. Of the other crater-chains several run from north-west to south-east towards Copernicus; altogether the craters number about 400, not including the multitude of minute craterlets due west of Copernicus. They vary greatly in size and were much under-estimated by Gruithuisen, really ranging from 3 miles in diameter downwards. The most favourable time for observation is when the east wall of Copernicus lies on the morning terminator. The principal crater-rows can then be easily seen in a 3-inch refractor and fully justify Webb's description: 'one of the most curious districts on the Moon'.

GAY-LUSSAC, SINUS, —350 +250. A deep bay in the Carpathian Mountains immediately north of Gay-Lussac, with short clefts and craterlets at its south end. The north end, opening into Mare Imbrium, is partly blocked by mountains; of these M5 is the highest, and has the crater B on its east. On the south are two craterlets, connected by a cleft.

GRUITHUISEN, —537 +542 [German physician and selenographer, 1774-1852]. A bright crater, 10 miles in diameter, with a craterlet on its north rim and another on the outer west slope. On the north is a mountain mass of some extent, running chiefly east and west and rising, at one point, to 6,000 feet. On its broad summit are some craterlets. On both the east and north are obscure rings, one of which has a mountain peak on its north rim, also some craterlets.

HEIS, —446 +536 [German astronomer, 1806-77]. A crater between Delisle and Caroline Herschel, with a craterlet, A, on its outer north. To the south-west is the crater D and, on the east, obscure rings, K and Q.

HERSCHEL, CAROLINE, —427 +566 [famous woman astronomer, 1750-1848].

This crater is 8 miles in diameter; on the floor, which is depressed 3,000 feet, is a small central hill. To the north is a prominent ridge and, on the east, a twin-peaked mountain, 1,400 feet in altitude, and several craterlets. Farther to the east are a crater, E, and a mountain, Eta, from which a cleft runs north-west.

KROSIGK, —458 +295 [German astronomer]. A small crater on the edge of the Carpathians and to the north-west of Tobias Mayer, with a long cleft running north-west from the wall. On the north are traces of old rings, with others farther to the north.

LA HIRE, —379 +463 [French mathematician, 1640-1718]. A mountain 5,000 feet high, with a base of 12 miles and with a craterlet on the summit. To the east are a lower mountain and some clefts. La Hire is bright at sunrise, but often fades, to brighten up again near sunset. Schröter and Webb saw it radiating when on the terminator.

LAMBERT, —322 +435 [German physicist, 1728-77]. This far from bright formation is 18 miles in diameter, with broad walls, finely terraced on the inner slopes, with a crater on the south crest and a break on the north. On the floor is a central crater, situated on a long ridge. To the west is a triangular mountain, rising 3,000 feet. A lower mountain mass lies on the east. L. F. Ball found an obscure ring filling the space between Lambert and Pytheas. C. S. Jones noted, 12 August 1902, a brilliant star-like point of light, equal to a third-magnitude star, on the dark side at co-longitude 18 degrees. This was followed for two hours as the terminator approached.

MAYER, TOBIAS, —469 +268 [German astronomer, 1723-62]. A beautiful crater, 22 miles in diameter, with a deep crater, A, on its west. This has a central hill, as also has Mayer. From the south wall a discontinuous ridge runs southwards, ending at a small crater. On the north is a mountain mass, with two craters at the end, while east of it are lower hills and craters. Where Mayer and A join, on the north, are two craters. Another more shallow crater lies on the south. On the interior of Mayer are some hills to the west of the centre. There are two craterlets on the east, also a crater on the inner north. To the east are low hills, a small ring, and farther east, a curved ridge on a light streak. This ridge is the west wall of an ancient ring. South of Mayer is a long cleft passing through four craterlets, and farther south is the crater F. Dr. S. R. B. Cooke has noted several domes in this area, some with summit craters. His drawing was published in the 10th Memoir of the B.A.A. Lunar Section.

PIETROSUL BAY, —381 +260. A bay in the coast-line of the Carpathian range, and north-east of Gay-Lussac.

PORTHOUSE, —307 +505 [English amateur astronomer]. A crater 4 miles in diameter, to the south-west of Carlini, and the largest of several in this neighbourhood. To the north-west are the small craters E and K.

PYTHEAS, —329 +351 [Greek navigator, *circa* 350 B.C.]. A very bright rhomboidal crater, 12 miles in diameter, with terraced walls and a central hill, which Thornton has found to be connected by a ridge to the north-west wall. There is a crater on the north wall, while a ridge runs from the south wall. The west wall is narrow, and not as bright as the eastern. To the east is a crater, A, and beyond, the double mountain, Dyson. On the south are hills rising 900 feet, and many craterlets. Pytheas is the centre of a light ray system, the brightest members of which extend from south to north. To the north-east are four bright craterlets in a line; many smaller lie around.

TIMOCHARIS, −202 +449 [Greek astronomer, *circa* 280 B.C.]. A perfect crater, 25 miles in diameter, isolated on the Mare Imbrium, with broad walls, finely terraced inside in a very complex manner. On the floor, which lies 7,000 feet below the wall peaks, are a central crater and some low hills or mounds. On the south is a fragment of an old ring. To the south-east is the crater C, and the crater group A, while farther east is the crater E, and south of it a mountain, M. Timocharis is the centre of an extensive but faint ray system, while its broad outer slope sinks into the plain with a gentle gradient, and the whole is surrounded by radial ridges. Under a high light, Timocharis is remarkably bright, and presents an appearance of freshness as though it was formed subsequently to the lava flow comprising the surface of the Mare Imbrium. Barcroft has seen an appearance resembling vapour filling the crater near Full Moon.

VIRGIL, −584 +265 [Great Roman poet, 70-19 B.C.]. A small bright crater to the north of Bessarion, with a hillock on the floor under the south-west wall. On the north is a large and obscure ring, S, and west of this a ruined formation, T, of which only the west wall attains any height.

WAGNER, −428 +212 [Hanoverian physiologist, 1805-64]. A crater to the north-east of Copernicus, with terraced walls, and situated in the midst of a very disturbed region, being surrounded by numerous hills and the fragments of ancient rings. To the east are two craters, B and K, also some clefts. On the north-east are the mountains M8 and M9, which are connected by a cleft which continues beyond M9 almost as far as the wall of Copernicus. The entire region surrounding Copernicus is far too detailed for written description, and reference should be made to the map in order to appreciate the complexity of detail visible even in instruments of moderate aperture.

WHIPPLE, MOUNT, −403 +474 [American photographer]. A bright, triple-peaked mountain north-east of La Hire, rising to about 2,000 feet. From the westernmost peak a cleft, η^2, runs south-eastwards, and another, η^4, north-westwards, while from the eastern mass a short cleft, η^3, runs north-westwards, parallel to η^4.

VI

The greater portion of this section is occupied by the dark Mare Nubium. The most important formation is the magnificent ringed-plain of Copernicus; other interesting objects are Stadius, Bonpland, Parry and Fra Mauro, all showing the effects of erosive forces in the past as also do the Riphæn Mountains. The predominance of Copernicus overshadows all other formations both on the map and in the telescopic view.

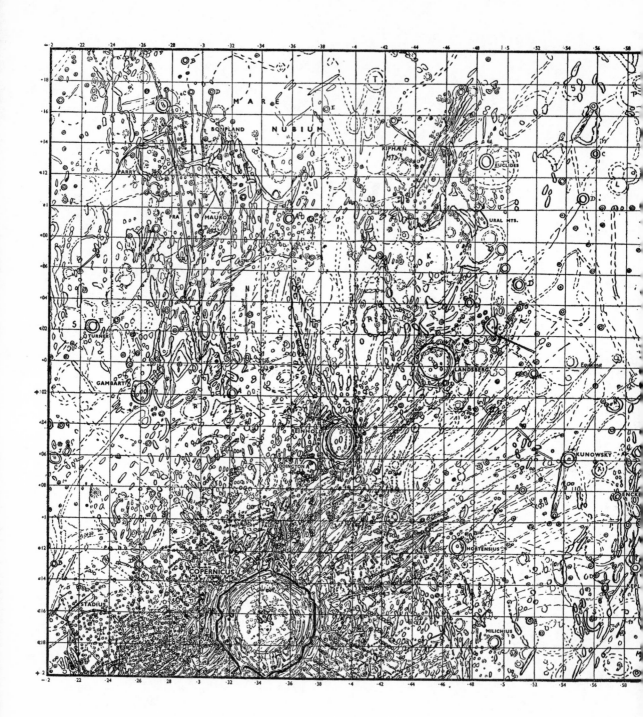

VI

BONPLAND, −293 −147 [French botanist, 1773-1858]. A fine example of a large ringed-plain. Of the southern wall facing the Mare, only isolated fragments remain; the other portions are continuous but low. On the interior are some craterlets and hillocks. Three clefts also traverse the interior; the most easterly commences at the crater, D, skirts a small but easily-seen buried ring adjoining the wall, and, after reaching one of the remaining fragments, reappears beyond, and crosses the floor to Fra Mauro. The second cleft begins at the crater, C, and dies out on the floor. The third cleft begins at the south wall, and after running across the floor enters Fra Mauro by a gap, as shown in a drawing by Dr. S. R. B. Cooke in the 9th B.A.A. Lunar Memoir.

COPERNICUS, −337 +167 [Polish astronomer and theologian, 1473-1543]. The finest ringed-plain on the Moon's surface, and situated on a raised portion of the crust near the northern border of the Mare Nubium. The walls, 56 miles in diameter, rise to a sharp thin crest, 12,000 feet above the floor, and although approximately circular consist of about twelve more or less linear portions, the whole of a decided polygonal outline. The outer walls are very broad with a gentle slope, and consist of a mass of concentric ridges, some of which, especially on the east, are evidently vast landslips. A great number of radial ridges also tend from the ring, gradually thinning out into invisibility, and are interspersed with a multitude of minute craterlets and craterpits, particularly on the west. We saw this appearance in grand perfection on 3 April 1952, with the great 33-inch refractor of the Meudon Observatory. Between every ridge were innumerable craterlets, and this appearance could be traced as far as the wall of Stadius. On the east are a great number of mountain masses and hillocks; from the north-east wall three clefts run radially towards the hinterland of the Carpathian Mountains.

South of Copernicus is a large double crater, once known as A, but now called Fauth, connected with the walls of Copernicus by lofty curved ridges, evidently partly ruined rings. South-west is a much smaller double crater, C, as well as numerous craterlets, some in chains. The north-west portion of the outer glacis exhibits several radial ridges, which, with a high ridge to the west, form several enclosures of irregular shape, and there is also a prominent depression on the north-west.

The crest of the enclosing wall contains about fifty little peaks, the most prominent, a, overhanging the interior on the west.

The inner slopes are richly terraced and separated by deep ravines, and exhibit many vast landslips, of which three prominent examples may be seen along the west wall when, at sunrise, the shadow of this wall has just cleared the multiple central mountain. The slopes below the lowest terraces are broken up into a number of hillocks.

The floor, 40 miles in diameter, is nearly circular, and contains a small, almost central multiple mountain, with large mountain masses to the west and the east. These are split up into separate peaks, of which seven can be detected under favourable conditions. These central mountains, the highest peak of which rises 2,400 feet, are worthy of this noble formation.

At the foot of the south inner slope is a distinct crater with two craterlets touching it on the east. R. Barker found, 22 June 1934, six craterlets on this portion of the inner slopes. To the north of the crater mentioned is a very shallow, small circular depression, and between this and the smaller central peak are two low hillocks, all in a line. Close to these, Barker has traced a fine cleft; Molesworth also noted a cleft which, after proceeding for some distance from the central mountain group, turned sharply to the east.

South of the most westerly of the mountain group is a low, curved ridge, open on the south-west and evidently the remains of an ancient ring. West of the group is a faint white ring, which, with two others farther north, is evidently the site of a submerged crater ring.

Along the inner slopes are at least twenty-three craters and crater depressions, as shown on the map; two of these craters on the north slope are visible as pits of black shadow for some time after sunrise. There is also a very prominent partial ring a little to the west.

The northern half of the floor is very smooth in comparison with the southern; there are, however, three exceedingly minute white rings, and a minute hillock due north of the small peak of the central group. The southern portion of the floor contains numerous low hills and ridges; all the objects on and around the margin of the floor exhibit clear signs of erosion; the central mountains themselves seem to be partly submerged by a rising lake of lava, the frozen surface of which now forms the floor. The cleft noted by Barker has been confirmed by Haas, using an 18-inch refractor. On 6 January 1933, Barker found another cleft running south from the centre.

At sunrise and sunset Copernicus forms a vast lake of black shadow; on one occasion at sunrise Wilkins saw the tip of the highest of the peaks of the central group appear faintly amid the shadow covering the interior; after a few minutes it vanished, to reappear hours afterwards in the normal way.

Copernicus is the centre of a very complex ray system, noted in the Introduction; many of the rays lie on the sites of very low ridges. At Full Moon, Copernicus appears brighter than the rays, and may be seen with the naked eye as a bright spot.

On the outer south slope are some craterlets with very dark interiors. On one occasion, when the shadow of the western wall was cast across the floor and on to the eastern inner slope, Wilkins noted that the shadow appeared deep brownish rather than black; the instrument used was a 6-inch reflector.

There is a complex system of light rays connected with Copernicus and related to it as a common centre. They are very irregular in width, exhibit many breaks and are most numerous in the immediate neighbourhood of the crater. The rays extending west radiate from the centre; those which extend northwards radiate from a point on the north wall, and also commence at a tangent to the west wall. One ray, between Pytheas and Timocharis, commences in the open country to the west of Copernicus and ends at an isolated mountain east of Timocharis. Two other prominent rays, roughly parallel with it, will be noticed. Pytheas lies between them. The spaces between the rays are darker than the other surrounding country. North and north-east the streaks or rays form a very complex pattern; from their numbers they unite to cause a large, bright patch in the direction of Kepler. The rays to the south-east are overlaid by a ray from Kepler, and where they intersect the junction is marked by large, bright patches.

The southern rays are confined to a comparatively narrow arc; on either side the surface is very dark, much more so than the Oceanus Procellarum or even Grimaldi. These dark areas appear more intense in photographs than to telescopic observation.

Fine photographs of Copernicus have been secured with the great Yerkes 40-inch refractor and the 100-inch Mt. Wilson reflector. One photograph was taken by Dr. Lyot at the Pic-du-Midi Observatory and shows much fine detail. Of the numerous drawings in existence those by Neison, Secchi, Fauth and C. F. O. Smith may be especially mentioned. A general view was given by Sir John Herschel, in his classic *Outlines of Astronomy*. The formation also formed the subject of a plate in *The Moon* of Nasmyth. There is also an enlargement of an early Lick photograph by Weinek.

The details given on Wilkins' map are largely to be picked out on the Mt. Wilson photographs, but large apertures are required to detect the more minute features. It is peculiar that no craterlets have, as yet, been detected on the interior, apart from the faint white rings already mentioned, and search should be made for any such, which doubtless exist. The entire formation is evidently raised high above the surrounding plain, and is situated not far removed from the central portion of the disk, so that it is also well-placed for telescopic study.

Recently Wilkins has found two delicate clefts running east to west and just outside the northern wall. A 12-foot diameter model of Copernicus has been made by Dr. Alter of the Griffith Observatory, U.S.A.

EDDINGTON, −367 +075 [Great English scientist, 1882-1944]. This crater was formerly known as Reinhold B, and is described under this heading.

ENCKE, −595 +080 [German astronomer, 1791-1865]. A crater 20 miles in diameter, with a depressed floor on which lies a discontinuous meridional ridge. There is a crater-let on the north rim, and a low ring under the inner west wall.

Encke stands on the edge of a large ring, on the south-west of which is the crater B; this crater is bright at Full. The old ring is at times seen in its entirety. In addition to the details already mentioned, there are confused, tumbled masses on the floor of Encke— small landslips, mounds, and other débris. To the west is a triple crater, first seen as such by L. F. Ball.

EUCLIDES, −488 −129 [Great Greek mathematician, *circa* 300 B.C.]. A bright crater, 7 miles in diameter, with walls rising 2,000 feet above the floor, which appears quite smooth. Euclides is surrounded by an extensive nimbus at Full, triangular in shape, and perhaps the finest on the Moon.

West is a bright little crater, A, and east the crater, D. This has a smaller crater, C, on the south. To the south and west of C are two peculiar enclosures, while on the north-east is a group of three obscure rings, L.

FAUTH, −342 +109 [German selenographer, 1867-1943]. A double crater on the south of Copernicus, and very conspicuous. It is in the midst of a region traversed by craterlet-chains and ridges from the great ringed-plain.

FRA MAURO, −290 −105 [Venetian geographer, died 1459]. A large ruined walled-plain to the north of Parry and Bonpland. The western boundary is common to Parry and Bonpland. On the east the wall is but slightly elevated above the outer surface, and falls steeply to the floor, which has a diameter of 50 miles.

The walls contain some crater-like depressions; on the exterior and on the inner slope is a partial ring, whose wall facing the interior of Fra Mauro has disappeared at one point. The portion which remains has been reduced to a thin ridge. On the eastern headland is the small crater, B. A long cleft traverses the interior, north and south of the central crater, A. East of A a cleft runs to the north wall and is prolonged beyond. Another cleft runs from the crater B, nearly parallel to the south wall. East of A is a low ridge, the remains of a partial ring on the south-east inner slope. Many small craters and longitudinal ridges can be detected on the floor, which also exhibits diversity of hue. There is a small dark area along the south wall, traversed by a cleft from Bonpland. Where the cleft passes from one formation to the other, the common wall has been disturbed by a small crater, and for a few miles consists of isolated hills. The dark patch, being of the same hue as the interior of Bonpland, suggests that the once-fluid floor of Bonpland has intruded into Fra Mauro, which would thus appear to be of earlier date. The whole of the north-west portion of the interior is occupied by a dark patch which projects southwards in long spires. There are two small ruined rings on the west wall. From the more northerly of these, two delicate clefts run to a bright mountain ridge tending northwards, and terminate at a conspicuous double crater. Another but shorter mountain ridge runs parallel to the first. To the east is a crater, A, with a smaller on its east, surrounded by a ring of isolated hillocks. North of these features are another crater and some hillocks; also a bright patch between this crater and A.

West of Fra Mauro are many small mountains, portions of what were once the walls of large enclosures, now almost entirely submerged. At Full, the region to the north of Fra Mauro is dotted by a large number of bright spots (craterlets?) and traversed by rays from Copernicus. Between Fra Mauro and Gambart is a partial ring, within which the long cleft traversing the floor terminates. This ring is easily traced at Full, also a portion of the cleft as a white line. Immediately to the east of the partial ring is a rimless area of similar shape and size, but much darker in tint, omitted from most maps.

GAMBART −262 +016 [French astronomer, 1800-36]. A ring-plain of somewhat peculiar shape, the east wall being less curved than the remainder. This formation is situated on the north of the discontinuous ridge running north from Fra Mauro. Adjoining the east wall is an ancient ring, with fragmentary walls; and farther east, beyond a dark bay, is the bright crater A. To the west are several craters, including B and C, the former with a smaller companion the east, while all around are craters, hillocks, also two bubble-like swellings. Between Gambart and the crater D, now called Turner, to the south, is an isolated mountain with a summit crater. Between it and the south wall of Gambart is evidence of the existence of an ancient ring.

The floor of Gambart is level, but there is a light patch on the south, and two low swellings on the north. There is also a small peak on the south wall. Gaudibert suspected a central peak, but this has not been confirmed by other observers. Between Gambart and Copernicus, and slightly west, is a large dark patch, very prominent under high illumination; also numerous hills and dark spots with some craterlets with very dark interiors, a most unusual feature. Some of these craterlets are less than one-tenth of a mile in diameter.

HORTENSIUS, —466 +113 [Dutch astronomer, 1605-39]. A deep crater, 10 miles in diameter, with a craterlet on the south crest, shown by Schmidt; a peak on the north crest and a central hill. The walls are bright, and there is at least one terrace on the inner slopes. Immediately south are some minute craterlets; north are five prominent and some lesser rounded hills or domes with summit craterlets. West is a crater, C, from which a valley-cleft running north was shown by Neison. This was doubted by Goodacre, and appears to be really a ridge. It is best seen near sunset, and after running 40 miles is continued by a broken chain of shallow depressions. From the north wall of C there also runs a delicate ridge to the north-east; on the east is a minute bright craterlet. South-west of C is a low ring, A, almost as large as Hortensius. Its eastern rim is higher than the western, and there is a pass on the south and a peak on the north. On its floor is some delicate detail, including minute craterlets and hills under the west rim. Between it and C are two irregular depressions, and further south two perfectly-formed craters.

KUNOWSKY, —536 +056 [German astronomer, 1786-1846]. A small ring with somewhat linear walls and a long but low central ridge. A bright ray starts at a tangent to the south wall, and extends south-east. On the outer glacis, where it begins, is a minute craterlet. West is a rough circle of isolated peaks; north-east is a plateau, the southern edge of which is marked by a few low hills. There is a small landslip on the inner west wall of Kunowsky.

LANDSBERG, —448 —006 [Belgian scholar, 1561-1632]. A prominent ringed-plain, 29 miles in diameter, with massive, rugged outer slopes pitted on the south by crater-like depressions. This portion of the wall is continued by a line of low hills south-east to the crater, C, which has a low central peak, a craterlet on its north wall and a shallow groove on the outer north slope. Outside the east wall of Landsberg is an obvious land-slip; north is a shallow ring from which a valley runs along the slope to the south-west.

West are many small isolated hills, the highest and most numerous being on the south. About 10 miles to the south-south-west of Landsberg is a cratercone, east of an isolated hill, and there is a similar cratercone slightly to the east of a line joining the centres of Landsberg and Reinhold, lying a little to the west of a ridge emanating from the north wall of Landsberg. On the opposite side of the ridge is a low dome with a minute summit craterlet.

North-east of the crater C is a low ring; another and much larger lies to the south-west. To the south-east are three bright craters, surrounded by haloes, centres of minor ray systems.

The walls of Landsberg are finely terraced on the inner slopes, and rise 10,000 feet above the interior, on which is a multiple-peaked central mountain mass and also some low mounds. On the inner east slope is a vast crescent-shaped terrace, probably a landslip, and separated from the wall by a deep ravine which is filled with shadow early in the lunar afternoon.

MILICHIUS, —495 +174 [German physician and philosopher, 1501-59]. A small bright crater, east of Copernicus, with low walls. To the east is a low dome with a very minute pit on its summit. South of this are two minute cones and a bright crater, A. Several cones have been found in this region by Dr. S. R. B. Cooke and other observers. A fine drawing by this talented observer will be found in the 10th Memoir of the B.A.A. Lunar Section. These cones, some of which bear summit craters, lie between Milichius and Hortensius. Goodacre shows little detail in this region. About 40 miles south of Milichius is a small double crater, while between Milichius and Hortensius is a curved ridge divided into three portions, but rising into four peaks, of which the second from the south is the highest and rises 3,000 feet. The peak adjoining it on the north rises 1,200 feet. Immediately east of this peak is a low hill, and farther east a low dome. The northern and isolated fragment of the curved ridge has a crater on its north slope.

PARRY, —268 —135 [English explorer, 1790-1855]. A ringed-plain, 28 miles in diameter, adjoining Bonpland on the west, with fragmentary walls, but more complete than those of Fra Mauro or Bonpland. There are passes in the west, north and south walls, and some bright craters on the interior. These are a little to the west of the centre. Others exist on the south and north, together with a few craterlets and hillocks. Under the south wall is a wide cleft which, after traversing the floor, passes through a pass in the west wall and continues beyond, curving to the north. Another cleft crosses the floor close to the east wall, originating under the east wall of the bright crater, A, south of Parry. A is 7 miles in diameter and has a central peak. The cleft passes into Fra Mauro and crosses the floor of this formation. Dr. S. R. B. Cooke found another cleft running across the floor of Parry southwards from the north wall, then curving sharply to the west and joining the wide cleft under the south wall, where it passes through this portion of the rampart.

Outside the west wall is a bright crater, and adjoining the north wall a partial ring. West of the crater A are some ancient rings, the walls of which are incomplete. Farther

116

south are numerous hills and pits. Between Parry and Guericke are some ancient rings, also a few hills.

Under a high light the east wall of Parry appears bright, while the centre of the south wall is concealed by a bright area extending slightly on to the floor. There is also a brilliant spot 40 miles west of Parry, at the centre of which Wilkins has seen a minute craterlet.

REINHOLD, —389 +059 [German mathematician, 1511-53]. A fine ringed-plain, 30 miles in diameter, with lofty walls rising, on the west, 9,000 feet above the floor. The outer east slope is very complex, consisting of a number of rocky masses overlapping each other. Adjoining the south wall is a partial ring, to the west of which is a bright isolated mountain. Further south are a number of little peaks rising only a few hundred feet. A strong mountain arm runs from the south-west wall, and another from the north wall; the latter extends for only a short distance and is succeeded by a number of hills arranged in rows curving slightly to the north-west. These, with ridges and craterlets, form an interesting vista in the telescope.

The inner slopes are distinguished by a deep ravine extending below the crest of the west, south and north walls, with a peak or small landslip partially blocking it on the south. Below the terrace thus formed is a steep slope to the floor, on which are a central mountain and some lesser elevations. On the south wall is a peak, and east of it an obvious crater, shown by Schmidt.

In addition to numerous craters around is the ringed-plain, Eddington, to the north-west, 15 miles in diameter, with low, linear walls, a craterlet under its south-east wall and others on its north wall. North-west of Eddington is a circle of isolated peaks forming the remains of an ancient ring, P, the central mountain of which can still be detected. Eddington has two passes in its north wall, and there is an old ring adjoining on the north-west. Wilkins (33-inch O.G.) found four clefts to the south.

RIPHÆN MOUNTAINS, —464 —150. A small range of mountains consisting of a curved arc, concave to the south-west, with two low peaks rising to nearly 3,000 feet. Another horseshoe-shaped and narrow ridge lies to the north, the space being filled with little hills. There is a crater on the eastern portion of this ridge, from which another low ridge curves north-east and may be traced in a circle, evidently the remains of an ancient ring. Another adjoins it on the south-east. The whole range is bright and is evidently the relic of once-prominent ringed-plains, now reduced to mere fragments by erosive forces. Towards the south, the range rapidly narrows, and ends at a small crater. East of this narrow portion is an isolated hill, also numerous lesser elevations. R. Barker found a cleft running south-west from the mountains, since confirmed by Wilkins.

STADIUS, —236 +183 [Belgian mathematician and astronomer, 1527-79]. A fine example of an ancient ring, the walls of which have almost entirely disappeared, the north-west showing the highest fragment. This portion may be seen even when at a considerable distance from the terminator and when all trace of the formation as a whole has vanished. The south border consists of mere mounds alternating with craterlets. On the east, the boundary is marked by a crater, A, a low ridge and a curved row of craterpits. The north wall is a mere ghostly outline marked by craterpits. Outside it is a crater, B, with numerous craterlets and a crater-chain.

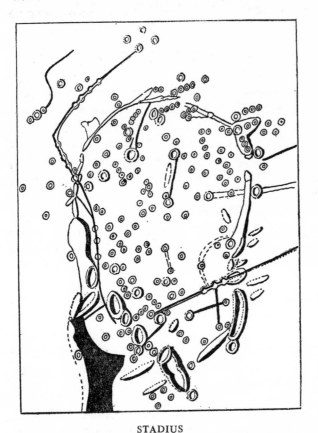

STADIUS

22 April 1953: 33-inch O.G. × 540. (Observatory of of Meudon) H. P. Wilkins

The interior of Stadius, 40 miles in diameter, is pitted with a large number of crater-pits and craterlets. The largest lie on the south and include a number of shallow valleys and crater-chains. Others may be traced from the northern border and under the fragment of the wall, on the west. Observers differ in their delineation of these delicate objects, as is fully to be expected. Schmidt shows 16 pits in his map but in the text he mentions having counted 50; Elger published a chart on which 41 craterlets and pits are shown (L.A.S., Vol. 5, p. 8). There is also a chart in the B.A.A. *Journal*, Vol. XXI, p. 188, and another was given by Goodacre, based on the Mt. Wilson photograph of 15 September 1919. This chart will be found in the 8th Memoir of the B.A.A. Lunar Section. Yet another appears in the book of Goodacre (*The Moon*, p. 133).

The above-mentioned charts, excellent in their way, do not show half of the astounding number of craterlets and pits on the interior of Stadius. Wilkins and Moore found the floor riddled with such objects, many of comparatively large size and down to minute pits of shadow, with the giant 33-inch Meudon refractor, on 3 April 1952. At the same time the surface to the east, between Stadius and Copernicus, was covered with ridges, between which were rows of minute pits.

The low banks comprising the existing borders of Stadius can be traced, when near the terminator, with a telescope as small as a 3-inch refractor. This aperture will also reveal a few of the more prominent craterlets on and around the rim. Telescopes of from 10- to 12-inch aperture are necessary to reveal the more delicate objects, while giant instruments are essential for the most minute.

Goodacre stated that some of the craterlets and pits between Stadius and Copernicus define the site of an ancient ring.

Between Copernicus and Eratosthenes, and thus north of Stadius, are numbers of craterlets, some in chains, one such chain passing into a true cleft at its north end. The more minute of these features require considerable telescopic power to be well seen, and this region evidently forms an extension of the pit-riddled surface of Stadius.

On the map about one hundred craterlets and pits, as well as seven shallow valleys, are shown.

Under high illumination, Stadius is covered by the light rays from Copernicus, and only the west fragmentary wall and one or two of the larger craterlets can be traced as bright spots. Under a very low sun the interior is seen to be slightly uneven, and thus presents a humpy aspect when on the terminator. Stadius is situated at the south end of the strong mountain arm from the south of Eratosthenes, which forms a guide to the detection of this curious formation when it is at some distance from the terminator.

TURNER, —228 —024 [English astronomer, 1861-1930]. A ring to the south-west of Gambart, with a smaller crater on the east. West is a low ring, S, and south a short cleft.

URAL MOUNTAINS, —475 —090. A mountain mass north of Euclides and north-east of the Riphæns, between it and Landsberg are the remains of several old rings, of which K is the largest.

119

VII

A large part of this section is occupied by portions of two seas, the Mare Nubium and the Mare Humorum. This part of the Mare Nubium is dominated by the great ringed-plain Bullialdus, a miniature of Copernicus with its radiating ridges and craterlet-chains. On and near the coasts of the 'seas' are many partially destroyed objects, such as Kies, Lubiniezky, Hippalus and Doppelmayer.

Of the clefts, the greatest is that associated with the crater Hesiodus; this is prominent enough to be seen with very small telescopes. The craters Ramsden and Moore are also associated with clefts, and others are to be found near Cichus, Capuanus, Mercator and Campanus. The complicated Ramsden system is second only to that of Triesnecker in interest, but a large instrument is needed to study it properly.

Of the smaller features, Hesiodus A and Marth are interesting owing to their double nature, the interior containing a complete ring concentric with the outer rampart, while Moore and Lenham contain dark radial bands of Aristarchan type.

Another interesting, though somewhat neglected, formation is Wurzelbauer, the rough interior of which is traversed by parallel rows of hillocks and craterlet-chains, so numerous that very little undisturbed ground is left.

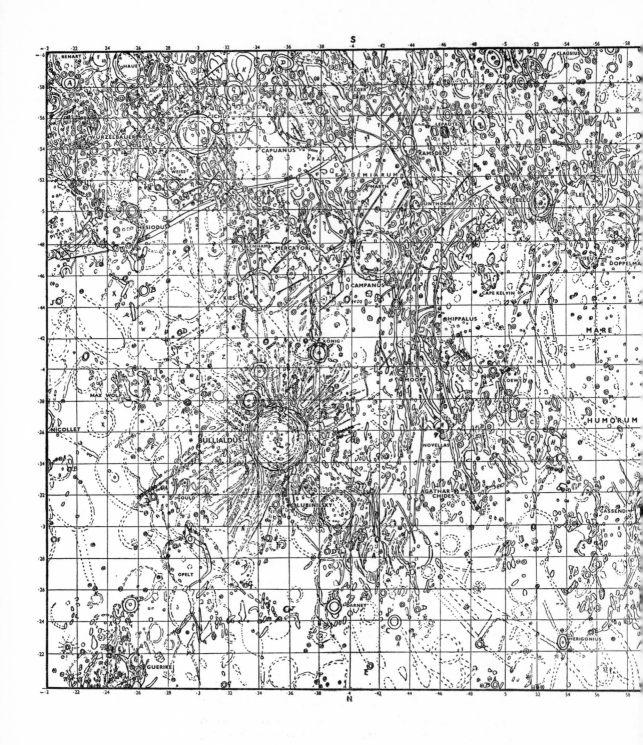

VII

AGATHARCHIDES, —484 —336 [Greek geographer and historian, *circa* 120 B.C.].
An irregular formation, 30 miles across, with walls rising 5,000 feet on the west, but
reduced to isolated masses on the north. Two valleys cut through the south wall. On the
interior are a low central mound and other irregularities. Here and there considerable
landslips can be traced on the inner slopes, especially on the west. West of Agatharchides
is what appears to be a lava-filled ring, 40 miles in diameter. This ring contains a cleft,
which traverses its interior from north to south. Many obscure rings lie in the neighbourhood, the most prominent on the south-east, as well as many hillocks.

BULLIALDUS, —354 —350 [French astronomer, 1605-94]. One of the finest of all the
lunar ringed-plains, 39 miles in diameter, and admirably placed on the Mare Nubium.
It has massive walls which exhibit a decided linear tendency, and rise to an average
height of 8,000 feet above the floor, which appears to be convex. There are many little
peaks surmounting the crest. The inner slopes are magnificently terraced, and exhibit
distinct landslips in places, also some craterlets. The outer glacis, which contains some
depressions, is surrounded by numerous ridges after the manner of Copernicus. There
is a gap in the south-east wall from which a crater-chain runs towards the crater, once
called C but now named König. This crater-chain loses that character and becomes a
cleft on the south.

In the interior of Bullialdus is a complex central mountain group, consisting of four
peaks and described by Goodacre and Moore as bright, but seen by Haas as dull. The
loftiest peak rises 3,200 feet. There are also a few mounds on the floor, and at least two
minute craterlets on the eastern portion, only visible in powerful telescopes. To the
south-west of Bullialdus is a prominent and deep crater, A, with traces of interior terracing, a small central hill and some mounds. There are also some craterlets on its walls.
On its south-east is another crater, B, connected with the wall of Bullialdus by a wide
but shallow valley. B has a central peak, and a craterlet on its south-east wall. Some
distance to the east is König. This also has a central hill and slightly overlaps an older
ring X on the east. This old ring is now reduced to isolated fragments. A similar ring, X1,
lies to the south of König but is not quite as much reduced as X. Between König and
Bullialdus are two oval, ridge-bordered enclosures, traversed by craterlet-chains resembling clefts; which indeed that on the west is, for a considerable distance. To the north is
a small crater, F, and still farther to the north, beyond a mass of little craters and
mounds, the remains of another old ring. This still has a considerable fragment of its
original west wall remaining, but that on the east now consists of isolated hillocks. In
addition to the numerous radial ridges from the walls of Bullialdus, the surroundings

123

contain numerous obscure rings; of these one, L, on the south-west, is especially prominent and still complete, although the walls are now mere ridges. Some observers have considered this as a formation of the Wargentin type, but Goodacre was right in pointing out that the floor is not raised above the level of the surrounding country. L has its highest point on the north-west, and here it rises about 600 feet. Immediately to the south-east is a low, rounded swelling, an example of a lunar dome but without any crater-like opening on its summit. The entire district is traversed by numerous crater-chains, discovered by Whitley. One row in particular is prominent, and the individual members are large but very shallow. Other chains consist of small craters after the pattern seen between Copernicus and Eratosthenes.

Haas has noted that the floor of Bullialdus contains a large number of tiny bright spots under high lighting, also a ridge 'which almost encircles the crater at the foot of the inner walls'. Under low illumination the floor is dark and uniformly shaded, but is bright under high illumination. It then contains several darker areas. One such area, to the north-east of the central mountains, apparently expands in a clockwise direction during the lunar morning to give rise to dark areas in the north-west and west parts of the floor. With the approach of sunset all dark areas disappear, probably due to the really rough floor being more or less covered by minute shadows. Many other formations might be instanced where the interiors appear to be of a rough nature or texture, largely covered by tiny irregularities too small for telescopic detection, and which are only made manifest by their combined shadows under low illumination.

CAMPANUS, —411 —469 [Italian theologian, *circa* A.D. 1260]. A fine crater, 29 miles in diameter, with walls rising 6,000 feet on the east above the floor, but lower on the west. A cleft cuts through this portion of the wall. On the somewhat dark floor are a central hill, two partial rings concave to the west, two craterlets between the central mountain and the north wall (that farthest north has a hill just west of it), and a crater-chain on the north. There is also a hill south of the central mountain, and three craterlets on the inner south slope. On the west is a partial ring with a cleft on the slope above it.

From the north wall a fine mountain arm projects, with three craters on its end and a cleft extending from east to west. A ridge runs to the crater, A. This is on one of the Hippalus clefts, and east of it are three minute craterpits. West of the crater A is the remains of an old ring. On the east are low and, in part, confluent craters. To the north-west is a small crater, and this has a circle of isolated hills to the north, evidently the relic of what was once a perfect ring.

CAPUANUS, —370 —560 [Italian astronomer, *circa* A.D. 1450]. A remarkable object, 35 miles in diameter, with a floor elevated above the surrounding country, thus resembling, in some degree, Wargentin. The floor is dark and contains some detail, chiefly low domes, depicted by Dr. S. R. B. Cooke in the 10th Report of the B.A.A. Lunar Section, and also seen by Barker and Thornton. Barker says there are at least four rounded hills on the interior, confirmed by Thornton, who depicts them as arranged in a quadrangle.

Barker noted a forked ridge connecting three of them. The bright walls rise to 8,000 feet in places but are lower on the north-west, and are broken by craters on the north. There are also three craters on the south-west, and a long depression on the south-east, where there is also a cleft. Krieger drew three light streaks and a cleft on the north-west. North of Capuanus is the relic of a once-complete ring, S. On the west is the remains of another, a. There is a partial ring on the inner east slope of Capuanus, and on the outer surface are three craterlet-chains on the south-east, two others on the west and a crater in a gap on the north-west, numerous hills and a distinct crater-chain running north. A fine mountain arm is associated with Capuanus, and this is cut through by the great cleft which begins at the east wall of Hesiodus. This division of the mountain arm is difficult to see, and has been denied by some observers, but its existence has been established by the observations of Barker and Wilkins.

CICHUS, −302 −548 [Italian astronomer, 1257-1327]. Another very interesting object, 20 miles in diameter, and situated on the edge of a small dark plain with a prominent crater, G, on its east crest. This crater is 5 miles in diameter and from it R. Barker has traced a delicate cleft running to the ruined ring, Capuanus a. This cleft was confirmed by L. F. Ball. The crater G was drawn by Schröter smaller than depicted by Mädler, and Webb thought there might be some suspicion of change in connection with this formation. Against the south wall are the relics of two rings, with a craterlet between them. The wall is finely terraced on the east, and here rises 9,000 feet; on the west it attains 8,000 feet, and here is a distinct landslip while a narrow cleft runs down the south-west slope.

On the floor of Cichus are two low hills, a little to the west of the centre. To the north-west is an ancient ring, on the north-west of which is the fine crater Hauet, with a central hill and a craterlet on its northern rim. To the north is another ruined ring, an interesting object as it is crossed by a cleft which begins at Hauet. Barker has noted a cleft to the north, and another which runs to the north wall of Cichus. The latter cleft has been confirmed by L. F. Ball. Barker, using his 12½-inch reflector, 7 November 1932, discovered a fine cleft from Hauet which crosses the mountain ridge associated with Cichus. This ridge is 3,800 feet in height, and the new cleft runs parallel with the great chasm from Hesiodus. This was confirmed by J. H. Ritcher. One of the Tycho light rays passes close to the west wall of Cichus.

DARNEY, −387 −252 [French astronomer, 1882-   ]. A small crater, terraced on the west, and situated on the plain to the north of Lubiniezky. A ridge runs from the south wall. On the north and west are obscure rings, West is the crater, J, and north-east a crater, E. On the east, beyond an obscure ring, is the crater C.

DOPPELMAYER, −580 −478 [German mathematician, 1671-1750]. A fine example of a large walled-plain, 40 miles in diameter, on the margin of one of the 'seas' and which has suffered from the action of erosive forces in the past, with the result that the portion of the wall abutting on the plain has largely disappeared, only fragments now remaining.

The interior contains a fine and prominent central mountain, 2,500 feet in height, divided by a ravine into two portions, which casts a strong shadow under low illumination. In addition to the central mountain there are some low ridges and hillocks. The southern and eastern ramparts are well marked and duplicated on the south-east, beyond which are two craters. On the concave floor there is evidence of a once-complete ring, now marked by a circular arrangement of hills. There are also at least two small craters to the north of the central mountain, while the southern portion of the floor is more rough than the northern, which appears to have been invaded by the material of the Mare Humorum.

On the plain to the north-west is a complete but low ring, Puiseux, while on the north-east can be traced an ancient ring which is about 49 miles across and through the centre of which runs a cleft, which is continued on the north-east as a ridge. Its true extent, overestimated by Neison, was first pointed out by Dr. S. M. Green. The only portion of this old ring which attains any altitude is on the north, where there is a small peak.

Some distance to the south of Doppelmayer is a large mountain mass, the most prominent of many such which are scattered on the surface as far south as Clausius.

DUNTHORNE, —454 —501 [English astronomer and engineer, 1711-75]. A crater with very broad walls, to the south-east of Campanus and on the east border of the Palus Epidemiarum. On the floor are two hillocks, and also two craterlets on the west wall. To the west is a cleft, part of the Ramsden system, while on the east are the concentric clefts bordering the western side of the Mare Humorum.

ELGER, —405 —578 [English selenographer, 1838-97]. An imperfect formation to the east of Capuanus. Between these formations is the long depression, P. North-east of Elger are clefts running to the south wall of Ramsden.

EPIDEMIARUM, PALUS, —380 —480 to —460 —580. 'Marsh of Epidemics'. A small dark plain to the east of Cichus, and traversed by the Ramsden cleft system, with many hills and craterlets on its surface. Mercator and Campanus limit it on the north, Capuanus and Elger on the south, and Cichus on the west.

GOULD, —280 —328 [American astronomer, 1824-96]. A low, ancient ring, open on the south and the north and with a crater, D, on its north-west rim, and a craterlet, A, in the centre of the floor. To the south-west of D is a craterlet-chain, which runs across the floor as a cleft and is continued on the east by another craterlet-chain as far as the west of Bullialdus. Around Gould are numerous obscure rings.

GUERICKE, —239 —200 [German physicist, 1602-86]. This formation is 36 miles in diameter with regular walls on the east, where there is an ancient ring, but with a gap on the south and a still wider gap on the west. This section of the wall has been reduced to the level of the plain. On the north wall is a peak of 2,800 feet. Some distance to the south is a crater, B. The most complete survey of the details on the interior is that obtained by Wilkins, 3 April 1952, at 22h. U.T., with the great 33-inch refractor of the Meudon Observatory.

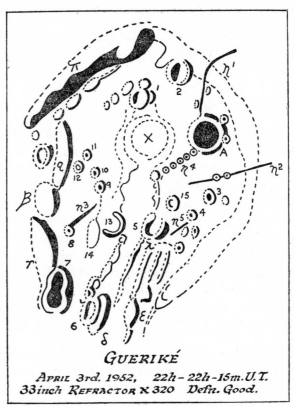

GUERIKÉ

APRIL 3rd. 1952,   22h – 22h –15m. U.T.
33inch REFRACTOR X 320   Defn. Good.

H. P. Wilkins

The details then seen included a prominent crater, A, on the south-east portion of the floor, from which a cleft, I, runs to the south and then cuts through the wall and turns east. From its north-west rim a craterlet-chain, 5 craterlets in all, runs towards the centre of the floor and close to a large ruined ring, X. Formation I consists of a crater with hills on both the east and the west, and another on the south. No. 2 is a deep and conspicuous crater. On the east wall of the crater A are two craterlets. Between A and the crater 3, to the north, is a cleft, 2, which passes through two crater-pits and thence through the wall. A short cleft, 5, runs from the small craterlet, 4, towards a well-marked ring, 5, which has a gap in its south wall. A row of hills runs to the crater, 6. East is a mountain mass, Delta. Four parallel ridges run from the ring, 5, towards the north-north-west. Above a double crater, 7, is a minute craterlet, 9, one of the group 9, 10, 11 and 12. There is an incomplete ring, 13, open on the south-west and close to it a hill, 14. South of 5 is a craterlet, 15. From the depression X a shallow valley runs north across the floor. In addition to the above there are some hills, and ridges, the hills are well marked, running parallel to the wall on the south-west. Most of the above-mentioned detail was unrecorded prior to its detection with the great telescope.

There has been some disagreement regarding the details inside Guericke. Goodacre mentions that Molesworth once saw a short cleft to the west of the centre. It seems certain, however, that this does not exist, as Wilkins was unable to find it with the 33-inch refractor; though several clefts were noted, none corresponds in position with Molesworth's.

HAUET, —243 —592 [French selenographer, 1878-1933]. A well-formed ring to the south-east of Wurzelbauer, with bright and broad walls and two large craters, E and F, on the north. On the floor are two hills, both near the west wall. From the north wall run two parallel rows of hills as far as the crater Cichus B, some craterlet-chains, and hillocks. North of the crater E is a smaller crater, H.

HERIGONIUS, —543 —231 [French mathematician, *circa* 1644]. A small but bright crater 10 miles in diameter. On the floor is a central hill. Herigonius is connected by ridges with a large, ancient ring on the west, while a smaller ring abuts upon the south-west wall. To the south-east are some hills, one of which rises 3,400 feet, nearly the height of Snowdon.

HESIODUS, —245 —490 [Greek poet, *circa* 735 B.C.]. A crater, 28 miles in diameter, to the east of Pitatus, with a pass into the latter and with gaps in its north wall. On the inner north-west is a crater, also a central crater with a smaller crater on its west. On the north is an old ring with a crater and a mountain on the south-east; the wall of the old ring is open on the north. Beyond is a larger ring, with a very broken western rampart and craters on the east. To the east of this ring is the crater, B, and on the north a ridge. West of the larger obscure ring is a low hill with a summit crater. On the south-east wall of Hesiodus is the crater, A, with a complete inner ring on its floor; west of A is a small, low, double ancient ring. A long cleft runs from the north-east wall eastwards to the mountain arm on the north of Cichus, and is continued beyond. A craterlet lies within the cleft near Hesiodus, and there are evidences of others farther east. Thornton found a small central hill in A and has seen the inner ring conspicuous at Full.

HIPPALUS, —456 —420 [Greek mariner, *circa* A.D. 120]. This is a fine example of a partially destroyed ring, on the western margin of the Mare Humorum. It is 38 miles in diameter, the east wall, facing the 'sea', having largely disappeared. From a converging point near Vitello, three deep and prominent cleft-valleys run towards Hippalus. The most easterly of these cuts through a small crater, skirts a hill on the west and ends at a hill. Continuing beyond this obstruction it cuts through a mountain and crosses the interior of Hippalus. In its course there are some enlargements or expansions; thence it can be traced to the south-east of Agatharchides. The middle cleft runs along the west wall, then crosses an ancient ring and passes several others and eventually passes into a wide valley. The most westerly of the clefts is interrupted by a mountain arm, but reappears beyond it and then skirts a ridge to the small crater, Campanus A, to the west of which are some little hills, probably the remains of old rings. The cleft then turns to the crater Moore, which crater has been found by Moore to have some dusky bands on the inner east slopes. A cleft also runs from A to the south wall of Hippalus, passing to the east of a hill while the main cleft continues beyond Moore and becomes wider and more shallow, eventually ending as a wide valley.

To the west of A are some very remarkable crosses, clefts, also little peaks and old rings. There are also some ancient rings on the north. The interior of Hippalus also contains some delicate craterlets, one of the most conspicuous being on the south-east, and the remains of an old ring on the northern portion, with hills and mounds only to be seen in powerful instruments, and even then only under good conditions. It still requires accurate observation and charting. Especially remarkable and suggestive is the deflection inwards of the middle portion of the west wall, and the manner in which the outer north glacis is disturbed by large but shallow depressions. The tint of the interior is similar to that of the Mare outside, proof that the material of the latter invaded the formation and probably caused the destruction of the south-eastern portion of the wall.

KELVIN, CAPE, —492 —450 [Scottish scientist, 1824-1907]. A mountain mass isolated on the south-western part of the Mare Humorum, with a plateau-like surface on which are ravines, and with a crater at its north-eastern point. South of it is a smaller mountain mass; both resemble islands. Kelvin rises at one point to 7,000 feet.

KIES, —344 —443 [German mathematician, 1713-81]. A low but complete ring on the plain to the south of the great ringed formation Bullialdus, and 25 miles in diameter. The rampart is highest on the south-east and here rises 2,500 feet. There are some gaps on the east, but probably they do not quite attain the inner level, which appears to be the same as that of the plain on the outside. On the floor is a light streak traversed by a delicate cleft; this Schmidt shows as a ridge. There are also some delicate craterlets. A prominent mountain spur runs from the south wall and is evidently a part of the eastern wall of an ancient ring. On the southern rampart of this ring is a crater, Lenham, with a smaller crater to the south and yet another on the west. Craterlet-chains run south from Lenham, and there are others on the north, from the north wall of Kies. Dr. Cooke detected many craterlets in this region. On the east is a well-marked dome with a distinct summit crater, an interesting object. D. C. Brown found, with a 10-inch reflector, a dark radial band in Lenham, which was confirmed by Moore, Lenham, D. C. Brown and Abineri. Lenham has a high peak on its north-east wall.

KÖNIG, —380 —410 [German mathematician, 1865-1927]. This crater used to be known as Bullialdus C, and overlaps an older ring on the east. This has had its wall reduced to isolated fragments, and there is another similar ring on the south. König is 14 miles in diameter, and has a central peak.

LEE, —558 —509 [English amateur astronomer, 1783-1866]. An incomplete ring, over 28 miles in diameter, the north-west wall being a mere ridge. The formation is situated to the south-west of Doppelmayer, and between this formation and Vitello. On the floor are low hills, some equally low ridges, and rings; of the latter one on the western portion is easily seen although overlooked by Goodacre. On the floor, near the east border, is a cleft, discovered by Goodacre. To the west of Lee is a still larger ring, even more ruined, and crossed by a cleft to the west of which is a buried ring. The north wall of this second ruined ring contains many craters.

LENHAM, —340 —474 [contemporary English selenographer]. This crater, 11 miles in diameter, is interesting on account of the dark radial band which runs to its inner east wall. Lenham used to be known as Kies A, and is described under that heading.

LEPAUTE, —462 —549 [French woman computor, 1723-88]. A small crater to the south-east of Ramsden, with a low ring, X, on the north. On the east is a large crater, D.

LOEWY, —500 —387 [French astronomer, 1833-1907]. A small and incomplete depression to the south of Agatharchides, and north of Hippalus, thus on the border of the Mare Humorum. The wall facing the 'sea' has entirely disappeared.

LUBINIEZKY, —385 —308 [Polish astronomer, 1623-75]. A ruined ring, 24 miles in diameter, with low, narrow walls broken on the south, while the interior is crossed by a bright streak; and although shown quite free from detail by Schmidt, contains several minute craterlets and hills. There is also a little peak on the northern wall. To the south is an ancient ring with its walls breached at intervals, a central mound and a cleft on the south. A smaller ruined ring abuts on the south-west wall. Several of these low rings are shown by Tobias Mayer as dark surface markings. The region to the north-east of Lubiniezky, occupied by these ancient rings, forms a bright patch under high illumination, which suggests that the interiors of many of these rings may not have been invaded by the material forming the present surface of the Mare Nubium. A prominent streak from Tycho passes a little to the south-east of Lubiniezky.

MARTH, —419 —517 [German astronomer, 1828-97]. A small crater associated with the Ramsden cleft system and remarkable for having a complete ring on its interior and concentric with the outer wall. Krieger drew a distinct pit occupying the centre of both rings, but Thornton does not confirm this. He finds the interior of the inner ring perfectly smooth, as though lava-filled.

MERCATOR, —386 —488 [Dutch geographer, 1512-94]. A fine ringed-plain about the same size as Campanus and forming with it a good example of a pair of ringed formations very similar in many respects. The interior is 28 miles in diameter, while the surrounding walls rise, in places, to 5,000 feet, with a crater on the western crest from which a short crater-chain runs south down the slope. Just within the crest of the rampart, on the east, are two craterlets. The outer walls are very broad, and three prominent rocky mountain masses project on to the Mare on the north. To the north of the most westerly of these promontories is a low ring which is connected with König by a discontinuous ridge.

The south wall of Mercator is cut through by a cleft which curves out on to the floor, ending at a small depression nearly in the centre. There are also some craterlets on the interior, which is rather dark in tint. The wall on the south-west expands into a large and broad mountain mass of considerable elevation, rising as much as 6,000 feet at one point and separated from another mountain, on the west, by a narrow ravine or valley. To the south of this mountain mass is a large depression; several hillocks also lie on the plain between Mercator and Capuanus. To the south of Mercator is Marth. Mercator and Campanus form the subject of one of the plates in Nasmyth and Carpenter's book on the Moon, and have since been finely shown on several of the best lunar photographs. South-east is the smaller crater, A, which at Full is surrounded by a bright rectangular nimbus.

MOORE, —437 —395 [English selenographer, and one of the Authors, 1923-]. This was formerly known as Agatharchides A, and lies to the north-west of Hippalus on the most westerly of the three great valley-clefts on the western side of the Mare Humorum. There is some object on the western part of the floor, probably a hill, and also two dusky bands on the inner east wall, discovered by Moore with a 6-inch refractor in 1949. With the great 33-inch Meudon refractor, Moore saw some small bright and circular patches inside the crater; the general effect is very like a miniature Aristarchus. To the south-west are two crossed clefts, also some hills arranged in a rough circle. A short, curved cleft runs from the south-east wall to a mountain on the south. North is the large cleft which continues after being interrupted by Moore, and passes through a crater, B, thence into Novellas. On the north-west is a massive mountain of no great altitude, and east of Moore is a delicate cleft.

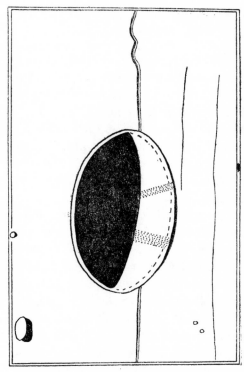

MOORE
6 June 1949, 21h., 6-inch O.G. × 325
Patrick Moore

NICOLLET, —200 —373 [French astronomer, 1788-1843]. A circular crater, 10 miles in diameter, with a hill just outside the east wall and a large ruined ring of which the western wall possesses some altitude. On the south are old rings with smaller on the north. On the west is a crater from which a ridge runs to the south-west. There is a ridge connecting Nicollet with the Prom. Ænarium.

NOVELLAS, —449 —345 [Spanish astronomer and chemist, 1874-1940]. A large enclosure to the west of Agatharchides, with very low, fragmentary walls and a cleft on the floor. This cleft runs to the ring, E, on the north. In addition to the cleft there is a central crater, also some hills and low rings on the floor.

OPELT, —292 —281 [German financier and patron of science, 1794-1863]. A large but low-walled enclosure on the Mare Nubium, some distance to the north-west of Bullialdus. The wall is tolerably regular and of moderate height on the east, but very low on the west. On the south wall is a crater, E, while the interior contains a small crater, A, many hillocks and some craterlets.

PUISEUX, −557 −466 [French astronomer, 1855-1928]. A ring of which only fragments of the wall remain, to the north-west of Doppelmayer. On the floor is a slight central hill.

RAMSDEN, −442 −543 [English instrument maker, 1735-1800]. A small ringed-plain, but of great interest owing to the very remarkable system of clefts associated with it, the whole bearing a strong resemblance to that of Triesnecker and of equal difficulty as a telescopic object. Like the Triesnecker system, the Ramsden clefts have a nodal point to the west of the crater, in the form of a small crater. From this crater a cleft runs north-west as far as the mountain arm from the north-east wall of Capuanus, and thus appears to be a displaced continuation of the great Hesiodus cleft, which is generally considered as terminating at the mountain arm. As a matter of fact, it cuts through this, but at an angle.

A second cleft runs slightly to the west of north and ends at a small crater; this is connected with Marth by a short, curved cleft. The third cleft from the node runs towards the north-east, where is the great triple system concentric with the western border of the Mare Humorum. So far, no definite connection between the two systems has been traced, the Ramsden cleft appearing to be lost at the hilly ground, but it is probably connected with the Hippalus cleft-valleys. Soon after leaving the nodal crater, it passes through a small crater, while the other two clefts present crater-like enlargements, in places, along their courses. From the south wall of Ramsden itself three clefts start: that to the west runs towards the south-west and crosses a cleft which begins at the nodal crater and runs south-east. This cleft is one of three clefts from the nodal crater which run towards the south-west; there is another on the south-east. The cleft from the wall of Ramsden, after crossing the last-mentioned cleft, passes to a small crater, where it divides into two: one short branch running due west, and the other, and longer, running to the south towards a small crater which is itself the terminus of a long cleft which runs, in a gentle curve, to the wall of Ramsden. Between these clefts a third cleft commences from the wall and bends towards the south-east, running almost parallel with the cleft which runs south-eastwards from the nodal crater, A. Between these clefts is a small crater, and there are others between or close to the various clefts.

From the north wall of Ramsden three clefts also make their appearance: two run northwards almost parallel with each other; that on the west runs into the long cleft, the most easterly of the three tending northwards from the crater A.

From a point on the wall very near to where the western cleft originates, another cleft begins, which runs to the north-east and connects with the more easterly of those from the north wall. A very long cleft begins from the more westerly of these clefts a few miles from its source at the north wall of Ramsden, and runs north-west as far as the outer glacis of Campanus; cuts through the wall of the latter formation and on to the floor, as already mentioned when dealing with this object. The above are the principal members of this remarkable system, but numerous finer and more delicate clefts exist, in part consisting of craterlet-chains, requiring very favourable atmospheric conditions for their detection and also a good instrument to see clearly their characteristic features.

Ramsden itself presents no features of interest, except for a small crater abutting against the outer south wall and two craterlets on the east wall. It has no central peak, and the walls are only of moderate height; the floor also is not deeply sunk below the outer level. Moore has recorded a bright area on the inner east wall (24 April 1953: 33-inch refractor). On the plain, to the east of Ramsden, there is a small crater on the south, and three more, forming a triangle, to the north-east, while farther to the east is the well-formed crater, B, and a large but imperfect formation, F, with very low walls, in part fragmentary and which has evidently suffered from the action of erosive forces in the past. This plain is separated from Vitello by a hilly region and craters; it contains, not far from the border in this direction, the remains of a large enclosure now reduced to mere ridges, and only visible when near the terminator. In this region also are some short clefts which are obviously part of the great cleft-valley system associated with Hippalus. Krieger gives a detailed chart of the Ramsden clefts in his *Mond Atlas*. All the features whose existence has been established are depicted on the accompanying map in the present work. Careful observation with considerable apertures will, doubtless, add to the number of objects already charted.

RENART, —212 —602 [Spanish astronomer, 1878-1946]. A large ring to the south of Wurzelbauer with a crater, A, on its north wall; another crater, F, on the east, and craterlets and hills on its floor.

VITELLO, —525 —506 [Polish mathematician, *circa* A.D. 1270]. A fine crater, 30 miles in diameter, with walls rising 4,500 feet on the east and with a crater on the southern crest. The wall is very low on the north. It is chiefly remarkable for a large and complete ring within the principal rampart, but not concentric with the latter, being nearer the western side than the eastern. Vitello also has a central hill, on the summit of which is a crater. South of this peak is a low ring, also a craterlet on the inner east wall, another on the north-east and some low mounds and ridges on the floor. To the west of Vitello is a valley, and beyond it a small mountain. On the north are isolated hills, craterlets and a low ring. The crater Vitello A, to the south-east, exhibits dusky bands on the inner slopes and across the floor, according to observations by Lenham. The crater D also has bands on its interior. Thornton has noted that at sunrise the inner ring of Vitello is seen as a chain of tiny beads of light partly encircling the Matterhorn-like central mountain. There is also evidence of a fault on the interior, as there is a decided dip close to the east inner wall.

WEISS, —285 —530 [Austrian astronomer, 1837-1917]. This is an enclosure to the north-west of Cichus, rather than a true crater, and has a gap on the north-east and many hills on the interior. At its north-west is a crater, with the remains of an inner ring on its floor; from this crater a cleft runs south-east, cutting through the west wall but seems to pass *under* the east wall of a peculiar formation immediately to the north of Cichus. To the north-east of this cleft is a shorter cleft, then a small crater, from which another cleft runs first to the north-west then to the south-east. Beyond this feature is the great Hesiodus Cleft. To the west of Weiss is a square formation, really a depression, L, and to the south-west the crater B.

WOLF, MAX, −260 −388 [German astronomer, 1863-1932]. A peculiar formation to the south-east of Nicollet, with a broad western wall cut through by two narrow valleys, and a crater, with a gap on the south partly filled by a small mountain. There is also a gap on the east. On the floor of Max Wolf are a low ring and two hills. To the south is the mountain Mu, close to the bright crater Hesiodus B. On the south-east are the crater G and the low rings T and L, the latter with two craterlets and two peaks on its walls and a craterlet on its dark floor. North of this is the small crater A, also some curved ridges and the crater F.

WURZELBAUER, −232 −556 [German astronomer, 1651-1725]. An enclosure about 50 miles in diameter with walls of some height, rising 5,500 feet on the west. It lies to the south of Pitatus and Hesiodus and west of Cichus, and is not quite circular. The walls consist of distinct segments, surmounted, here and there, by little peaks. On the south a large crater, with a smaller on the east, abuts on to the wall. Immediately to the north-west of this is an intrusive mountain mass with a crater to its north-west. Farther to the north the wall is deflected inwards, and is followed by a linear portion to the northern end where craters occupy the crest. The eastern wall is tolerably continuous, and broken by a small crater at one point. On the inner slope, here, are some craterlets and also terraces. The interior is very rough, and contains much detail, all comparatively minute and consisting, chiefly, of rows of hills and craterlet-chains. Two of the latter are especially prominent, and run almost due north and south, one nearly central and another chain to the west. Of the numerous hillocks, one is nearly central, and to the east of this is a rough circle of hills, probably the remains of an ancient ring. On the northern portion are some larger hilly masses and a distinct crater to the north-east; there is also a small crater, of some depth, at the foot of the inner south slope which contains several small craters. To the south-east of Wurzelbauer is a large, finely terraced crater, D, with a smaller, E, on its north. The crater D appears to possess no central peak, but there are some craterlets on the inner slopes. To the east is the dark plain, extending to Cichus. This plain is traversed by at least three craterlet-chains. The surface between Wurzelbauer and Pitatus exhibits many examples of old rings, one of which, E, is double. West of Wurzelbauer is Gauricus, the separating wall being common to both of these formations. Much of the coarser detail on the floor is visible even in a telescope as small as a 3-inch refractor, but larger apertures are required for the finer features—especially the craterlet-chains, which are only visible for a short time under a low angle of illumination.

VIII

This section consists mainly of rugged country, and contains many formations of great interest. On the westernmost part of the Mare Nubium, the only 'sea' area in the whole section, lies the so-called Straight Wall, by far the grandest and most conspicuous of the lunar faults; and near by is the interesting little crater Birt, which is associated with several clefts.

There are a number of large walled plains in the section, notably the two southern members of the Ptolemæus group (Alphonsus and Arzachel) and the great chain composed of Walter, Regiomontanus and Purbach, as well as the vast ruin Hörbiger. Several pairs of craters are to be found (Aliacensis and Werner, Apianus and Playfair, Airy and Argelander), and other interesting objects are Alpetragius, with its enormous central mountain; Thebit, west of the Straight Wall; and the peculiar compound formation Vogel.

No mountain chains are included in this section.

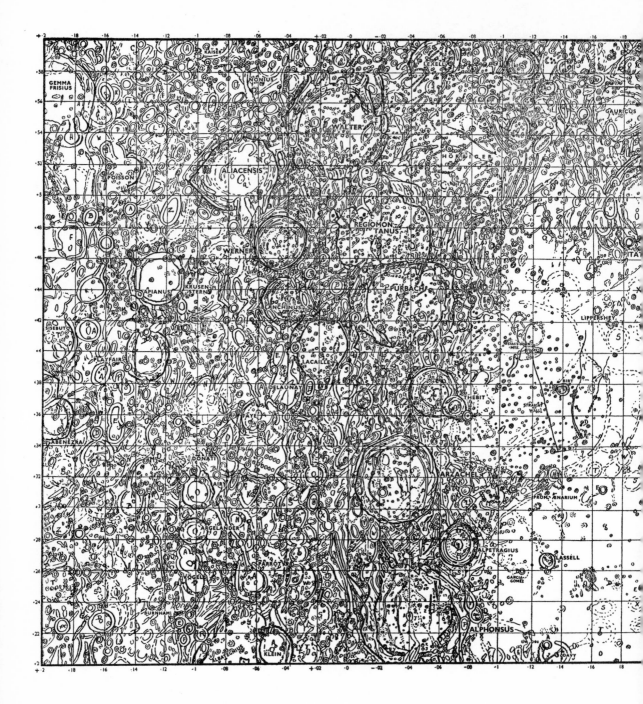

VIII

ABENEZRA, +192 −358 [Jewish scholar, 1092-1167]. This fine crater is 27 miles in diameter, and has lofty walls rising 15,000 feet on both east and west. On the floor is a central mountain, which is connected by a ridge to the south wall. Abenezra overlaps an older ring on the east, and this ring contains at least eight craters and two hills, while there are craters on its walls. The inner slopes of Abenezra are richly terraced. To the north of the old ring is the crater B, and farther to the east a peculiar double depression, E. North of the crater B is a partial ring, T. There are other fragmentary rings on the west and south. On the floor there is a crater at the foot of the north wall, and another on the south wall.

ÆNARIUM, PROMONTORIUM, −133 −320. This lies to the north of the Straight Wall, and has a peak rising 5,000 feet. At the east end of the cape is a small ring, N, with craterlets on its flanks; and north-west of this is a large but imperfect formation, M. This latter object has a crater on the east, and some craterlet-chains on its floor. To the west are three craters, the most prominent of which is k. Craterlet-chains run from the north wall of M, together with numerous ridges and hills.

AIRY, +092 −312 [Astronomer Royal, 1801-92]. A beautiful crater 22 miles in diameter, with finely terraced walls, broken in places by craters, and with a landslip on the east. The floor contains a central mountain, and some hills and mounds. To the south-west is the ring, G, on the floor of which are several craterlets, the largest being almost in the centre. West are old rings, and north a strong ridge with summit craterlets, running to the low ring A. On the north-east begins a long valley, which eventually passes into the interior Parrot. South-east is the crater, B, at the north-east angle of the deformed ring of Donati. On the west a long ridge connects the craters A, B and F with Burnham. There is a small crater on the south-west crest of Airy, and a smaller one, J, on the outer south slope.

ALBATEGNIUS. This formation lies partly within this section and partly within Section I. It is described in the latter section.

ALIACENSIS, +079 −510 [French theologian, 1350-1420]. A great crater 52 miles in diameter, with broad, terraced walls rising to 12,000 feet on the west but much higher on the east, where peaks attain 16,500 feet. There is a landslip on the west, and a double crater on the south rim; the floor contains a central mountain. There is a wide gap in the north wall, from which a valley leads into a depression with a central hill. The inner west slope of Aliacensis is very complex, with numerous terraces, craterlets and large mountain masses—a fine sight under suitable illumination. All along the outer west wall are craters, notably a cluster under the peak Beta, while the peak Gamma abuts on to a crater. On the inner north-east are two craterlets with their walls in contact, while on the south lies a partial ring. There is a deep double crater on the outer south-east, a very prominent object, and also numerous craterlets and mountain ridges. To the north-west is the large but low-walled crater, Z.

ALPETRAGIUS, −075 −276 [Arab astronomer, *circa* A.D. 1100]. This is one of the finest craters on the Moon, considered as a telescopic object. Although it is only 27 miles in diameter, it has finely terraced walls over 12,000 feet high on the west, and broad inner slopes. The small floor is largely occupied by an enormous central mountain rising over 6,000 (Schröter, 7,000) feet, and somewhat dome-shaped.

Wilkins examined Alpetragius on 3 April 1952, with the great 33-inch Meudon refractor, and saw a distinct craterlet on the summit of the central mountain, surrounded by four almost overhanging peaks. This was at once confirmed by Moore, with the same instrument. In 1953, using the 33-inch refractor under very favourable conditions, Moore detected a second summit-crater, at once confirmed by Wilkins. It is smaller than the first, and lies symmetrically on the north portion of the great central mountain mass.

There are three small craters on the southern part of the floor, and two on the east. Many spurs of rock run down to the floor. On the outer west is a fine valley, and on the north-east a ruined ring, with a low eastern wall and three hills to the west of the centre.

ALPHONSUS, −048 −233 [Spanish king, 1223-84]. This is the middle member of the great group made up of Ptolemæus, Alphonsus and Arzachel. It is 70 miles in diameter. The walls are of extraordinary breadth and complexity, rising in places to 7,000 feet, though they are lower on the south. To the west is a very long valley, running from a large ring with a central hill to a crater west of Arzachel. On the south-west, where the walls are cut through by valleys, is a crater. The north-east wall is also cut through by parallel valleys.

The floor abounds in interesting detail. Nearly in the centre is a mountain, with its highest peak on the north and with two craterlets on the crest on the south. There are over fifty craterlets on the interior, together with numerous old rings on the south-east. The most interesting objects, however, are the dark spots, considered by some observers as patches of vegetation. There are three of these near the west wall, each with a craterlet in the centre. A winding cleft connects these spots; it also traverses an old ring, and bends on the south to run north again a little to the west of the central mountain. This cleft also bends round on the north, so that a portion of the interior is completely surrounded.

On 3 November 1958 N. A. Kozyrev, using the 50-inch reflector in the Crimea, observed an outbreak near the central elevation in Alphonsus. This was no chance observation; Kozyrev had been studying the area following some observations by D. Alter, in America, which indicated that periodical obscurations might occur there. Subsequently a reddish patch was described by Wilkins, G. A. Hole and others, though other observers (Moore, for instance) have been unable to detect it.

The spectograms taken by Kozyrev show conclusively that a disturbance did in fact occur, though it was not, of course, in the nature of a major volcanic eruption. This is not the first time that activity has been suspected inside the crater; Klein drew attention to apparent changes as long ago as 1882. It is evident that the formation merits close and continuous attention.

Further activity was suspected by Kozyrev in 1959, but on this occasion the evidence was inconclusive. Moore, who was observing the crater at this time, failed to see anything unusual.

APIANUS, +123 −452 [German mathematician, 1495-1552]. A fine crater 39 miles in diameter, with terraced walls rising 9,000 feet above the floor, on which are some craterlets. An ancient ring to the east is full of craterlets and pits, with a double crater on the north-west. On the north are some large craters; there is a crater-chain to the west, and a valley running from the south to a small crater.

ARGELANDER, +097 −285 [German astronomer, 1799-1875]. A fine but rather small crater, 20 miles in diameter, with beautifully terraced walls rising to sharp crests. On the floor is a central mountain, and there is a crater on the north-west. To the north are three confluent rings. A large ring on the east gives rise to a valley which runs to Parrot. There are some old rings on the north-west, most of them open to the south. West is the bright crater, A, with numerous craterlets to the north.

ARZACHEL, −035 −316 [Spanish-Arab astronomer, 1028-87]. This is the third member of the prominent group consisting of Ptolemæus, Alphonsus and Arzachel, and lies on the south. It is 60 miles in diameter, with complex and richly-terraced walls rising 13,500 feet on the west but only 10,000 feet on the east. The floor is depressed 3,000 feet below the outer level. The word 'level' is hardly appropriate, as the entire surroundings are very rugged.

On the floor there is a central mountain 4,900 feet high, with two minute crater pits on its crest. On the western portion of the floor is a deep crater, A; there are smaller craters to the south and east. To the north-west of A are two craterlets with their walls in contact; the smaller rather overlaps the larger. From this double object a fine cleft runs to the south, passing through a very low-rimmed ring to the west of crater A. East of the central mountain there is a craterlet, and also three low, confluent depressions. Altogether there are over twenty-five craterlets and hills on the floor, well shown on one of the Mt. Wilson photographs. On the outer west is a fine valley, V, and on the south-west an old ring. D. P. Barcroft has found that the sunrise shadow of the central mountain is darker than that of the west wall.

BALL, −118 −585 [English astronomer, died 1690]. Although this crater is only 25 miles in diameter, it is a very remarkable object. The walls, which are magnificently terraced on the inner slopes, rise 5,000 feet above the floor. On the south-west crest is a craterlet, and there is another on the south-east. The most remarkable feature is a deep and broad groove which descends the inner south slope from the crest to a crater on the floor south of the central mountain. On the west crest are three craterlets. The central mountain is very large, and rises 2,500 feet; a craterlet touches it on the south-east. On the floor are some other ridges and pits.

On the south is a double crater, and on the west a crater-row. North-east is a ring with a central mountain and some craterpits on the floor; this is known as A. On the east is a ring, M, with three craterlets on the eastern portion of its floor. To the north-west is a remarkable group of large but low-rimmed rings, the best-formed being C, which has a pit on its north rim and two craterlets on the inner south. The surroundings contain several fine examples of craterlet-chains.

BIRT, —137 —380 [English selenographer, 1804-81]. This fine crater lies to the east of that remarkable object the 'Straight Wall'. It has a deeply-sunken floor, 6,000 feet below the crest of the walls, which are broken by a smaller crater, A, on the west. On the interior of A is an object that may be either a central hill or a landslip from the wall. Where A and Birt join is a craterlet, first distinctly seen by Moore, 3 April 1952, with the 33-inch Meudon refractor, and immediately confirmed by Wilkins. On this occasion Moore also found a very reduced ring about the same size as A and abutting on it to the north-west, as well as a minute hill on the floor of Birt itself, east of

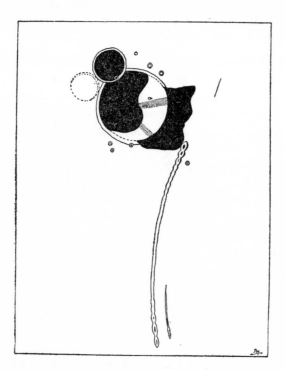

the centre and just south of the main dusky band which runs up the inner slope. On the east is a fine cleft, passing on the north through a low dome. In the giant telescope, this cleft was seen to have at least a dozen enlargements closely north of the two distinct craterlets in which it originates on the south. On the same night Wilkins, with the 33-inch telescope, found a short cleft immediately to the east of the dome, beginning on the north at three craterpits and bending on the south towards the main cleft.

On 1 April 1941 E. J. Reese, of the U.S.A., discovered two dusky bands on the inner east slope, and also some semicircular bands concentric with the wall at the inner foot. The two main bands are not difficult objects.

BLANCHINUS, +041 —425 [Italian astronomer, *circa* 1458]. This formation lies between Werner and Lacaille, and has regular walls except on the east, where there is a large depression,

BIRT AND CLEFT
3 April 1951, 22h. 15m., 33-inch O.G. (Meudon Observatory), Patrick Moore

B. The floor is full of detail, consisting of a central pit, craterlets, pits, ridges, old rings, and a fault crossing the interior. On the north is a double crater. On the inner slopes there are some crater-like depressions. To the west is a very peculiar arrangement of ridges interspersed with craters. Between Blanchinus and Apianus is a ridge-bordered enclosure now called Krusenstern; on its interior there are some craters.

BURNHAM, +122 −242 [American astronomer, 1838-1921]. This object is a ring with low walls, at the north end of a long valley which runs southwards to a ring on the west of Airy. On the interior of Burnham are a crater and two hills. There is a small mountain on the outer north-east wall.

DAVY, −138 −204 [English scientist, 1778-1829]. A 20-mile crater, deep, but with a gap in the north wall. On the south-west a crater, A, intrudes; and this has a central hill. The wall is low to the east of A.

Davy has a low central mountain, and a cleft crosses the floor. On the north-west are a cleft and some craterlets. South-west is an old ring, and there is another, T, on the south-east, with a central craterlet. To the south of T is a smaller and shallower ring, S, with two others, X and Z, on the east.

DELAUNAY, +043 −378 [French astronomer, 1816-72]. A very irregular formation, divided into two parts by a high ridge. On the north wall are some craters, while on the south there is an imperfect formation with high peaks on its walls. On the interior of Delaunay, either side of the dividing ridge, are several hills. Faye lies to the north-west, and Lacaille to the south-east.

DONATI, +083 −354 [Italian astronomer, 1826-73]. An abnormal, defective formation, with broken walls open on the north. On the north-west crest are three craters, and there is a deep crater on the outer north. South of this crater is what looks like a shallow lava-pit. Donati has a central mountain, and there are some craterlet-chains on the floor running to a craterlet on the west. Donati adjoins Faye on the north-west.

DUBLIER, −014 −260 [Contemporary Spanish astronomer]. An irregular formation 13 miles in diameter on the south-west wall of Alphonsus. (On the Map the name appears at −036 −253.)

FAYE, +062 −365 [French astronomer, 1814-1902]. An irregular and imperfect formation, with a large central mountain and a smaller hill on its east. There is a gap in the south wall, and an imperfect formation on the south-east. On the north wall is the crater, B, which has a pit on its south rim. On the floor of Faye, in addition to the central mountain and its companion, there are craterlets, hills, and a ridge running from the central mountain to the north-west wall. To the north-east is an ancient ring with a hilly interior, while on the north is a large enclosure with a central crater and some crater-chains on the floor. West of this latter ring is the large double crater, T.

GARCIA-GOMEZ, −115 −261 [Contemporary Spanish astronomer]. A perfectly round, symmetrical bright crater six miles in diameter, lying between Alpetragius and Lassell.

141

GAURICUS, −182 −558 [Italian scholar, 1476-1558]. This large object, 40 miles in diameter, is irregular. The inner slopes are very wide, and the surrounding walls rise 9,300 feet above the floor on the east, though they are lower elsewhere. There are several craters on the inner east slope, while on the western inner slopes are crater-chains. The floor contains craterpits and many ridges. An old ring adjoins Gauricus on the north, and there is another on the south. Just outside the west wall is a crater connected to a mountain mass on the south by a ridge. On the south-west is the crater B, with two craterlets on its floor; from this, a crater-chain runs south. Between Gauricus and Pitatus are mountain masses and craterlets. Some distance to the north-west is a double formation, V, and south of this an elongated depression, Q, with numerous craters and hills.

GEMMA FRISIUS, +187 −562 [Dutch scientist, 1508-55]. A great formation about 80 miles in diameter, with irregular walls, broken in places by craters; on the north-west a large formation, Goodacre, intrudes. The western wall is tolerably even, and commences on the north at a crater, east of which—on the floor of Gemma Frisius—is a partial ring, D. A large ring abuts on the outer south-west; this is known as A, and has a remarkable crater group on its inner east slope. On the south crest of Gemma Frisius is a crater-chain. East of this the main wall runs in a bold sweep to the north-east, where its continuity is destroyed by the intrusion of two large rings, both open on the south, so that their interiors are in communication with that of Gemma Frisius. The larger of these rings, H, has very broad walls. On the floor of Gemma Frisius is a nearly central hill, as well as some craterlets and a dark spot on the west. On the outer east is a large enclosure, G, with two overlapping rings, D and K, at the end of the south wall—which is prolonged, and with a gap between it and the wall of Gemma Frisius. The ring, D, has a central peak. On the outer south-east there are many craters.

Deslandres

HELL, −114 −535 [Hungarian astronomer, 1720-92]. A prominent crater 20 miles in diameter, with terraced walls broken by a craterlet on the south. The floor is full of hills, mounds and some craterlets. There is a small central hill. A crater-chain runs all along the outer north and north-east wall. A little distance to the north-east is an oval ring, A, with a craterlet on its north rim, while on the south-west, beyond some craterlets and a small mountain, is a crater, C, which has two craterlets on its floor. North of C are some craterlets, from which three clefts run north-east to a group of small craters north of Hell. Hell lies on the eastern part of the vast but indefinite enclosure, Hörbiger.

Deslandres on LAC charts

HÖRBIGER, −080 −530 [Austrian cosmologist, 1860-1913, strong advocate of the glaciation theory of lunar craters]. A vast plain to the west of Walter; really the relic of an old ring, after the pattern of Hipparchus. On the south it is bounded by Lexell and Ball, on the east by Hell, and on the north by the confused hilly region to the south-east of Regiomontanus. Its vast surface, over 100 miles across, is pitted by numerous craterlets, craterlet-chains, hills and craters. The western portion contains some mountain masses concentric with the wall of Walter, and in this part of the floor are found the largest crater-chains. On the south, many craterlet-chains run across the surface from Lexell, while the south-eastern portion contains a group of craters between Lexell and Hell. A little to the north-west of the centre is a small crater, H, from which a chain of hills runs to the west wall of Hell. South of H is a cleft, beginning at a hill on the west and dying out on the floor. On the north is a crater, from which a fine craterlet-chain runs to a small crater situated midway between the first crater and Hell. East of this, and marking the north-eastern border, is a long but shallow formation traversed by a row of hills, similar to Hell A; to the north of this is the deformed crater, N. In addition to the above, the interior of Hörbiger contains numerous objects—far too many to describe individually, but noteworthy near sunrise or sunset.

KAISER, +090 −594 [Dutch astronomer, 1808-72]. A large ring to the south-west of Nonius, with a crater, A, on the outer west and many smaller craters on the north. On the floor are two craters on the north, and two craterlet-chains on the south. To the north-west, beyond a crater group, is the somewhat square formation, B, with craterlets on its walls and some hills and pits on its floor. All around Kaiser are craters and hills.

KLEIN, +044 −207 [German selenographer, 1844-1914]. This was formerly known as Albategnius A, and lies on the south-east wall of that great formation. Klein has a central mountain; there are two craterlets on the inner east and one on the south, while the southern inner slopes consist of detached masses. There is a large crater on the north rim. At the foot of the outer south-east wall is a small crater, B. Immediately east of this is an ancient formation. East is another old ring, T, with the remains of a central mountain and some craterpits on its interior. On the south-west, and thus on the floor of Albategnius, what appears to be the relic of an old ring, U, abuts on the wall.

KRUSENSTERN, +093 −445 [Russian explorer, 1770-1846]. A large enclosure bounded by ridges. It lies near Blanchinus, and is described with that formation.

LACAILLE, +019 −400 [French astronomer, 1713-62]. A beautiful and nearly circular crater, 35 miles in diameter. The walls are highest on the west, where they are also broad, and contain a crater, D. The south-west wall contains many little craters, and there is a larger crater on the south-south-east. On the north-east is a small crater, from which a valley runs northwards, opening into a large enclosure, T, which is full of hills, and also contains some craterlets. There is a large elongated crater, B, on the north wall. On the interior of Lacaille are some hills and craterlets, and two shallow depressions, one on the south and the other on the east.

LASSELL, −132 −267 [English astronomer, 1799-1880]. A crater on the Mare Nubium, 14 miles in diameter, with low walls, and craterlets on both the south and north crests. On the floor are four hills, one forming a central peak. On the outer north is a small crater. To the north-west is the crater B, on a bright area, while to the east is a remarkable arrangement of craters, G, beyond which is a craterlet, D, on a bright area. D is brilliant under high illumination. North of it are the faint traces of two old rings, S and T. East of D is the small crater E, and north of it two old rings, X and Z.

LEXELL, −058 −581 [Finnish astronomer and mathematician, 1740-84]. A fine example of a partial ring. It is more or less open on the north, as this portion of the wall has been destroyed. Lexell resembles a bay on the borders of Hörbiger. On the floor is a low central hill, and also numerous craterlets, some in chains. On the south crest is a small crater, H, while a crater-chain occupies the eastern portion of the floor. South is an ancient ring. In addition to the features already mentioned, a cleft crosses the floor on the north. North is an ancient ring, also opening on the north. A fine craterlet-chain runs across the floor of Lexell, from H to a small crater on the site of the former north wall; here it subdivides, one chain curving towards the tip of the remaining portion of the west wall, the other running towards Walter.

LIPPERSHEY, −161 −437 [Dutch inventor of the telescope, died 1619]. A small crater 4 miles in diameter, between Birt and Pitatus. To the north-east are some old rings, S, T and W, and on the south-east another, X. X contains a craterlet, and there are several others in the neighbourhood.

MILLÁS, +022 −318 [Spanish philosopher, 1897-　]. The northern component of a very remarkable formation to the west of Arzachel. In reality it is made up of two rings in contact, a valley connecting their interiors. Where this valley enters the rings there are wide gaps in the walls. Millás has a large central mountain, and a craterlet on the north wall. There are terraces on the inner slopes. On the west is a cluster of rings, of which M, P and S are the largest. These rings are very irregular; P contains some hills and a craterlet-chain on the western portion of its floor. To the west of P is another abnormal ring, K. Both P and K lie on the north border of a small plain which is crossed by craterlet-chains radiating from Millás.

NONIUS, +060 −570 [Portuguese mathematician, 1492-1577]. This formation is 20 miles in diameter, with broken walls, and an interior filled with ridges and large, low rings. Between Nonius and Walter is a depression, within which is an old ring with craterlets on its east and west. To the north are numerous craters. On the south-east is a double formation, R, with a smooth floor.

NUBIUM, MARE, (Western), −300 −300. 'Sea of Clouds'. One of the great dark plains termed 'seas', bounded on the west by Thebit, Alphonsus and Ptolemæus. The western portion contains numerous craterlets, especially in the region to the east of Thebit. This is really the relic of a once-complete ring, well over 100 miles in diameter, and crossed by the Straight Wall. The most detail-crowded part is, however, the bay which extends towards Lexell, and now called Hörbiger. Like all the plains, the Mare exhibits many ridges, and there are numerous examples of old rings of which only traces now remain.

PARROT, +055 −255 [German physicist, 1792-1840]. An irregular formation, 40 miles in diameter, to the south of Albategnius. Its ramparts rise on the west to 5,000 feet above the interior, which is largely occupied by large rings. Of these, A is the most prominent. South of A, which has its wall broken on the west, the floor of Parrot is occupied by some hills. A valley from the eastern side of Airy can be traced to the wall of Parrot, through which it cuts, and thence over the floor into A. The floor to the east of A contains some hills and craters. There is a gap in the south wall, a small mountain filling the breach; and east of this is a double crater. The inner south-east slope is broad, and there are craters on the crest. To the east is a partially overlapped ring, C, on the south-western portion of the floor of a larger ring, W. This has a double wall on the east. The entire walls and surroundings of Parrot are very complex, and crowded with craters, crater-chains and hills, the whole presenting the appearance of having been subjected to pressure and erosion in the past.

PITATUS, —203 —498 [Italian astronomer, *circa* 1550]. This grand object is a magnificent lagoon-like ring, 50 miles in diameter, on the southern shore of the Mare Nubium. It presents many indications of having suffered from erosion in the past. The northern wall, facing the 'sea', is broken, with wide gaps. The entire walls are, in fact, irregular. On the west crest is a large ring, G, with a feeble central hill; it abuts on a partial ring to the north-west. Beyond this is a double crater, and a row of depressions to the crater E. West of E are some lower and imperfect rings. The fragmentary north wall is low, and in the gaps are small craters, while the rampart is straight to Hesiodus. The south wall is ringed with craters just beyond the crest; there are also some on the inner slope. Here and there are great landslips, and south-east lies a double crater. On the interior is a not-quite-central hill, a crater under the south wall, ridges, hills, and a few pits. On the southern portion are two white patches, with another on the north, contrasting with the dark ground of the interior. On the north-western part of the floor there is a cleft, and another on the north-east. Under favourable circumstances, a cleft can be traced all round the interior, close to the walls. A remarkable crater-row lies on the crest of the south-east wall; Neison mentions five components, but Wilkins shows seven. To the north, and on the Mare, are craterlets, old rings and some hills. On the north-east is a partial ring, F, and south of this a cleft runs to the north wall of Hesiodus. Where Pitatus joins Hesiodus there is a gap in the wall, so that the interiors are in communication with each other. Wilkins, (33-inch O.G.) found eight clefts and forty pits within Pitatus.

PLAYFAIR, +136 —397 [Scottish mathematician, 1748-1819]. This object is 28 miles in diameter, with terraced walls bearing craters on the east, south-west and north. On the floor are hills and craters, chiefly on the north. There is a gap in the south wall. On the west are the rings A and D, together with some partial rings. On the east is a peculiar object, W, with a wide gap in its south wall. North of W is a large ring, E, full of small craters, and with others on its walls. Between Playfair and Apianus are craterlets and a mountain ridge.

POISSON, +142 —513 [French mathematician, 1781-1840]. A most irregular object to the west of Aliacensis, consisting of the fusion of several large ruins. Where the south wall should be are the rings W, P and S. The west wall is double, with a wide valley on the outer component and a ridge concentric with it on the east. On this part of the floor are some craters, including B. The northern wall has altogether disappeared; in the gap is a small crater. The east wall has a very broad outer glacis, partly due to the inclusion of some large rings; at the north end is the deep crater A. At the other or western side of the gap is the crater B (distinct from the floor-crater bearing the same letter), and between A and B is a craterlet-chain. The region to the south-east is crowded with rings, of which C, L and E are the most distinct. On the eastern part of the interior is a ridge with a small peak midway along its crest.

PURBACH, —029 —428 [German astronomer, 1423-61]. A great ring-plain 75 miles in diameter, with walls rising 8,000 feet on the west, and a landslip on the inner slope. The southern wall is common with that of Regiomontanus, and is narrow in parts. On the east, the wall is tolerably regular, but bears crater-rows on both inner and outer slopes; there is also a summit crater half-way along. The outer slope here is very complex, abounding in craters and craterlet-chains. The north wall has been largely destroyed, and there is an intruding crater, G, full of pits. The interior of Purbach swarms with detail. There is a nearly central ridge, with a craterpit row on its west. This ridge seems to form part of a once-complete ring, of which fragments of the former wall can be traced at intervals. North of this ridge are two very low rings, of which only fragments now remain. Near the east wall is a large oval ring, while on the south-east are some old rings, one being marked by a curved row of craterlets. All over the interior are scattered numerous craterlets, many in chains. Of the latter, a very noteworthy example will be found running to the south-west wall. On the inner south wall are some other low rings, and a craterpit chain.

REGIOMONTANUS, —020 —475 [German astronomer, 1436-76]. Another great formation, 80 miles from east to west but less from north to south, where it measures 65 miles. The very irregular walls rise in places to 7,000 feet. The interior is full of interesting detail. On the northern portion and a little west of the centre is a large mountain mass A, with a crater on its flank. West of this mountain are some craterlets and hills. The inner west slopes are very broad, and on the outer side is a large crater. The southern wall is very irregular, and here a large ring has intruded; this ring is open to the north, but still bears the remains of a central peak. East of this ring is a wide gap, partly occupied by craters. The east wall is massive, and very broad on the south-east. On the eastern portion of the floor are some low rings, small craters and numerous craterlets. Some of these by their arrangement suggest the outlines of former craters. The surface between Regiomontanus and Blanchinus is one mass of detail—craters, craterlets, ridges and hills. Of the craters, the largest is B. Outside the east wall is a similar confusion of objects, including many partial rings. Everywhere are crater-chains and ridges.

SISEBUTO, +177 —413 [Spanish king, reigned A.D. 612-621]. An imperfect but quite

146

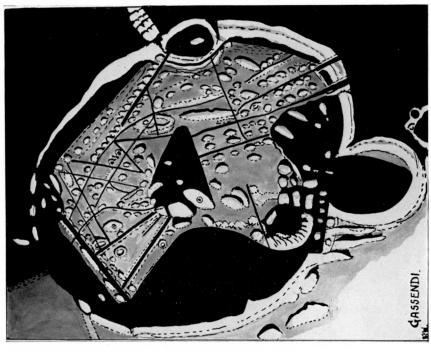

3b. Gassendi, drawn by H. P. Wilkins with the 33-inch
refractor at the Observatory of Meudon

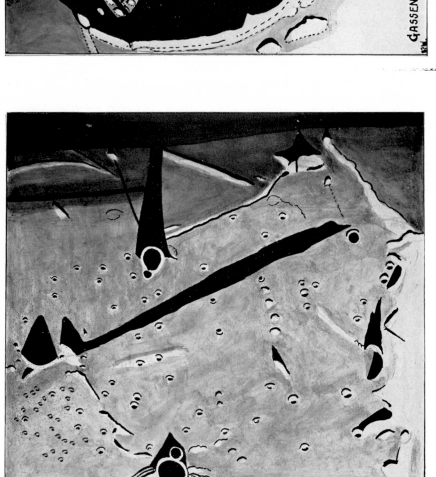

3a. The Straight Wall and Surrounding Area. Drawing made by
H. P. Wilkins with the 26-inch refractor at Washington

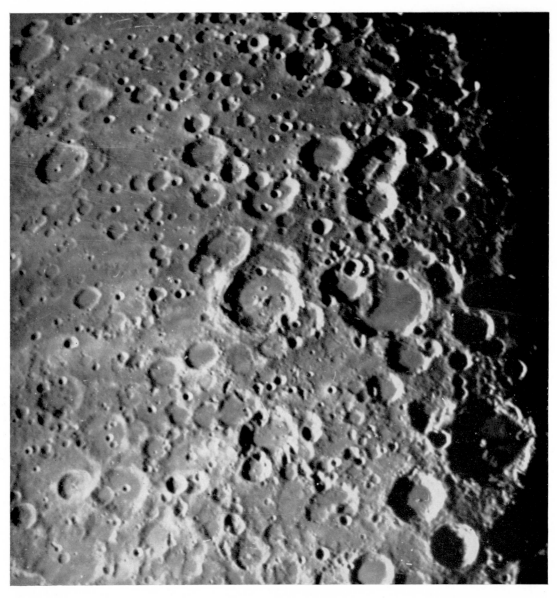

4. Maurolycus, Stöfler and District. Photograph by E. A. Whitaker, Greenwich Observatory

prominent object to the south of Azophi, and open on the south. On the interior is a central hill, and there are some other hills also. Outside the east wall is a deep crater, A, with a central hill, to the south of which is a minute craterlet. To the west are the craters E and F. There is a fine example of a double formation on the outer north-eastern slope.

STAG'S-HORN MOUNTAINS. These mark the southern termination of the Straight Wall, and are described under that heading.

STRAIGHT WALL, —114 —400 to —136 —339. A most remarkable formation on the western side of the Mare Nubium, between Birt and Thebit. It is 60 miles long and in reality a fault in the surface, which is 800 feet lower on the east than the upper, western side. The difference is less at the northern end, where it ends a little to the east of a small crater. The wall, although called 'straight', is not absolutely so, and there is a slight break nearly midway, where a segment has been misplaced. Many minute craterlets and craterpits lie on both sides of the Wall. Moore, using the Meudon 33-inch refractor, on 22 April 1953, charted 92, most of them of small size. The Wall also becomes lower on the south, where it ends at a peculiarly-shaped mountain mass, the Stag's-Horn Mountains, with an altitude of 1,900 feet. The Wall lies inside and nearly in the centre of a large old ring, now barely traceable.

H. Hill has seen two breaks in the Wall; a dusky streak from Birt to the base of the Wall, 'like a narrow ditch', was also seen by him. B. G. Dale found a minute craterlet between Birt A (the crater on the western rim of Birt) and the Wall, close to the foot of the latter. This is shown as one of twin craterlets in the map, and also appears faintly on the well-known Mt. Wilson photograph. R. Barker noted a cleft at the foot of the Wall, and this has also been suspected by other observers: so far we have failed to confirm it, but nevertheless it certainly exists. Barker's cleft runs along the foot of the Wall, and branches at the northern end to a small craterlet on the east. Recent studies by G. Fielder show that the angle of slope of the Wall is much less sharp than was previously believed.

THEBIT, —065 —375 [Baghdad astronomer, 826-901]. A deep and well-marked crater west of the Straight Wall, 30 miles in diameter. Its walls are both high and terraced, but with a break in the south, and a crater on the west crest. On the north-east is a large intruding crater, A, 12 miles in diameter; this has bright walls, a central hill, and a craterlet on the inner north. On the north-east rim of A a still smaller crater has intruded. This crater has a very minute central hill.

On the floor of Thebit is a nearly central ring, with a segment projecting on its east and forming a sort of central mountain; but only a few hills now remain of the former west wall. On the north-west is a low hill, and there is a still lower hill due west, while on the south are some hills arranged in a circle—evidently marking the site of an old ring. On the south-east are six hills, and there is a shallow pit at the foot of the rugged inner slope. Some of these 'hills' may in reality be landslips. On the north are low, curved

147

ridges, and a well-marked partial ring adjoins the central ring on its north. On the inner slope, near the intruding wall of A, are two craterlets.

A circle of isolated hills lies to the south-east of Thebit, and on the north a chain of hills runs to the Straight Wall. To the west are ridges, and a crater-chain. From the outer slopes many ridges run, some as far as Arzachel, and, on the west, to a ring; south of this last formation is an ancient ring open on the south, the gap being filled by a crater.

VOGEL, +098 −257 [German astronomer, 1841-1907]. A very peculiar formation, formed of three craters now fused together and with the interiors in communication. The central component has a central mountain, and there is also a hill in the centre of the component on the north. Moore (33-inch refractor: April 1953) detected a very delicate cleft under the inner east wall. Many small craters lie on the east wall. To the west is the long valley from Burnham. East are crater-chains and the remains of an old ring, D. Wilkins found a cleft from the Burnham valley to the south component.

WALTER, +010 −548 [German astronomer, 1430-1504]. A great walled-plain about 90 miles in diameter, with wide, massive walls, divided by valleys on the south and with a large double crater at the west side. From this formation a pass leads on to the floor of Walter. On the east are many craters, and a crater-chain. Peaks on the walls rise 10,000 feet above the interior, on which are a mountain to the west of the centre, several large craters on the west, a crater-chain on the south-west, and numerous ridges and craterlets. On the eastern portion is a crater, with a smaller one on the south-west and a concave depression between them. There are also many craterlets and craterpits. On the south-east part is a dark area.

On the outer north are depressions along the crest, and a large double crater, while on the north-east is an overlapping treble crater. The east wall is low, with a large, low-rimmed ring outside. In places, especially on the inner north-east, are landslips.

WERNER, +052 −470 [German mathematician, 1468-1528]. This is one of the most circular of all the lunar rings; it is a grand object 45 miles in diameter, with magnificent terraced walls rising in majestic peaks to 15,000 feet above the interior. On the interior is a grand central mountain 4,500 feet in altitude, with curved ridges and many hills on either side. On the inner north is a bright little crater, and a bright area, within which is a craterlet on the north-east. Webb considered that the bright spot at the foot of the north-east wall had faded since the time of Beer and Mädler. Wilkins found *two* minute craterlets within this spot, best seen in the waxing Moon. Webb saw one, which Neison declared to be a cratercone.

Between Werner and Regiomontanus are craterlets and hills, but the surface is less disturbed on the west, where are found some old rings. On the south-west is the peculiar ring connected to the interior of Aliacensis, while on the north lies Blanchinus. Wilkins, with the 33-inch O.G., also found a delicate cleft on the floor of Werner, running from the centre to the south-east wall.

IX

This section is crowded with detail, as there is only one Mare area included in it (the eastern part of the Mare Nectaris). Neither are there any cleft systems of note, and only one range of mountains (the Altai). Walled formations, however, abound, the chief being Piccolomini, Cyrillus and Catharina (the two southern members of the Theophilus chain), and the great bay Fracastorius.

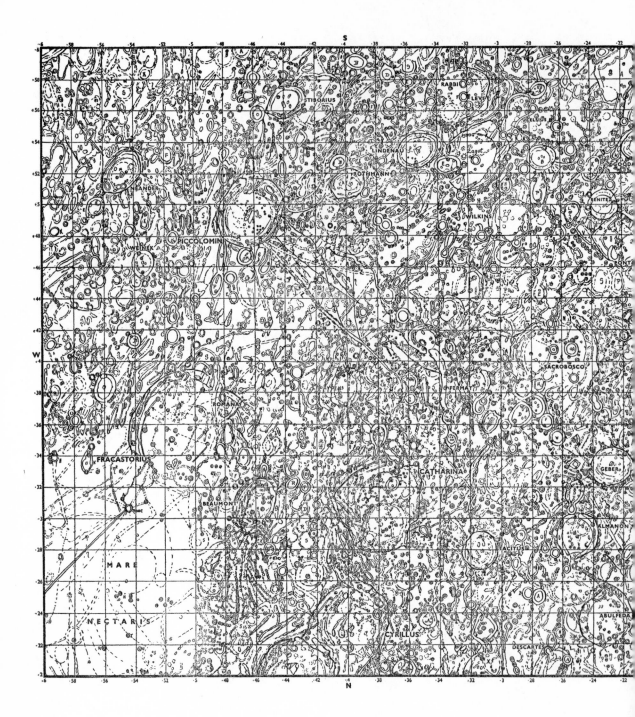

IX

ABULFEDA, +235 —241 [Arab geographer, 1273-1331]. A ring-plain 40 miles in diameter, with circular walls beautifully terraced on the inner slopes. The walls are crowned with craters on both north and south; they rise 9,000 feet on the west and 10,000 feet on the east. The north-east portion is cut by a ravine, flanked on the north by a mountain; farther north the wall narrows, with several craters on the outer slopes and two on the inner. On the extreme north is a crater, from which a ridge runs on to the floor. On the outer west are depressions, and a large ring with low walls, to the west of which is a craterlet-chain. On the south-west and the east are portions of a large, ancient ring. From the south wall a crater-cleft runs south-west to a crater to the north of Almanon, and is continued beyond by a series of craters and mountain-ridges. Outside the south wall, and beyond this remarkable crater-row, is a mountain mass. The interior of Abulfeda contains some detail. There are craterlets on the south-east, and also two craterlets on light patches, one in the centre of Abulfeda and the other near the east wall. A third patch lies near the inner north slope, and there are other details besides. The northern half of the floor is darker than the southern. West of Abulfeda, and east of a mountain-ridge running north from Tacitus, is a low ring with a twin crater, B, on its south-east rim and another ring on its southern part.

ALMANON, +251 —290 [Arab prince, died A.D. 833]. A ring-plain to the south-west of Abulfeda, but smaller. The walls are much lower than those of Abulfeda, and remarkably broad on the inner west, where the crest rises 6,000 feet; on the east the wall is 2,000 feet lower. On the outer north-west slope is a crater, C, on the line of continuation of the crater-cleft or row connecting it with Abulfeda. C has a smaller crater on its west rim, from which a craterlet-chain curves south-east to a low ring abutting on the south-west wall. On this portion of the wall of Almanon is a crater, A, with a much larger one, B, on the south. B has a prominent crater on its west rim, and a small central peak. On the east a valley runs north-east to the crater Abulfeda B. East of this is a depression, beyond which is the bright crater, A; north of the latter is a low ring with craters on its south rim. On the interior of Almanon are some hills, a curved ridge (probably part of an ancient ring), and—under the south wall—a further obscure ring on the south-east, abutting on the inner slope.

ALTAI MOUNTAINS, +350 —410. A fine range of mountains extending from the east wall of Piccolomini to the east of Catharina, an extreme length of 315 miles.[1] The range rises steeply from the plain on the west, averaging 6,000 feet, with one lofty peak

[1] On the map the name follows the principal cleft parallel to it.

(*a*, west of Polybius), rising 13,000 feet; but the range is only slightly elevated above the surface to the east.

It may be divided into three distinct portions: (1) that nearest to Piccolomini, (2) the lofty mass to the south-east of Polybius, (3) the section on the north. These sections are separated by lower portions.

Commencing at the east wall of Piccolomini, the range is of considerable height, with a crater on the crest and a smaller crater near its eastern end. The portion between the larger summit crater and the west wall of Piccolomini is serrated into four distinct peaks. At the foot are some craterlets. There follows a low section, at the foot of which is a crater, with a smaller to the south. Just north of the crater a cleft runs to the north wall of Piccolomini. The second section is the loftiest, with a serpentine outline and a crater on the crest on the east. On the plateau to the south are some low depressions. Opposite Pons the crest is low, with one little peak, but again rises and continues, curving to the north at its east end. There are three shallow depressions on the crest, doubtless craters filled with lava almost to their brims. Finally, the range ends in a narrow, pointed ridge. Its course is, however, continued farther north by isolated mountain masses, and there can be little doubt that it represents the border of an ancient 'sea', the remains of which are represented by the Mare Nectaris—as was suggested by Fauth and Goodacre. On the once-smooth eastern portion the gigantic group composed of Theophilus, Cyrillus and Catharina now stands.

AZOPHI, +205 −378 [Persian astronomer, 903-986]. A crater 25 miles in diameter, with lofty walls bearing peaks 11,000 feet above the floor; on the floor are some low ridges. There is a crater on the inner north-west, and a crater-chain on the south-west. To the south is a mountain arm, part of an old and once-complete ring, open on the south and with a peak to the south-east. On the west is a crater, while other low rings will be found on the north. To the south-east is the crater A, which has a central peak. On the south crest of Azophi is a crater; there are others on the outer south-west, and one on the north-east. West lie the crater C and the low ring T.

Azophi and Abenezra form a pair of craters, Abenezra having overlapped Azophi. Immediately to the south is the imperfect ring Sisebuto, already described (Section VIII). Between the walls of Azophi and Sacrobosco are many craterlets.

BEAUMONT, +457 −310 [French geologist, 1798-1874]. A ruined ring-plain 30 miles in diameter, the wall having been reduced greatly, by erosion, to the present low altitude. On the west there is a wide gap; a narrow gap has also been noticed on the south, close to a craterlet on the crest, and there is still another gap in the east. The north-west wall is broad, with a crater-chain running at the bottom of a ravine. There are also crater-like depressions on the north wall. On the light-grey floor are numerous craterlets, the largest lying near the west wall. There is a double craterlet a little east of the centre. Dr. Sheldon, in a sketch dated 12 June 1891, showed a large dark patch on the south-east, a narrow dusky streak under the south-east wall, another dark area on the south-west and, in the gap on the west, yet another; also a ridge south of the centre.

When near the terminator the interior is seen to be covered with minute asperities, and over twenty craterlets or pits. In 1953, Moore discovered two clefts on the floor, one running from the main floor-crater to the north-west wall, and the other (an extremely delicate object) below the west wall. From the north wall a long and, in places, broad ridge runs north towards the west wall of Theophilus, casting a prominent shadow near sunset. Under morning illumination a cleft has been noted at its foot on the west. On this side a large number of ridges, very low and branching, and many craterlets (often in chains radiating from Theophilus) and hillocks will be noted near sunset, gradually sinking into insignificance the farther west they intrude on the Mare Nectaris. At its north end this ridge is separated from Theophilus by irregular depressions. South-east of Beaumont is a mass of craters; and a little beyond the outer north-east glacis, crossed by a delicate cleft and a crater-chain, is a small ring, with perfect but very low walls, and containing a little central hill.

BENITEZ, +231 −499 [Spanish astronomer 1879-1954]. A crater 19 miles in diameter. It used to be known as Pontanus A, and is described with Pontanus.

CATHARINA, +378 −310 [Saint, *circa* A.D. 307]. A great but somewhat irregular walled-plain, about 55 miles in diameter, with broad walls torn by explosions and much deformed by depressions (the largest of which lies on the inner north-west slope), but still attaining 16,000 feet in places. A very prominent valley runs down the inner west slope and is, in part, a crater-chain. The outer north-west slope is altogether deformed by valleys and a mass of depressions, intruding upon each other. The crest of the wall on the south-east and south is disturbed by small craters; on the outer slopes, among numerous craters, is the ring C, connected to Polybius by a ridge and to Catharina by a valley. In contrast with the rugged walls, the interior of Catharina is comparatively smooth. On the south is a low ring, with a central peak and a break in its north rim, On the northern portion of the floor is a large low ring with a narrow border; on the south of this rim is a low peak, almost in the centre of Catharina. Another hillock will be found on the floor of this low ring, which is depressed below the rest of the interior. Both within this ring and on the floor outside are numbers of low hills and craterlets. Under evening illumination a high mountain mass connects Catharina with Cyrillus; this is one side of a high valley which can be seen in its true aspect under moderately high illumination. Towards the east the ground slopes so gradually as to cast little shadow. Observed soon after sunrise, the valley, however, appears full of shadow. Many of these features are shown on a fine photograph taken by G. W. Ritchey on 12 October 1900, with the 40-inch Yerkes refractor, full aperture, at the visual focus, using screens in contact with Cramer's instantaneous isochromatic plates.

CELSIUS, +285 −558 [Swedish physicist, 1701-44]. A peculiar object south-south-east of Zagut and east of Rabbi Levi. On the interior are a deep but small crater, two craterlets on a ridge concentric with the south-west rampart, mounds, and two low rings to the south-east, close to two larger craters which occupy the site of the wall at this point. From a double crater to the north-east a long craterlet-chain runs north-east as far as the outer south glacis of the crater Zagut B. Adjoining on the south-east is the ring A, with a partial crater on the southern portion of its floor. A overlaps an older ring, B, while on the south is the fragmentary enclosure, D. West of Celsius and separating it from Rabbi Levi is a wide valley, traversed by ridges.

CYRILLUS, +398 −230 [Saint Cyrillus, died A.D. 444]. A great formation, 55 miles in diameter, somewhat square and intruded upon by Theophilus. The west wall is finely terraced, and there is a crater on the south-west crest. The north wall is naturally partly destroyed by Theophilus, but the eastern fragment is continued north as a lofty ridge. Between this ridge and the east wall of Theophilus are some lower ridges, and craters. On the inner south-east slope of Cyrillus is the very distinct crater A, with a bright peak on its western crest. To the north of A the great wall is double. On the interior of Cyrillus is a fine central mountain group, the highest peak being to the west of the centre; and west of this peak is a magnificent valley, V. South of the peak lie a low plateau, and many ridges and craterlets. A cleft runs from A to a mountain on the north wall. South of this mountain is a shallow, concave depression. East of Cyrillus is the crater A, with broad south walls, bearing two craterlets, and north of this the crater B. There are also numerous craterlets and some craterlet-chains. On the south-west is the low ring, R, and north of it, touching the west wall of Cyrillus, is the smaller, spoon-shaped object, S. Farther west are two small but prominent craters, and several craterlet-chains from the great ridge, which, commencing at the west wall of Theophilus, run across the eastern side of the Mare Nectaris towards Beaumont. Between Cyrillus and Catharina is a wide valley, only well seen as such under low illumination. The surface here is occupied by several craters, some, like V, being decidedly oval. On the south-east is the remarkable object R, apparently an old ring divided into two by a low ridge and with craterlets on each portion. South of this is a small crater, with a central pit and traces of another concentric ring on the interior.

DESCARTES, +262 −206 [French philosopher, 1596-1650]. This has low walls and is 30 miles in diameter. The wall is partly wanting on the north, but rises 5,000 feet on the south, where is an intrusive crater, with a break in its north wall and a larger formation east of it. On the inner south-east slope is the deep crater A, and adjoining it on the west the relic of an old ring. From A a craterlet-chain runs on to the floor. There are two craters on the north-west wall. In addition to the craterlet-chain, and a companion, there are some low ridges on the floor. West is a cleft, passing through craterlets and running north to the old ring, X. To the south-west of X is a formation, S, with walls open on the north and with several craterlets on its interior. A crater-chain can be traced along the outer west wall of Descartes, and north-west is a small but deep crater on the east side of a smooth enclosure, D.

FERMAT, +313 −387 [French mathematician, 1601-65]. A crater 25 miles in diameter. The walls rise 6,000 feet above the floor in places, and there is a crater, A, on the north wall on the eastern side of a break. On the western side of this break are some craters, and a short crater-chain. The south wall bears an intruding crater, and there is a craterlet on the broad west wall. On the floor are some hills. West is a partial formation, C, its western wall being part of the Altai Mountains. At the south end is the crater B. On the south is a large enclosure, full of rings and with the deep crater F on its west rim. F has a craterlet on its south wall, and a small crater abutting on the north. To the north-west, and at the end of the Altai range, are two shallow and obviously partly lava-filled craters, A and B, both containing a few minute hillocks. To the north-east are several large craters. Of these D, S, F and W are associated with Sacrobosco. There are some craterlet-chains to the north of Fermat, well worth looking for under favourable conditions.

FRACASTORIUS, +505 −363 [Italian astronomer, 1483-1553]. This is one of the finest examples of a partially ruined ring on the lunar surface, under all but low illumination appearing as a great bay on the southern shore of the Mare Nectaris. It is 60 miles in diameter; of the original north wall only a few mounds now mark the position, and these can only be detected under a low sun. From the north-west end the wall (here a delicate ridge) has a regular curve, with small crest craters, to a crater on the outer south slope, east of which a crater-chain runs south from the crest. The wall is here broad, with a gap farther east into a double crater on the outer east slope; turns north, and is deformed by the triangular depression Romana, which contains craters on the south and some mounds, one forming an almost central peak. The north-east wall is a confused mass of depressions, one, F, bearing a central peak. The wall ends, on the north, in three large craters. Farther north-west there is a discontinuous ridge to a small crater on the border of the low ring S. There are three craterlets within S, and south-west of it three little mountains. A gap of 30 miles intervenes between S and the beginning on the western wall; within this gap are two craters, of which Goodacre only shows one. There are also some mounds. On the inner west wall are several craters, and on the outer surface some large craters, the deepest being B, with a central hill and small craters flanking its outer slopes. To the north-west is the peculiar object K, a deformed crater, with a central peak, two craterlets on the extreme south and a small crater on the south. This is connected by low ridges to Fracastorius. Other low ridges can be seen under a low sun, one running to Rosse; and there are two clefts at least, one terminating at the small crater Rosse A. To the south are the craters C, G and K, the latter double.

The floor of Fracastorius is one of the most often observed regions on the Moon. Observers differ in their delineation of the details; the Special Chart depicts all we have been able to find with certainty. In the centre are the remains of a central mountain, now reduced to several isolated hills of little altitude. Goodacre records four, but Wilkins six. They are visible at sunrise on a circular patch, the only illuminated portion of the floor, and evidently a small plateau. North of this group of hills is a distinct craterlet, with three other craterlets on its west, and farther north is the small crater A. Between A and the site of the north rampart is the mountain mass already mentioned, with three peaks. West of it are two craterlets and a low ring. Wilkins found 25 May 1936, with 12½-inch reflector, a low ring, Z, between the craterlets and the triple-peaked mountain mass. East of this group are some craterlets and a short cleft. Concentric with the west wall is a long ridge, probably a cleft or a cleft on the side of a ridge, with craterlets at intervals. On the eastern side of the floor is another ridge, also with craterlets, but not so strongly marked as that on the west. A cleft crosses the floor just to the south of the central hills, and immediately south of this is the craterlet M. Goodacre shows no clefts on the floor, though they are shown by Gaudibert and by Neison. On the extreme

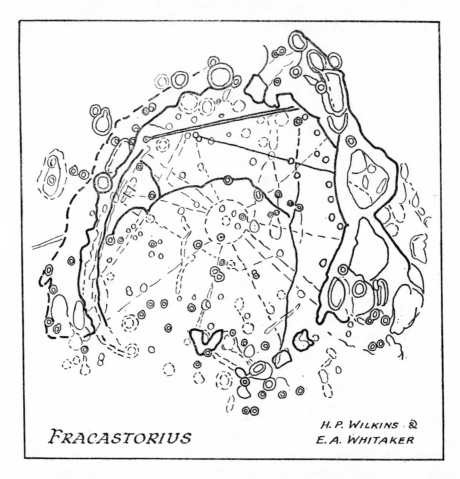

FRACASTORIUS

H. P. WILKINS &
E. A. WHITAKER

southern portion of the interior are several craterlets, some low rings and hillocks. A ray from Tycho runs to a crater on the east wall, and this crater, like one on the west, is then very brilliant. Under high illumination a dark patch appears under the east wall, the floor then being covered by a network of delicate light-streaks and whitish spots, somewhat resembling the floor of Plato under a like angle of illumination. Fracastorius will repay careful study with the largest aperture at the observer's command, but the bulk of the details are so delicate that they can only be seen under the most favourable atmospheric conditions.

North and due west of Beaumont is a short cleft passing through two craterlets, and between these craterlets and Rosse are two craterlets situated on a light-streak. This cleft ends at the low ring, S, on the surface of the Mare Nectaris.

GEBER, +227 −333 [Spanish-Arab astronomer, *circa* A.D. 1145]. A crater 25 miles in diameter, with walls rising 9,000 feet on the west and remarkably regular. On the north-east is the crater A, slightly encroaching upon Geber; A also slightly encroaches upon a lower ring, L, on the floor of which are four craterlets. Between L and the wall of Geber is a craterlet-chain, and there are many small craters on the outer slopes. On the south-west are the remains of two old rings; only curved segments of the once-prominent walls now remain. There is another old ring on the south, just to the west of a small crater with a craterlet on either side. On the south-east is a large but low-walled en-closure with a small floor, on which are a craterlet and some hills, but with thick walls bearing some craters on the east. Close adjoining this is another old ring, S. On the floor of Geber lie a small twin-peaked central mountain, traces of terracing on the inner slopes and a few craterlets, chiefly just below the south-east crest.

GOODACRE, +206 −540 [English selenographer, 1856-1938]. This crater is 30 miles in diameter, and lies on the north-west of Gemma Frisius. It has lofty walls, broken by the crater B on the south, with broad inner slopes and craterlets on both the slopes and floor. There is a low central hill on the floor, a craterlet north of it, and one to the east. On the outer west is a ring, W, open on the south, and south-west of this are some over-lapping craters. Farther west is the crater K, formed by the fusing of two craters with the common wall destroyed. East of K and north of Goodacre are numerous craters and craterlets, also a few hills and the remains of old rings.

LINDENAU, +353 −535 [German astronomer, 1780-1854]. A crater to the west of Zagut and east of a large ancient ring. The finely terraced walls rise 12,000 feet on the east and 8,000 feet on the west. On the inner north slope is a craterlet. West is a con-fusion of ridges, craterlets and small craters, one of the most prominent being H; there are also some craterlet-chains. On the interior of Lindenau is a group of low hills near the centre; also a few mounds, chiefly on the south-western side, and a couple of pits. On the inner south slope is the relic of a former crater. A ridge runs concentric with the outer east wall. On the north are several low rings.

NEANDER, +549 −520 [German mathematician, 1529-81]. A crater 36 miles from north to south but less from east to west, but with broad, terraced walls rising 8,000 feet on the east and a central mountain of 2,500 feet. On the inner north-west slope is a crater, B, and on the north-east the smaller ring A, both easily seen. On either side of the central mountain, M, is a craterlet. Where the broad inner slope of the south-east wall reaches the floor is the remains of an old ring. There are also some low hills on the interior. A ridge runs on the outer south concentric with the wall, and there are some mountainous masses and small craters in this region. To the north-west is the crater E, also somewhat deformed and with an old ring at its south end. West of E is a mass of craters, several joined by their walls, and two clefts on the south-west. That to the east begins at an old crater on the west of Neander to the southern crater, H, which seems to have interrupted it. The cleft begins again at the other side of H, and, after touching the wall of the crater, J, turns to the south and runs to the termination of the great Rheita Valley. On the east of this long cleft are many craters, some most interesting objects, one consisting of four craters arranged in a square with their walls in contact; north of this is a small crater with another touching on the north. This latter crater has a wide gap in its north wall, but still exhibits a central peak. East of Neander are some notable craters, especially F, N and the remarkable group, P. Nearly all of these objects have low walls, but are striking objects under low illumination. To the south-east are many rings, ridges and craterlets.

NECTARIS, MARE, +540 −250. The 'Sea of Nectar' is a dark, approximately square, plain, 180 miles across, Fracastorius forming a bay on its southern shore. On the eastern part is a prominent ridge from Theophilus to Beaumont; the surface to the east of this is very rugged, with numerous ridges, hills and craterlet-chains, most of them radiating from Theophilus. Similar, but fewer, features can be seen on the west side of this great, though short, ridge, with some superb examples of craterlet-chains radiating from Theophilus, numerous craterlets and a cleft. There are also some old rings, now almost submerged by the lava of the plain; of these Z and S are the most prominent. Of the small craters B and A are the largest.

   The largest crater on the surface of the Mare is Rosse, which is the node of several ridges running west, east and north. They cross other ridges concentric with the west border. The entire plain appears to be concave, and the ridges mark the successive levels. On the south-west and also the north are ancient rings. About 150 craterlets are scattered over the floor. Wilkins found, 9 January 1935, a shallow depression, 60 miles in diameter, in the centre of the Mare, marked by shade—obviously an ancient crater. Also, 26 May 1936, three 'ghost' rings between the centre and the west border with craterlets on their northern rims and all connected by a light-streak. From Rosse a cleft runs across the plain, and there are other clefts on the west, associated with Bohnenberger. Of the larger craterlets, A, R, I and U, with the groups N and S, all on the north, are the most noteworthy. On the south-west is H, a small crater with four craterlets along its western ramparts, and east of this the peculiar crater, Fracastorius K.

PICCOLOMINI, +463 −496 [Italian archbishop and astronomer, 1508-78]. A magnificent and most prominent formation, 56 miles in diameter, with beautifully terraced walls of great height, with peaks here and there of 15,000 feet. The southern slope is very peculiar, apparently of a 'ropy' nature, just as though once-plastic material had overflowed at this point. It falls gradually to the floor in a gentle slope very different from the other portions of the ramparts. Moore has seen here a very shallow depression, of some size ($12\frac{1}{2}$ inch reflector, 1952). At sunrise the inner terraces stand out boldly from the shadow and present a fine telescopic picture. On the outer south-west is a large crater with a small central hill, while on the north is the crater, M, and west of this the two spindle-shaped objects, resembling shallow valleys, S and P. East of the almost circular crater, M, are some remarkable overlapping rings. The inner south-east slope is very broad, with some craters. On the interior is a central mountain in two parts, or rather one mountain cut through by a ravine. Near the east slope is a craterpit and a hill between it and the central mountain. On the northern portion Wilkins found, 20 January 1934, with a $12\frac{1}{2}$-inch reflector, four craterpits arranged in a square and very delicate objects. There are some craterlets to the west. Moore had a fine view of Piccolomini with the 25-inch 'Newall' refractor at Cambridge University on 26 September 1953, and discovered the remains of an old ring closely south of the central mountain mass, with indications of another old ring to the east. Altogether, twenty-four craterlets and five hills were seen on the floor. From the north-east wall begins a most interesting and complex system of clefts, roughly parallel to the Altai Mountains, which also begin at the east wall of Piccolomini. The widest and most prominent cleft lies farthest west and is, in part, a craterlet-chain. This cleft runs to a triple group of craters to the east of Polybius. East of this long cleft is a much finer cleft, which runs parallel to the first, passing in its course just south of a small crater, H, and then to a craterlet on the south wall of the crater B. This crater has a smaller crater on its south-east, and three craterlets on its west. Between these two clefts and near Piccolomini is a short cleft. This cleft is crossed, a little to the east of H, by a fine cleft from the great cleft, and runs to the Altai Mountains. From the craterlet to the south of B, already mentioned, another cleft begins and runs to the same point of the Altai Mountains, where the cross-cleft converges. Just west of B is another cleft, running almost north and south and crossing the two running to the craterlet south of B. This cleft ends at a low ridge just to the north of the crater A. There are other short clefts in this region, and some low ridges, also craterlets and hills. North-east of B is a most remarkable triangular object, K, from the east rim of which a delicate craterlet-chain runs northwards. From a small, double craterlet to the east of K a cleft runs to the strong section of the Altai Mountains mentioned in connection with Fermat. Between Piccolomini and the crater of Rothmann are some very deformed rings, oval rings and many craterlets. Due south is the formation B, and on the east of this is a craterlet-chain. Due west is a crater pair, near the crater Weinek C.

POLYBIUS, +400 −383 [Greek historian, 204-122 B.C.]. A crater, 20 miles in diameter, to the south-west of Catharina. There are craters on the crests of the south and north walls, and a row of three on the south-west. On the floor is a ridge a little to the east of the centre, three craterlets on the west forming a short chain, one on the south-east and two at the south, and a hill. Polybius is connected by a ridge to the crater Catharina C, the elongated crater south of Catharina. On the west is a mountain ridge concentric with the wall; this ridge is prolonged north, and expands into a considerable mountain mass. Just before this expansion there is a deflection to the east, really the east wall of a former ring. Between the mountain and C are numerous craterlets, some in chains, and low rings. On the south is a great cleft from the east wall of Piccolomini, with some small craters between the cleft and the wall. West are many low rings; of these, S is the most prominent. South-west of S is the deep crater A, with a smaller ring, containing another crater, on its north. To the east is the triple formation F, described under Piccolomini, and rings, craterlets and ridges in abundance between the two formations. A portion of the wall of the northern component appears to have become displaced, and now appears as a spur of rock partly jutting on to the floor.

PONS, +330 —429 [French astronomer, 1761-1831]. A most interesting and abnormal object, 20 miles in diameter, on the highland to the east of the crest of the Altai Mountains. Its walls are of extraordinary thickness, and more or less perfect except on the south-west, where the crater A has intruded. On the other portions of the wall are some craters, all shallow, ridges and a few ravines. The small interior contains two craterlets on the east at the foot of the wall, a minute pit on the west, to the east of what looks like a landslip along the western rampart, a hill on the south and a short ridge. There is no definite central peak. Immediately to the west is a great and lofty mountain arm, a sort of spur from the main crest of the Altai Mountains; probably a portion of an ancient ring, for it is curved on the east, and there is a gap on the south. On the north-east side of this old ring is the prominent and deep crater, B. To the north-west, and adjoining Pons, is another ring, with a gap in its west wall which forms part of the Altai Range. On the floor of this ring are a crater, two craterlets and a hill. Due north of Pons is the crater F, with a craterlet on its south rim and a small crater adjoining on the north. East of F and Pons are ridges, interspersed with craterlets and some abnormal objects South is a small plain, on which the most prominent objects are the crater C, the low rimmed D and some hills. This plain is bordered by craters on the west and a mountain ridge on the east; on the south are some imperfect rings associated with the crater Wilkins. A delicate ridge runs from Pons A to the crater C.

PONTANUS, +218 —477 [Italian poet and astronomer, 1427-1503]. A fine crater, 28 miles in diameter with broad walls, broken by a partial crater on the north. On the floor is a nearly central crater, A, connected with the south-east wall by some ridges, several craterlets, and some hills. The inner crest of the south-east wall is remarkable for the row of craterlets so prominent in the telescope; from some of these craterlets a ridge runs down to the floor. On the north-east slope is a short cleft. Adjoining on the south-west is the great and deep crater Benitez, with a craterlet on the crest of its west wall and a smaller on the east. There is a most minute central peak within Benitez, and some ridges. To the south of Benitez are several small craters and the ring Goodacre K. West of Benitez is the low-rimmed formation L, with a central pit and some craterlets on the walls. Adjoining L on the north-west is a small square formation, which in its turn touches a much larger and more prominent elongated formation V. This object, probably the result of the fusion of two craters, extends to the west wall of Pontanus. North-west of it is a most remarkable and easily-seen craterlet-chain which may be traced as

160

far north as the two low rings S and P. On the east and north-east of Pontanus are some abnormal formations, many craterlets and numerous ridges.

RABBI LEVI, +330 —570 [Spanish-Jewish astronomer, 1288-1344]. A great but somewhat irregular formation, 50 miles in diameter, with walls of no great height and cut through, on the inner south, by a series of prominent parallel ravines. There is a double crater, or rather two small craters with their walls in contact, on the south wall. Along the outer south-east slopes are some elongated depressions and small craters, while a ridge flanking Celsius on the west, encloses a shallow valley between it and the wall of Rabbi Levi. On the north-east is Zagut, and on the north-west Lindenau, between the ramparts of which and Rabbi Levi are some craterlets, notably a short chain ending, on the north, in a small square object. There is a gap in the west wall of Rabbi, which is partly filled by a partial ring, R. On the inner slope above R are two craters. The interior of Rabbi Levi contains many interesting features. The principal object is the crater F, a little to the east of the centre. Adjoining F is the crater A, and there are some very low-rimmed rings associated with these two craters. On the south-east is a group of four craters, arranged in pairs. At the foot of the inner west wall is another crater pair, while nearly all the inner north-western portion is occupied by a large, low ring. There are some craterlets, especially on the south, and three minute hills to the west of the centre. On the outer west are many craters, some overlapping, as for example D, while D and E are connected by a smaller ring overlapped on the west by D and itself overlapping E on the east.

ROMANA, +478 —372 [contemporary Spanish astronomer]. A triangular depression 21 miles in diameter, on the east wall of Fracastorius. It used to be known as Fracastorius D, and is described under that heading.

ROSSE, +545 —307 [Irish nobleman and astronomer, 1800-1867]. A bright, deep crater 10 miles in diameter, in the Mare Nectaris, north-west of Fracastorius, to which it is connected by ridges. A light streak runs to the north-west from Rosse across the Mare Nectaris, with a cleft to the west of it and a ridge to the east.

ROTHMANN, +400 —514 [German astronomer, died *circa* 1600]. A fine crater between Piccolomini and Lindenau, with finely terraced walls and a mountain not quite in the centre. A prominent ravine runs down the inner south slope, and can be traced to the central mountain. The northern rim is serrated, and there is a linear segment on the north-west. On the south-west is the crater B, with a craterlet on its north wall, while on the north is the small but bright crater A. On the surface to the east are many objects, in particular the craters F and K; while on the north-east is a most extraordinary formation. This consists of a pair of craters adjoining a larger crater to the north. A tongue of rock curves down the south wall of this crater and on to its floor, which is otherwise quite smooth. The outer wall of this crater is flanked by craterlets. West of this, and filling up the space between it and the Altai Range, are the remains of an old ring, somewhat difficult to make out. From the north-east rim of this ancient relic, a craterlet-chain runs northwards to a shallow and, apparently, lava-filled ring south of the crater Pons B. The curved ridges from the east wall of the great formation Piccolomini end close to the west wall of Rothmann.

SACROBOSCO, +260 −400 [English mathematician, died 1256]. One of the great lunar rings, but irregular and about 52 miles in diameter, with broad and lofty walls, rising 12,000 feet on the east, where is a landslide. There is a wide gap in the south wall, filled up by a mass of craters and a low ring, N. The south-west segment of the wall is complete, and due west is the crater A, one of a pair; beyond this the north-west wall has altogether vanished, its site being occupied by a confused mass of craters, forming in general a great crater-row. Of the craters in the direct line are, from the south, D, with a spur on its interior; S, with three craterlets and two hills on its floor; F, with a craterlet on the north; and W, with a craterlet on its west wall and traces of terracing. Adjoining S, on the west, is another crater, D, which has on its floor a small partial ring and a craterlet on the south, a craterlet on the north and two hills. The north-east portion of the wall of Sacrobosco is also deficient, and is chiefly a gap occupied by ridges and some craters. On the extreme north-east is a double crater, with a ring, T, on its north. At this point the wall resumes its true character, and runs south to the low ring N, on the south. On the interior are many objects. South of the centre are two craters, A and B, both with central peaks. South of them are several craterlets. North of A and close to the inner slope is a crater, C, while on the north-west is the partial formation H. This portion of the interior contains some old rings. On the outer east are numerous craterlets, ridges and the remains of ancient rings as far as the wall of Sisebuto. South is the imperfect formation, E, with a mountain mass to the north-west.

STIBORIUS, +439 −565 [Austrian astronomer, 1465-1515]. A fine crater, 23 miles in diameter, with terraced walls bearing a crater on the north and situated on the western rim of a large, low ring. This ring contains several smaller and some craterlets on its interior. On the interior of Stiborius are a peak, not quite in the centre; some lower hills, and a craterlet on the west. The north-west portion of the wall is drawn out, and there is a deflection inwards to the east of it. Touching this pointed portion of the wall is a crater with a central peak, and south of it are several craters, E bearing a craterlet on its northern rim. Farther south is the crater A. From the crater E a shallow valley runs south, passing the east wall of A. North is a peculiar arrangement of shallow enclosures, ending in a square formation close to the small but deep crater L.

TACITUS, +313 −280 [Roman historian A.D. 55-120]. A polygonal formation, 25 miles in diameter, situated between Catharina and Abulfeda. The walls are beautifully terraced on the inner slopes, and rise 11,000 feet above the floor, on which are a central craterpit, some mounds and a trace of an old ring on the north-west. On the inner slope west of this is an oval depression. West of the central craterpit is a dark area, and there is a large, low mound on the west, on which is a pit. A small crater lies just beyond the south-west crest, and from this a ridge runs to the south, becoming higher and more prominent as it proceeds. West are some craterlet-chains, and a ridge half-way to Catharina; east are several craters, mainly in rows, some mountain arms and hills. To the north-east is the fine crater pair, A and B, the latter having slightly overlapped the former, while due north, at the end of a ridge, is a square enclosure partly filled with craterlets. South-west of this formation, and nearer Tacitus, are the relic of an old ring P, the crater B, and innumerable craterlets and ridges.

WEINEK, +535 −462 [Hungarian astronomer, 1848-1913]. A prominent crater to the north-west of Piccolomini, with the smaller crater, C, between them. There is a crater on the north crest, and one on the inner south-west, while on the floor are a small central hill, five hillocks and two craterlets. On the south-west is a low ring, also the deep crater, A. West are a number of abnormal and ridge-bounded formations; of these E is the largest. To the north is the crater F, with a small gap in its north wall. East of F is G, with a large central hill, and a crater on the inner north, while intruding on the north-east is the fine double crater, K. On the east are several small craters, and two elongated depressions, S and P, the latter touching the wall of Piccolomini. There is a remarkable arrangement of small craters on the north-east of Weinek, arranged so regularly as to excite astonishment.

WILKINS, +295 −495 [English selenographer, and one of the Authors, born 1896 at Carmarthen, South Wales.] This formation was formerly known as Zagut S (Goodacre).

This is an irregular formation, terraced on the inner slopes, especially west, while on the floor and close to the west wall are two hills and a light spot. On the north-east rampart is a distinct double crater, the components lying north and south. On the north wall is a more shallow ring, also double. The components of this ring lie east and west of each other. The walls are nowhere of any great height, while the floor is 40 miles in diameter. On the northern portion is a hillock, and there is some object crossing the floor from east to the north-west, possibly a low ridge. On the outer west slope is a crater-chain, the components of which diminish in size towards the south.

ZAGUT, +317 −530 [Spanish-Jewish astronomer, *circa* 1480]. A very irregular and complex formation, 50 miles in diameter. On the west is an intruding ring with a central hill. On the floor of Zagut is a ridge from the south wall, a low ring, and a craterlet on the west; also other rings on the east and north-west. On the north are several craters. To the south-east of Zagut is a large, low ring, open to the north, with craters on its north rim and chains of craters from both ends on the north. This was named Celsius by Schmidt. To the north is a large, low ring with a double crater on its east wall. On the floor of this ring are low mounds, and at least nine craterlets. To the south is the crater B, with numerous craters between it and the east wall of Zagut.

163

X

This section includes some of the finest of all the lunar formations, including Petavius, with its grand double rampart, central mountain and cleft; Vendelinus; and Furnerius. The northern central portion is occupied by the dark Mare Fœcunditatis. Near the limb are the giant Wilhelm Humboldt and many little-known rings.

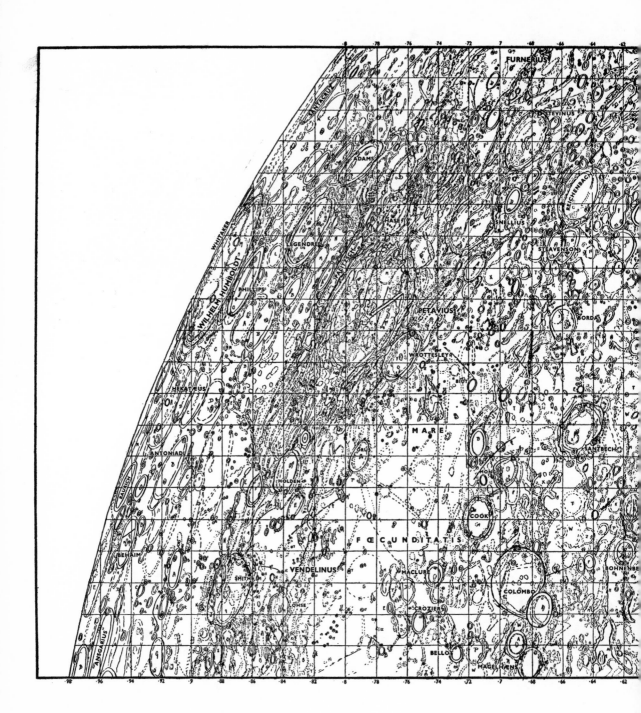

X

ADAMS, +791 −525 [English mathematician, 1819-92]. A fine crater, with a central crater and hills on the floor. There are craters on the crests. To the north is an old ring, and, on the south, a crater-chain. On the east is a wide valley, V, running to an ancient crater, F. To the west of F is the crater A. The crater-chain is continued on the south by the row of four large craters. To the west is Santacruz, with a craterlet and a ridge on the floor and a craterlet on the north crest. Outside the west wall of Santacruz is a mountain, M, followed by two large rings. Beyond the valley on the east is a group of depressions flanking the west wall of Hase. Of these B and K are the largest. A wide crater-valley, V, runs north from the north wall of B. Adams A has very bright walls, and is of considerable depth.

ANSGARIUS, +960 −220 [German theologian, 801-864]. This crater lies close to the limb, which makes it difficult to observe. It is 50 miles in diameter, with a smooth floor except for a few low hills. To the west is a crater, and there is another on the east. There are also two craters on the south-west wall. The crater B, on the west, has a crater on its south-west rim, while close on the south-west is the ring C, and south-east of this the smaller D, from which a valley runs to the south-east wall of Ansgarius.

ANTONIADI, +913 −330 [Greek astronomer, 1870-1944]. A large ring to the north-east of Hekatæus, with two craterlets on the floor. East is a crater, C, with a smaller, F, on its east, and a crater, E, on the north. To the north-west is a mountain, Eta, and a deep crater. This crater has a central hill. Close to the limb is the crater D.

BEHAIM, +943 −285 [German navigator, 1436-1506]. A fine crater, 35 miles in diameter, with a central crater, and a hill and a cleft on the eastern part of the floor. There are also craters on the walls. To the north-west is a large ring, E, close to the limb. On the south-east outer slope of Behaim is the crater B. On the south are many craters.

East is the crater A, which, with its surroundings, was examined under good conditions, 4 October 1952, by Wilkins, with the great 25-inch 'Newall' refractor at Cambridge University Observatory. North of A is another crater, B, connected by a ridge to A. On the interior of A is a ridge under the west wall. Immediately west of A are three minute craterlets from which a fine cleft runs north, following close to the wall, curves at a small craterlet and then runs due north, ending in two craterlets. Close to and south-east of B is a peculiar deformed crater, while numerous craterlets were also detected, especially on the south and east.

BELLOT +728 −215 [French explorer, 1826-53]. A small crater, 12 miles in diameter, with a smooth floor which is remarkably bright. On the north-east are some old rings and the distinct crater B. Wilkins found a craterlet on the floor of Bellot close to the south wall. Immediately to the east is the old ring, P, of which only the east wall is of any height. North of P are indications of a much larger ancient ring, only traceable with difficulty.

BIOT, +718 −385 [French astronomer, 1774-1862]. This crater is 10 miles in diameter, and is situated on the Mare Fœcunditatis to the east of a short ridge. From the south wall a cleft runs towards the east wall of Petavius. On the north is a smaller crater, while to the east is the brilliant crater, A. To the north of A is a low plateau, on which is an old ring. On the west is another old ring with well-formed walls on the north and west but open on the south. This is a very striking object under low illumination.

BOHNENBERGER, +619 −279 [German mathematician, 1765-1831]. An interesting object on the western border of the Mare Nectaris. It is 22 miles in diameter, and there is a gap in the north wall. On the floor is a nearly central ridge running north and south, a craterlet on the south, and some hills. There are also two clefts on the interior. On the outer north-east is a low ring. The west wall is prolonged on the north as a lofty mountain ridge, with craters on its crest, and the crater F on its east flank. On the south is the crater G, on the north edge of an old, cleft-crossed ring. West of Bohnenberger are the Pyrenees Mountains, and on the open plain to the east several clefts. One of these runs from the crater F to Rosse, and this cleft is bordered on the west by a low ridge. Between Bohnenberger and Santbech are many low rings, and a craterlet-chain.

BORDA, +660 −425 [French astronomer, 1733-99]. This formation is 26 miles in diameter, with low walls, highest on the north and with gaps on the south. It has a central hill, and the south-west portion of the floor is occupied by a low ring. There are also some hills on the interior. On the north wall are two craters, the remains of an old ring; also a peculiar valley-like feature, E. West is a fine mountain with a peak rising 11,000 feet. On the north-west are a crater-chain, some low rings and many hills. To the south is an elongated ring, with other craters as far as Steavenson and B. East is the crater F, with a craterlet on its north rim, while further east are the craters B and another on the north-west; also two mountain masses. Some distance to the south-west is the deep crater A. This has a smaller crater on either side, together with ridges and craterlets.

COLOMBO, +686 −260 [The discoverer of America, 1446-1506]. This fine and prominent object is 50 miles in diameter, and has a large intruding ring, A, 25 miles in diameter, on the north-east. A has a central hill and some other details on its floor. The interior of Colombo contains much interesting detail. In the centre is a group of six hills arranged in a rough circle, and this is evidently the remains of an old ring. On the west are craterlets and curved ridges, probably the remains of other old rings. There are at least ten craterlets on the interior, of which C, on the south-west, is the largest. On the western portion is a fine cleft. West are some old rings, while on the south-east, and close to the wall, is the small but bright crater B. From the east wall of Colombo a cleft runs to the south-east as far as the crater E, passing a mountain on its way. On the outer east slope of the intruding ring, A, is a crater-chain ending, on the north, at a crater. Abutting on the wall, near A, are two low rings, W and X, and the deep crater, Magelhæns A.

COOK, +713 −300 [English naval explorer, 1728-79]. Although this is only 26 miles in diameter, it is easily found on account of its dark floor. The walls are low, nowhere exceeding 500 feet, with a few little peaks on the east and a small crater on the south crest. The interior contains a crater on the south-west, and a small circle of little jutting spurs north of the centre. On the north is a ridge, and west are two low rings. South is the crater A, with a central hill. On the outer west is a crater from which a cleft runs south, seen by Wilkins 3 April 1938.

CROZIER, +753 −234 [English explorer, 1796-1848]. A crater, 15 miles in diameter, with a central hill and a craterlet on the southern part of the floor. West is an old ring, D, with the crater, E, on the south-west. On the south is a group of low-walled and old rings, S, T and D being the best defined. North-west is the bright crater, B, and south-west of it a mountain, forming part of the wall of an ancient ring.

FŒCUNDITATIS, MARE, +680 −360 to +840 +100. The 'Sea of Plenty'. A great and dark plain on the south-west portion of the disk, bordered by Petavius, Vendelinus and Langrenus on the west, and 640 miles from north to south and 415 miles from east to west. The area is 160,000 sq. miles. The Mare is narrow on the east of Vendelinus, but expands again on the south, eventually ending to the east of Petavius. At Vendelinus it is only 132 miles wide, and the peaks on either side rise 5,400 feet and 3,300 feet but, as Neison remarks, would not be in sight from each other owing to the rapid curvature of the globe. On the surface are numerous ridges, craters, craterlets and many obscure rings.

FURNERIUS, +704 −587 [French Jesuit mathematician, *circa* 1643]. A great walled-plain, being the most southerly of the great group beginning on the north at Langrenus. It is 80 miles in diameter, with terraced walls rising, on the north, to 11,500 feet. The interior contains much interesting detail, recently subjected to a careful scrutiny by Abineri and Arthur. There is a gap in the south wall, where are some craters. On the inner south-east is a landslide, while on the floor the most prominent object is the bright crater, B. This has a central hill, a craterlet on the north and on its east is a ridge with a long, low hill. There are fourteen large craters and many craterlets on the interior, also a fine cleft on the north. This cleft curves south-west of B and divides; the branch to the east traverses two craterlets. Near the north-west wall is another cleft, which is convex to the west. A delicate cleft also crosses the extreme southern portion of the interior, visible at sunset and confirmed by R. Barker. The walls and immediate surroundings are very complex and reference should be made to the map for the details. There is a chain of depressions on the inner west, while beyond the crest is a gorge. On the north-west crest is the crater, A, and on the south-west the wall has been disturbed by the crater G. To the south-east is Fraünhofer.

HASE, +770 −485 [German mathematician 1684-1742]. A large ring south of Petavius, the walls rising 7,000 feet in places, and with three craterlets on the inner west slope. The floor contains a large number of minute pits and there are vast numbers of pits in the area to the west of Hase, towards Legendre and Adams. With the 25-inch 'Newall' refractor of Cambridge University Observatory Wilkins found, 4 October 1952, the following details on the floor of Hase:

On the northern portion is a large crater, with two craterlets on its east. North of this crater is a craterlet, and a spur from the north wall. On the east wall, opposite the crater, is a depression. On the central and eastern portion is a craterlet-chain of five craterlets, and south of this a small crater. This has a still larger crater on its south, on the rim of an old ring abutting on the south-eastern wall. A little to the south-west of the large crater, on the north, are three craterlets and the remains of an old ring. On the inner north-west wall are a crater and a depression, with a high mountain between them. There is a crater-chain on the outer north-west slope. On the outer south-east is a crater-chain.

Thornton has noted a peculiar arrangement of ridges on the outer north-east, which shows up at sunset as an illuminated cross. Moore, in 1952, noted eight craters on the west wall with his 12½-inch reflector. South is the ring D, the walls of which have been broken on the south by a crater.

HEKATÆUS, +920 −360 [Greek geographer, *circa* 476 B.C.]. This object, which lies close to the limb, is pear-shaped and has lofty walls rising 16,000 feet on the east and nearly as high on the west. Abineri and Moore have seen indications that Hekatæus is the result of the fusion of two old rings. On the floor are a central mountain, ridges and some small craters on the south. On the east are rings, A and B, containing ridges. On the north is a ring containing a row of four craters. The finely terraced walls contain little peaks on the west, and two minute craterlets on the inner north-west. There is also a very bright spot, probably a crater, on the south-west and just below the crest. On the extreme northern portion is a low ring. On the outer north-east a double crater will be seen. Of the three great rings extending along the outer east, that farthest north has two craters on its east crest, the central ring has craterlets on its floor, and the ring farthest south has a ridge on its dark floor. Abineri, 15 October 1951 (8-inch reflector), recorded three narrow valleys connecting the floors of Hekatæus and Wilhelm Humboldt.

HOLDEN, +838 −328 [American astronomer, 1846-1914]. This ring lies on the south border of Vendelinus and is fully 25 miles in diameter. On the floor are a ridge and a crater, A. To the south is a smaller crater with a central hill, while on the north wall are two craters and a third on the west. To the north-west is the ring, F, and north east, E, with some craterlets on the south. East of Holden are a depression and some craterlets.

To the south-west are numerous ridges from Petavius, while the inner slopes of Holden are terraced.

HUMBOLDT, W., +878 −457 [German statesman, 1767-1835]. A grand ring, 120 miles in diameter, with lofty walls rising in majestic peaks to 16,000 feet on the east and little, if any, inferior on the west. On the interior is a central chain of hills, with a crater on its north. There is also a crater on the north-east, some dark spots on the north and south, while a cleft crosses the floor. Wilkins has also noted a fine cleft crossing the floor near the northern end. On the inner west are some landslips. Humboldt overlaps an older ring on the north-west. The double nature of the north wall is a striking feature. To the east of the centre of the ridge in the interior are two hills. The central ridge rises into lofty peaks, but separated by breaks; at sunset the shadows of these peaks reach the west wall in grand spires of shade. There are two craters on the west, and two more on the east. On the far west and on the averted hemisphere are some large rings. Of these C, D and L, and Whitaker (Stereographic Chart) are the most prominent.

LEGENDRE, +822 −483 [French mathematician, 1752-1833]. A ring 46 miles in diameter, with low walls. Wilkins examined Legendre, 4 October 1952, with the great 25-inch 'Newall' refractor at Cambridge. As then seen the following details were recorded: The wall is broad on the west, and contains a craterlet on the inner slope; on the outer surface, to the west, is a short cleft. On the extreme south is a group of craters, one having a small crater on its south rim. On the north Legendre abuts on to a large ring, the dividing wall being broken by passes. On the interior of this ring are at least six craterlets, two minute hillocks and a short ridge. On the interior of Legendre is a somewhat discontinuous central ridge, and there is a low ridge on the west, concentric with the wall and probably a landslide. On this ridge is a craterlet. On the eastern portion of the floor is a craterlet-chain near the centre, five craterlets on the south and three on the north. Under low illumination some shallow depressions can be seen on either side of the central ridge. On the outer east is a small crater with a large craterlet on its north, from which a short cleft, convex to the east, runs to a craterlet on the north. South-east are numerous craterlets.

LOHSE, +843 −247 [German astronomer, 1845-1915]. A crater on the north-east of Vendelinus, with a mountain not quite in the centre of the floor. The walls, which are terraced, have a gap on the south, where also is a crater. There is a craterlet on the west crest. In the north wall is a gap which opens into a ring, E, crossed by a cleft and with craters on its walls.

MAGELHÆNS, +681 −208 [Portuguese navigator, 1480-1521]. A crater 25 miles in diameter, with low walls; a dark ring, containing a central craterlet, and another lie on the inner south-west. To the south-east is the ring, A, with a central hill. East are some curved ridges and hills. Some peaks of the Pyrenees Mountains also rise on the east.

McCLURE, +742 −264 [English explorer, 1807-73]. This crater is 15 miles in diameter, and has a central hill, connected by a ridge to the north wall. There are also two low hills and two craters on the inner south slope. On the south-east wall is a crater, while to the north of McClure is a curved ridge, part of an ancient ring and with a crater on its north rim. To the south is a crater-chain. East and west are many obscure rings. To the east is the bright crater, A.

MONGE, +695 −334 [French geometer, 1746-1818]. A ring to the south-east of Cook, with a deformed west wall and a crater on the south crest. On the floor are some hills and low rings, also a minute pit close to the inner north-west. West is a crater, G, and south of it is a fine cleft passing through two craters. To the south-west is the large crater, B, with a mountain ridge on the south and a crater on the north. East is the obscure ring, S, which opens into another ring on the north. There are two obscure rings, F and K, on the north and a craterlet-chain.

ORÚS, +790 −340 [Spanish astronomer]. This crater, formerly known as Petavius B, is 19 miles in diameter, and lies some way to the east of Holden. It is fairly regular in form, with a central mountain, and presents no special features. Adjoining it on the north is the remnant of a very old ring, P, on the northern border of which lies a mountain mass, M, of some altitude.

PALITZSCH, +801 −457 [Ger-

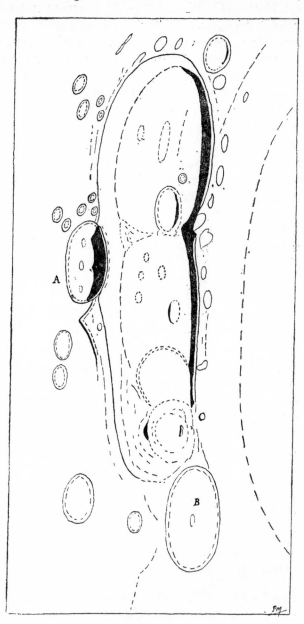

PALITZSCH

4 October 1952, 22h. 25-inch O.G. (Observatory of Cambridge), Patrick Moore

man astronomer, 1723-88]. Although far less imposing than its great neighbour Petavius, Palitzsch is undoubtedly one of the most interesting objects on the whole Moon. It is generally described as an irregular, gorge-like formation 60 miles long and 20 wide, and it has often been suggested that it was formed by a meteor ploughing its way through the still-plastic lunar surface.

On 4 October 1952 Moore, using the great 25-inch 'Newall' refractor at the Cambridge University Observatory, had a superb view of Palitzsch, and its true nature was at once evident. It is not a gorge at all, but a vast crater-chain, as is clear from the drawing reproduced here.

The southern component contains what appear to be the remains of a central height, and the old wall on the north can still be traced; there is also a prominent crater here. The western wall is broad and lofty, disturbed in the north by the intrusion of a fine, deep crater, A, with three hills on its floor. The central component of Palitzsch has walls of rather less altitude, but still fairly high; on the floor are five hills. The northern component is disturbed by two old rings, the smaller of which is not easy to trace. Outside the northern wall of Palitzsch is a crater, B, with low walls and central hill; this has often been included with Palitzsch, but is really a separate formation.

Between Palitzsch A and Legendre lie two old rings, M and N. To the south is Hase, and on the east Palitzsch abuts on the majestic Petavius.

PETAVIUS, +785 −430 [French chronologist, 1583-1652]. A great ring, one of the finest on the entire lunar surface and a grand object under low and medium illumination, but obliterated at Full. It is over 100 miles in diameter, measured from crest to crest, with massive, broad and very complex walls rising in peaks of 11,000 feet on the east, where the wall is double, and 7,000 feet on the west. There are traces of a once-complete double rampart, the inner one being lower and less regular than the outer and main wall. The interior is decidedly convex, the central portion being 800 feet higher than that adjoining the walls. In the centre of the floor is a grand, complex mountain group, the principal peak rising 5,600 feet and casting a long shadow under a low sun. This, and the details of the group, are best seen under evening illumination.

From this mountain group runs one of the finest clefts on the entire Moon, towards the south-east wall, cutting through the inner component into a valley between the walls. In places this great cleft, which can be seen with a very small telescope (Wilkins has seen it with 1½-inch), has raised banks, like a canal.

Where the cleft ends, on the east, is a small ring. On the south portion of the floor are several craters, two easily detected. From a craterlet near the south wall a cleft runs to the central mountain group. To the west is a more delicate cleft, and there is another, which, beginning at the south-east outer border, runs towards the great cleft, crosses it and thence to the north-east wall. Several other clefts exist, one ending on the north, in a ruined ring. This ruined ring is only one of several such on the floor. The majority of these clefts on the interior are very delicate and difficult to see; some are, in part, craterlet-chains. From the south, and in particular the north walls, radiate many ridges,

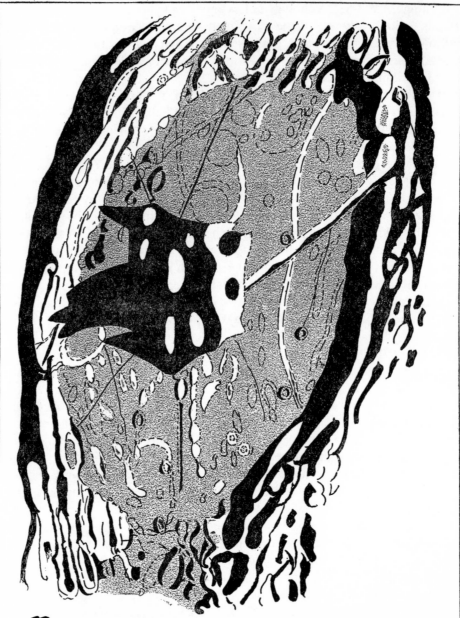

PETAVIUS   H.P. WILKINS, F.R.A.S.

Oct. 5, 1952. 30 - inch Reflector x 300

with shallow valleys between them, the whole forming a complicated region well shown on one of the Paris photographs. Petavius is almost invisible, not at the precise Full, but when the solar altitude is highest, some three days after first quarter. Mädler produced a good special chart which, in some respects, is superior to the map of Schmidt.

A magnificent observation of Petavius was secured by Wilkins, on the evening of 5 October 1952, with a power of 320 on Dr. W. H. Steavenson's 30-inch reflector at Cambridge. The drawing shows what was seen on this occasion with this fine instrument. At the first glance the floor was seen to be covered with numerous mounds, clefts, craterlets and ridges, while the central mountain group cast a long and curiously serrated shadow. On the eastern slope of the principal mountain a distinct oval depression, full of shadow, like a pit shaft, was noted.

The surrounding region, as already indicated, is very complex, consisting of ridges gradually fining away, valleys, and some crater-chains. Of the latter the most prominent is that which runs from near the outer east rampart towards Snellius. On the outer south-east is an old ring, P, with a larger, F, on the south. On the north several craterlets can be detected between the ridges and a valley, V, due south of Holden.

PHILLIPS, +865 −450 [English geologist, 1800-74]. A large ring on the east of Humboldt, about 75 miles in diameter, with a long, central ridge and some low rings on the northern portion of the floor. According to Schmidt, there are two craterlets on the north-eastern part. There is a small crater on the crest of the north wall. On the outer south-east is a fine, deep crater, A, while on the north-east are two low rings, A and B. B is the more prominent; both have some craterlets on their interiors. North of B is a smaller crater, with its west wall fringed with hillocks and two craterlets on the inner east. South is a short crater-chain, the craters 9, 10 and 11, also the peculiar object, F. Between Phillips and Legendre is a ring, L, with very low walls. Phillips appears to have overlapped an older ring on the north; traces of this can be seen under favourable conditions. Between Phillips and the west wall of Petavius is the deep crater B, with a hill on the western part of the floor.

PYRENEES MOUNTAINS, +640 −160 to −220. A small range of bright little hills, on the western side of the Mare Nectaris and east of Gutenberg. The highest peak rises 12,000 feet on the north; on the south there is a peak of 6,500 feet. The range rises abruptly on the east from the plain, and is, in parts, double. This is well seen near Bohnenberger and east of Colombo, where are the two parallel ranges, M, and that from the north wall of this formation. Due east of Colombo A it also divides, and there is an isolated mountain between the ranges.

RAURICH, +944 −320 [Spanish astronomer, 1868-1949]. A ring north of Humboldt and between it and Ansgarius, 30 miles in diameter. West are a small crater and some rings.

REICHENBACH, +647 −504 [German optician, 1772-1826]. This formation is 30 miles in diameter, with lofty walls, rising 12,000 feet in places. On the south-west crest is the crater, G, and on the west the crater 3, while on the north wall is a depression, R. The walls are broad and are terraced, with craters in places; of these I, on the south, is the largest. On the floor is a low ridge east of the centre, some still lower ridges, hills and a crater, 2, near the north-east inner slope. On the outer north are the craters Steavenson and B, the former overlapping the latter and both with central mountains. North of Steavenson are some rings, the most prominent being K. East is a confused mass of depressions, and a mountain, M. Farther east is a double object, V, and the large, deep crater, C, with a central mountain. North of V is the large ring, D, with a deep crater, E, on its north. Within D is the relic of another ring. South, beyond some small craters, is a very peculiar object, C, another example of a confluent formation. West, between the wall and Stevinus, is a craterlet-chain.

SANTACRUZ, +820 −564 [Spanish astronomer, *circa* 1560]. A large formation about 50 miles in diameter, close to the limb and some distance west of Adams A.

SANTBECH, +650 −356 [Dutch astronomer, *circa* 1561]. A fine crater, 44 miles in diameter, with lofty walls, rising 15,000 feet on the east but only 10,000 feet on the west, and cut by valleys on the north and south-east. There are craters on the west and the east crests. On the inner slopes are some craters, and there is much débris at their foot. On the interior is a not-quite-central hill, which lies at the south end of an ancient ring, X. On the inner east slope is the crater, A. South is the small but distinct crater E, while on the west is a small isolated mountain, M, which lies on the south rim of a very low ring, S. This ring contains a central hill. Its north wall is breached and opens into a second ring, X. The east wall of this ring is massive, and rises into a considerable peak facing Bohnenberger A. To the north-east are two craters, B and C, with others. East of B is a fine cleft, and there is a craterlet-chain some distance to the north. Wilkins found, 10 December 1934, a cleft from the south wall of Santbech to the south-east, and another cleft running north for 25 miles from the east wall. Due east is a ridge, M, and the formation G, formed of several craters fused together.

SMITH, +873 −252 [English amateur astronomer, 1874-1949]. A large ring on the west wall of Vendelinus, with craters lining its west wall. These are G, 8 and J. On the south-west crest is the crater, M. On the east, just below the crest, are some craterlets, and there is a small crater on the east crest. On the floor are some mounds, and the relics of former rings. On the outer east are two peculiar semicircular objects, with numerous craterlets on their walls and interiors. North is a confused region, with low rings and the craters G and X. To the west is a fine crater, A, with a small crater, N, on its west wall. On 4 October 1952 Wilkins, using the 25-inch 'Newall' refractor at Cambridge, saw a number of minute craterlets in this area. Farther north is another crater, and between them and slightly overlapped by A is the low ring B. There are some craters, traces of a crater-row and the deformed crater K, between B and the wall of Smith. On the south-west is an elongated depression of little depth. This is N, and is followed by a series of rings to the crater Holden F.

SNELLIUS, +719 —488 [Dutch astronomer, 1591-1626]. A great crater, 50 miles in diameter, with finely terraced walls, rising 7,500 feet, and with a small crater on the west crest. On the floor is a central hill, west of which a curved valley-cleft runs to the south wall, through which it passes. There are some crater-like objects on the inner east, and at least four craters on the floor. On the south-east, the wall has been slightly deformed by the craters 9 and 11; east of the former is the deep crater B. To the north-east is the great ring, A, with a central craterlet. On the south-west are numerous ridges and rings.

STEAVENSON, +664 —474 [celebrated contemporary English amateur astronomer]. This crater was formerly known as Reichenbach A, and is 22 miles in diameter. It contains a central peak, and there is a craterlet on the inner south-east slope, also a craterlet on the south crest where it adjoins Reichenbach. To the south-west is a curved crater-chain with short ridges, while from the north wall a strong mountain arm runs north, ending some distance south of Borda and defining the east wall of an irregular enclosure. Steavenson intrudes upon the ring B, on the east, while on the far north, east of the strong mountain arm already mentioned, are two large craters. Farther east are the low-walled ring T, and the distinct crater D, with three hills on its floor.

STEVINUS, +683 —540 [Belgian mathematician, 1548-1620]. This crater lies to the south of Snellius, and is a good example of the twin or paired craters so common on the lunar surface. It is 50 miles in diameter, with lofty and finely terraced walls rising 11,400 feet on the south but lower on the north. The inner slopes contain some craterlets on both the north and the south. On the rather dark floor are a long central mountain, a few lower hills and some mounds. There are two craterlets on the north-east portion, close to the wall, and there is another on the extreme south. Outside the south-east wall is a crater, C, while on the west is a valley, V3, with a large ring at its south end and the remains of a smaller ring on the north. The ground to the west of this valley is very complex; there are many craters, some in chains, and the craters Hase D, N, L and F. The latter crater is double. On the north a cleft, which runs along the outer west, traverses the hilly region and thence through a gap in the walls and on to the floor of Snellius. To the south of Stevinus are some craters and mountain ridges, also a small crater-chain beginning at a craterlet near the crater F and running towards C. The crater F is one of a pair of craters, the other being D, to the west of the peculiar confluent formation, C, described under Reichenbach.

VENDELINUS, +850 —275 [Belgian astronomer, 1580-1667]. This is one of the great irregular lunar formations, and forms the central component of the grand group of Langrenus, Vendelinus and Petavius. It is over 100 miles from north to south, but always appears foreshortened into an ellipse, although with somewhat square 'corners'. Vendelinus appears to have suffered considerably from erosive forces, and is in a more or less ruined condition. On the west the ring C.F.O. Smith intrudes. This ring, formerly C, is 45 miles in diameter and is described under its proper heading. On the floor of Vendelinus and east of Smith is a crater, H, with some smaller craters to the east. Elger and

M   177

Maw noted, and drew, a cleft from H which was described as running to the wall on the north. It cut through this portion of the rampart and was traced as far as the crater L, on the outer north. This cleft was doubted by R. Barker but has been seen, at least in part, by both Thornton and Haas, one with an 18-inch reflector and the other with an 18-inch refractor. Wilkins, however, could find no trace of it using power 500 on the Mt. Wilson 60-inch reflector, 17 June 1954, but discovered two delicate clefts in the neighbourhood. On the north-east wall is Lohse, and the wall from this crater towards the south is remarkably straight, although it is broken at one point by a craterlet. On the south are Holden and the large crater E, which intrudes considerably on to the interior. To the north-west of E are three craters, one being the larger of a slightly overlapping pair. On the south-east part of the floor are some small mountain masses and a few delicate craterlets. A cleft cuts through this portion of the wall, and can be traced as far as the mountain, M1, to the north of Holden B. Near the centre of the floor is a delicate ancient ring, 8, while just south of the crater H is a most delicate cleft running west from two minute pits to the west of the craterlet 12. This cleft runs to the peculiar semicircular objects, old rings or vast landslips, on the outer east slope of Smith. The outer west wall is very complex, broad and, in part, double, near Smith in particular, where it contracts owing to the depression 4. South of this is the old ring, S, containing the craterlet 3, and then the crater Holden F. On the north there is no true wall, merely a hilly tract with numerous ridges and small craters, of which L is the most distinct. The irregular formation, Lohse E, is traversed by a delicate cleft, Lohse itself being merely a crater on the north-east wall of Vendelinus. West is a plain, with craters and ridges. Some of the latter are parallel to the wall, and evidently mark the sites of rings, formerly prominent but now reduced by erosion.

There is a crater-chain flanking the west wall of Smith, while to the west of this formation, and thus of Vendelinus also, is a small elongated crater which was seen by Wilkins, using the 25-inch 'Newall' refractor, to have craterlets at both the south and north ends, a most peculiar object.

WHITAKER, +910 −480 [contemporary English astronomer]. A great crater on the south-west wall of Humboldt, with hills and craters on the floor. It is 70 miles in diameter. *Now Barnard*

WROTTESLEY, +764 −406 [English astronomer, 1798-1867]. This fine crater is easily found, as it lies close against the east wall of Petavius. The walls are lofty, attaining 8,000 feet in places, and are broken by a crater, B, on the south. There is a considerable peak on the western crest, which casts a fine shadow. On the floor are a twin-peaked central mountain about 1,700 feet in height, several mounds and two craterlets on the north. There is also a short cleft on the inner west slope. East is the crater E, also some craterlets. On the north-east the very peculiar object already mentioned under Biot, attracts attention. On the north-west are many ridges, none however of any particular height, some craters, and hills. One of these ridges marks the border of the Mare Fœcunditatis at this point. A crater-chain extends towards Snellius A. From the north wall a fine mountain ridge runs northwards, with some craters at intervals on its western side. Near its northern termination is a small, double crater. East of this ridge are some delicate craterlets, good tests for the defining power and general excellence of a telescope.

East of Wrottesley, and on the dark surface of the Mare Fœcunditatis, is a ridge through which passes a cleft from the south wall of Biot. South of this the Mare rapidly narrows, and its southern termination may be considered as indicated by some low ridges to the north of the crater Snellius B. On the west, Wrottesley is overshadowed by the great wall of Petavius, here double.

XI

This equatorial section of the western limb contains some notable objects, including the great walled-plain Langrenus and the craters Goclenius and Gutenberg, each with a system of clefts. The eastern portion is largely occupied by the dark Mare Fœcunditatis while, on the extreme north, the southern tip of the Mare Crisium is included. This coast-line of the Mare Crisium is most interesting, and consists of more or less detached mountainous masses, of great altitude, separated by winding valleys, forming an indented coast-line of interesting aspect and a magnificent view in the telescope. Among the other and smaller features are the two craters Messier and Pickering, suspected of changes in shape and visibility.

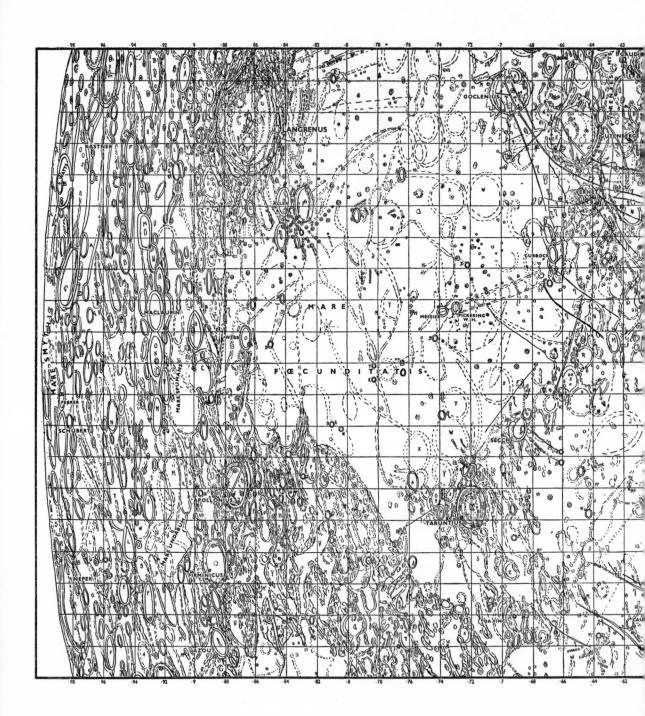

XI

ALLER, +841 −102 [contemporary Spanish astronomer]. A crater 17 miles in diameter, lying north-east of Langrenus. It is of some depth, and has a central peak. It used to be known as Langrenus K. It is one of three very similar formations, the others being Langrenus F and B.

APOLLONIUS, +872 +078 [great Greek mathematician, *circa* 220 B.C.]. A fine crater, 30 miles in diameter, with walls bearing peaks rising 5,000 feet above the floor on which are ridges, a crater on the inner north-east and a prominent diagonal ridge. On the west crest are two shallow craters. To the east is a valley, V, and beyond it three confluent craters. To the north are two central-peaked craters. Large overlapping rings lie to the west, while on the south is a large but low ring, S, and west of this is a prominent ridge running to Webb. On the south-west a crater-chain runs to the Mare Spumans. Between Apollonius and the Mare Fœcunditatis are numerous hills, depressions, mountains and craters.

AZOUT, +885 +178 [French astronomer, 1622-91]. Although only 18 miles in diameter, this is an interesting object. It has a low central mountain and two lower hills on the floor. To the south is a fine mountain arm, while on the north are a lofty ridge, and a high mountain on the border of the Mare Crisium. East is a low ring with a central hill. This ring lies on the floor of a valley running towards the Mare, and has a high mountain to the east. The floor of Azout is a dark grey. On the south, and west of the mountain arm, is the crater A, with a craterlet on its north rim. A smaller crater, B, lies to the west of A. Numerous ridges, in places of considerable altitude, are prominent under low illumination. North is the great mountain, Beta, on the shore of the Mare Crisium.

CAUCHY, +616 +166 [French mathematician, 1789-1857]. A small crater 8 miles in diameter, and remarkably bright, very conspicuous at Full. Barcroft has noted apparent variations; under low illumination it seems round and deep, but under a high sun it resembles a mountain. To the south-west is a delicate craterlet-chain. The chief interest in Cauchy lies not in the crater itself but in the two long clefts which, originating at a mountain on the west, runs eastwards, one on either side of Cauchy. There are also some low hills and craterlets in this region. The crater D lies to the north-west of cleft 1. There is a third cleft to the north-west of D, also some craterlet-chains. There is also another cleft which, unlike all the other clefts, runs from north-west to south-east. Cleft 1 throws off a short branch to the south. Just outside the south-west wall of Cauchy is a short craterlet-chain.

DA VINCI, +692 +161 [Italian genius in many fields, 1452-1519]. A ring situated to the east-north-east of the crater Taruntius, with gaps in the north and south walls and a central craterlet on a slightly marked meridional ridge. There are some craterlets on the west side of the floor. On the south-west is the crater D. The outer north slope contains two large craters, and many smaller ones. On the east, two craterlet-chains have been detected; from the more easterly a cleft runs north-east, parallel to the Cauchy cleft. There is a peculiar low-rimmed crater, Z, on the south with a crater on its east wall. Farther east is an ancient ring, M, at the south end of a wide but shallow valley which runs to the north.

FÉBRER, +987 +022 [contemporary Spanish astronomer]. A ring to the south of Schubert and on the border of the Mare Smythii.

FIRMICUS, +887 +127 [Sicilian astrologer, *circa* A.D. 330]. A crater 35 miles in diameter, with a very dark floor, which makes it easily recognizable under any conditions of illumination. There is a very low central hill, and a craterlet under the western inner wall. Outside, to the east, is a crater-chain; to the west, a narrow valley outside the wall. East of this again is another valley, which runs towards the Mare Crisium. On the west are some low-walled, dark-floored rings; also the Mare Undarum. On the eastern border of the Mare Undarum are two considerable craters, B and C, with two smaller craters, A and D, to the south. To the north-east is a mountain of some height. Closely outside the north-east wall of Firmicus is a small 'lake' of Mare material, almost as dark as Firmicus itself, and shaped like a letter F without the centre stroke.

The wall of Firmicus is highest on the west, where it rises to 4,950 feet above the sombre floor.

GAUDIBERT, +602 −188 [French selenographer, 1823-1901]. A large ring to the south-east of Gutenberg, with many ridges and craters on its interior. On the outer south-east wall are some craterlets. To the north-west is a low ring, with a crater, B, on its north border. West is a small crater, J, and beyond this the Pyrenees.

GOCLENIUS, +695 −173 [German scientist, 1572-1621]. A large crater, 32 miles in diameter, with walls rising 5,000 feet on the west but imperfect in places, especially on the south. On the inner south-east is a partial ring, open on the north, and with two hills in the gap left by the destruction of this portion of the wall. This feature was omitted by Fauth. On the floor there are also a central hill with a craterlet to the west, and a cleft which, coming from the south-west, passes through the north-east rampart and is continued beyond. Fauth showed a cleft on the inner north-west. To the north is a crater from which a cleft runs parallel to the cleft from the south-west. Fauth also shows two short clefts from the north wall, and another crossing the larger, parallel clefts. This was confirmed by Goodacre in 1927. Schmidt omits the cleft to the east. Wilkins has found another cleft to the north of the crater K.

GUTENBERG, +650 −148 [German printer, 1398-1468]. A most interesting object, about 45 miles in diameter, with an intruding ring, 14 miles in diameter, on the north-west and a smaller ring to the east. In the south wall are some gaps, and there is a craterlet on the east crest. On the floor is a central mountain, which is really part of an ancient ring, now greatly reduced by erosive forces. Fauth shows three craterlets on the summit of the central mountain, but these want confirmation. Two clefts run to the north wall, and there is another under the west wall. The craterlet-chain outside the east wall was shown as a ridge by Fauth. To the west are two low rings. On the south-east wall is the large crater A. The slope below A is broad, and divided by terraces in a most interesting manner. A fine craterlet-chain runs along the outer east wall; this is the one depicted as a ridge by Fauth. On the north-west is the intruding ring E, with a small central hill and breaks in both the east and the west walls. On the north wall, both inside and outside, are craters. A cleft from Goclenius passes close to the east and then to the north-east, cutting through a curved ridge, probably part of what was once a complete crater; on this ridge is the crater H, and thence the cleft runs to a mountain, where it ends. Beyond this barrier the cleft reappears. On the floor of Gutenberg, and adjoining E, is a very low ring, through which passes a cleft, dividing at a craterlet, one of the branches ending at the north wall; the other reappears beyond and runs north of the crater E. On the south, between the craters B and E, are some craterlet-chains, and a cleft from the ring A. A delicate cleft also crosses the southern portion of the interior, while on the outer south-west are the low rings, H and X. To the south is a considerable and rough mountain mass, and several craters. At the eastern side of the large, low ring, G, on the north, begins another cleft, which bends and eventually reaches the imperfect formation, N. Gutenberg is the focus of a minor system of roughly parallel clefts to the north, obviously a part of the great line of weakness extending from Goclenius to Hyginus.

KÄSTNER, +974 −111 [German mathematician, 1719-1800]. This name was originally given to the grey plain now called Mare Smythii, but the modern Kästner is a great ring very close to the limb, with walls broken on the south. Under the west wall is a crater, and there is another on the east. To the west is a large ring which is connected with Kästner by a pass in its east wall. East is a ring with a central hill. The wall is lowest at a point on the north-east. The large ring on the west has a smaller one on its west wall. Farther to the west, and thus close to the mean libration limb, is a mountain peak, Eta, with another, Alpha, on the north and a third, Epsilon, on the south. Abutting on the north wall of Kästner are the large crater G, and, to the south-east, the deep crater A. To the east of A is a long mountain ridge from Lapeyrouse. A row of large craters, of which D, M and N are the deepest, flank G on the east. West of G is a mountain, and there are two other peaks on the north-west and on the surface of the Mare Smythii. South-west of Kästner are some small craters and a mountain, Alpha, which is on the limb at mean libration. The floor of Kästner appears quite smooth except for a ridge running from the north wall towards the centre, and two low peaks on the inner south, noted by Moore on 9 August 1949, with a 6-inch refractor. East is the crater F, and north of it is a long valley-like depression, V. This is flanked by large craters on the north. The crater F is almost surrounded by craters and long ridges, on the south, as far as the crater Lapeyrouse F. Where the large crater, B, joins Kästner, and in the gap in their walls, are two small craters, shown by Goodacre and confirmed by Wilkins. Further observations will, doubtless, result in the detection of other features.

LANGRENUS, +863 −155 [Belgian selenographer, 1600-75]. This majestic object, 85 miles in diameter, is a most imposing object despite its unfavourable position near the limb. The walls rise 9,000 feet high on the east; the inner slopes are divided by a series of narrow terraces and are broken also into a valley skirting the outer glacis. The inner slopes are broad, while the outer slopes are complex with many craterlet-chains on the immediate surroundings. On the floor is a bright, twin-peaked central mountain; the most western peak rises 3,300 feet. On the southern portion are some hills and a buried ring on the south. The walls are prolonged on the south. From a craterlet at the foot of the north wall a cleft runs to the north. Wilkins found a duplicate cleft on the south, 6 December 1937. To the east is an isolated hill. On the west is a ring, B, with a central hill, one of several similar craters. A triple-peaked mountain often appears in profile on the limb. West of Langrenus is a plain extending to the limb, with a crater at the north end.

To the south-west of Langrenus is a crater, M, close to a larger ring. R. W. Potts, of Cambridge, found extraordinary shadow effects in M near sunrise. As the sun rises on the crater, the whole of the interior becomes bright except for the central portion, which preserves a dark circular spot, filled with shadow. This slowly diminishes for a few days. The interior of M appears to be funnel-shaped and of considerable depth. When the comparatively small floor is at length free from shadow, it appears as a small, dark grey plain. The appearances mentioned have, in part, been confirmed by Haas and Wilkins.

R. M. Baum saw, 28 August 1948, a long, bluish mountain mass on the limb to the south-west.

The outer south slopes of Langrenus are very complex, with numerous ridges, craters, craterlet-chains and pits, and this complexity also extends along the west wall, where are craters and a fine valley, V. To the north this rough surface broadens, with ridges and craterlet-chains running to the three craters, B, F and Aller, on the north-east. All these craters possess central mountains and are connected, on the north, by a series of craterlets, B and F being connected by a craterlet-chain. Farther east is G, and south-east of it the crater A. From the middle of the east rampart of Langrenus a delicate cleft, in part craterlet-chain, runs north towards Aller. West of Aller and due north of Langrenus, is the small crater C. On the far west are the craters K, 1, G and G1, the last two forming an overlapping pair. Still farther west, towards Kästner, are the imperfect formations H and F, which lie at the south of a long valley, V, which can be traced almost as far as Maclaurin. In addition, there are numerous other formations around Langrenus, some of considerable interest and importance, which may be identified from the map.

LA PEYROUSE, +956 −185 [French navigator, 1741-1788]. A large ring, with a ridge in the centre of the floor and a crater on the southern portion. The floor is also crossed by a delicate cleft, and there are some hills and a delicate crater-chain on the east wall. To the north-east is a bright crater, A, with a markedly bright hill near by. West is a deep ring, containing a central hill and a crater, while on the east is the large crater F, with a still larger crater B to its east. From the north-east wall of La Peyrouse runs a row of four craters, the furthermost being lettered A. Ridges tending to the north-west connect with Kästner. (Name omitted from map.)

LUBBOCK, +666 −068 [English mathematician, 1803-65]. A bright crater, 8 miles in diameter, situated on the north rim of an older ring. To the west is a small mountain mass, while on the north is a rocky surface and a small crater. Two parallel clefts begin here, and run north-east towards the crater M. The ancient ring to the south of Lubbock has the fragments of others on the east, from which issues another cleft connected with the Goclenius system. A little to the east of this long cleft is another, which passes through a craterlet, and then continues for a few miles to the south. These clefts are crossed by another, which runs to a low-walled enclosure, G, on the interior of which are a low ring and some mounds. To the east of Lubbock is the peculiar object, N, a double crater with another, F, on its south. Between Lubbock and N are several craterlet-chains. The well-known twin ray from Messier and Pickering nearly reaches Lubbock.

MACLAURIN, +927 −033 [Scottish mathematician, 1698-1746]. This is a 30-mile crater with a concave floor, and some faint detail on the interior. It has overlapped an older ring on the east, while on the south is the crater A, and north the larger, K, with a hill and a crater on its floor. Maclaurin is really one of a remarkable series or chain of craters which extends from the west of Langrenus to the Mare Undarum. On the west is the crater H, and north of it a most peculiar object, being the remains of a once-perfect crater, C. The eastern wall is of great thickness and considerable altitude, but most of the west wall has disappeared, and the crater now opens into the Mare Spumans. East of C, and between it and Webb, is a long craterlet-chain.

MESSIER, +738 −033 [French astronomer, 1730-1817]. A deep crater, 9 miles in diameter, forming the more westerly of a pair, the other being W. H. Pickering. It is situated on a light-streak, and is elliptical from east to west, with gaps in both the south and north walls. The latter was seen as a craterlet by Arthur Mee. The western wall is higher than the eastern. Arthur Mee also detected a ridge connecting Messier and Pickering. There are many craterlets in the neighbourhood. Pickering found striking changes in both craters which he ascribed to surrounding patches of hoar-frost. (See Pickering, W. H.) Changes do occur, but the Authors regard them as due to optical effects only.

NEPER, +980 +155 [Scottish mathematician, 1550-1617]. A great and important crater, very close to the limb; the west wall at times actually lies on the limb. It is 70 miles in diameter, with terraced walls of great height, 10,000 feet in places and cut through on north and south by valley-clefts. On the inner east slope are two craters; and there is a central hill, bearing a summit crater, and this peak is part of a mountain ridge traversing the floor. There are also some small hills, or cones, and a craterlet on the west. To the west are three peaks, sometimes seen in grand profile on the limb, and situated on the averted hemisphere. On the outer west wall is a deep valley, beyond which is a large ring, rarely well seen, while to the south-west is the crater R. East of Neper are many craters; of these F, P and L are the most prominent and lie at the northern end of the Mare Undarum.

PICKERING, W. H., +730 −035 [American astronomer, 1858-1938]. This crater, which is the companion to Messier, is elliptical from north to south, and there is a break in the north wall. On the east is a small attached ring. Within Pickering are two ridges, one from the south wall and the other from the north wall; between their ends, and in the centre, are three low hills. There is also some object on the east. From Pickering two light-streaks run, in a gentle curve, to the north of Lubbock, somewhat resembling the tail of a comet. Between these streaks Goodacre found the relics of five once-prominent craters, that on the east has the remains of a central hill. These have not however been confirmed by the Authors. Mädler thought Messier and Pickering alike, both in size and shape. Prof. W. H. Pickering, however, found that this similarity only exists at nine days after sunrise, Pickering being the larger near sunset and immediately after sunrise, but Messier appears to be the larger three days after sunrise. These changes are easily verified even with a small telescope. South of Pickering Klein found four pits, or perhaps only light spots. Wilkins and Moore have seen both Messier and Pickering very dark under a moderate angle of illumination.

SCHUBERT, +987 +047 [Russian scientist, 1789-1865]. A crater, 46 miles in diameter, with low walls and a smooth floor, except for a small crater. To the west is the Mare Smythii and east some ridges and the bright crater A. There are some little peaks on the east wall. South is Fébrer, and south-east the crater E. To the east are the craters N, D and F, and a chain of craterlets.

SECCHI, +689 +042 [Italian Jesuit astronomer, 1818-78]. A bright crater, with a break in the south wall, east of which is a small ring with a central hill. To the south-west is a long, delicate cleft, and south of this is another from a small mountain towards Pickering. On the south-east is a low ring, from which a long cleft runs south, and crosses the two mentioned in connection with Lubbock. On the floor of Secchi is a low ring on the inner east. To the north are what appear to be fragments of an old ring. L. F. Ball found, 2 May 1949, two valley-clefts, in part a crater-row, from the east wall, both ending in small craters, A and B respectively. Beyond these craters are the craters F and E, and two mountains. A third short crater-chain to the west of the two clefts was omitted by Goodacre.

SMYTHII, MARE, +995 −030 [English admiral and astronomer, 1788-1865]. A plain on the west limb, brought completely into view by favourable libration, when the east wall appears continuous but low in the centre, where are some craters. West of Schubert are two elongated depressions. On the south the border extends west of Kästner. On the surface are ridges, craters, craterlets, hills and obscure rings. The first detailed chart was produced by E. F. Emley (B.A.A. Journal, 47, 4), and subsequent charts have been made by Wilkins and by K. W. Abineri. Under high lighting many bright spots and light areas appear, probably hills or else crater-cones, on the walls of ringed-plains. Burrell, Barker and L. F. Ball have found periodic changes in brightness. The west border of Mare Smythii is occasionally visible in profile on the limb, with several rounded peaks, which may well be the nearer walls of ringed-plains permanently hidden from view.

SPUMANS, MARE, +910 +020. The 'Foaming Sea'. A somewhat ill-defined plain to the west of Mare Fœcunditatis, with a great bay, C, on its east, and four considerable rings, K, P, M and Maclaurin, on its west.

TARUNTIUS, +722 +092 [Roman philosopher, *circa* 86 B.C.]. This crater is 38 miles in diameter, with narrow walls rising to 3,500 feet above the concave floor. The floor is of exceptional interest, as it contains a complete inner ring—a good example of what F. H. Thornton has called 'concentric crater' formation. Moore (1 January 1952, $12\frac{1}{2}$-inch reflector) saw this 'inner ring' as much darker than the rest of the floor.

Taruntius has been closely studied by A. P. Lenham, who has recorded a number of hills and ridges on the floor, as well as a hill very closely north-east of the central mountain. On the central mountain itself Gaudibert discovered a summit craterlet, confirmed by Lamèch; and south-west of the central heights Wilkins has found a dark area.

The walls are crowned by several craterlets; there are three to the north-east, one to the east, one to the south-east, and two craterlets and a hill along the western wall, discovered by Lenham, who has also seen three bright spots on the west wall, each with rays extending westwards.

There are many landslips around the gentle outer slopes, with landswells and narrow ridges. To the west lie several rings, from which area a delicate cleft runs to the mountainous region south of the Palus Somnii. South of Taruntius is a pair of overlapping rings, K and L; farther south, on the Mare, are some large, low-walled rings, W, X, Y and T.

UNDARUM, MARE, +927 +122. The 'Sea of Waves'. A dark area west of Apollonius and Firmicus, with the remains of old rings, M, R, S, on the south, and the craters B and C on the north. The floor contains many old rings now almost obliterated by lava. Mare Undarum can be found without difficulty under high lighting, as it then appears very dark.

VERNET, +644 −103 [Contemporary Spanish astronomer]. This broken but quite conspicuous formation lies north-east of Gutenberg, and was formerly known as Gutenberg G. It is 21 miles in diameter. On 26 September 1953 Moore drew it under good conditions with the 25-inch 'Newall' refractor at Cambridge University Observatory, recording a rounded central mountain, five hills and an old ring on the floor, as well as a number of ridges, and four craterlets in the wall—two on the inner west, and two on the north-eastern crest. The wall is highest in the north-west, where closely outside the glacis there is a decided drop in ground-level. Two parallel ridges pass right through the southern part of Vernet.

There are many clefts in this area, particularly in the areas to the south and east of Vernet. These are described with Gutenberg.

WATTS, +988 −114 [contemporary American selenographer]. This crater was formerly known as Kästner B, and is described under that heading.

WEBB, +866 −016 [English clergyman and amateur astronomer, 1806-85]. A bright crater 14 miles in diameter, with a rather dark floor upon which stands a central hill. There is a crater on the north wall. Webb stands at the end of a long ridge, flanked by a crater-chain. To the south is the crater H, and to the east are two more craters, D and B. There are also some old rings and low-walled depressions. Moore has found that it is the centre of a system of somewhat short and inconspicuous rays.

XII

This section includes the Mare Crisium, one of the most interesting of the smaller lunar 'seas'. Among the ringed-plains are Cleomedes, Gauss and Geminus. The section also includes the brilliant crater-ring Proclus, the centre of a ray system and which exhibits peculiar bands on the inner slopes. On the limb to the south-west of the Mare Crisium is a dark plain, known as the Mare Marginis but described in Section XI since the greater portion lies within that section. The most prominent of the ringed-plains is Cleomedes, but the largest is Gauss, which but for its foreshortened appearance near the limb would be one of the most imposing objects on the entire lunar surface.

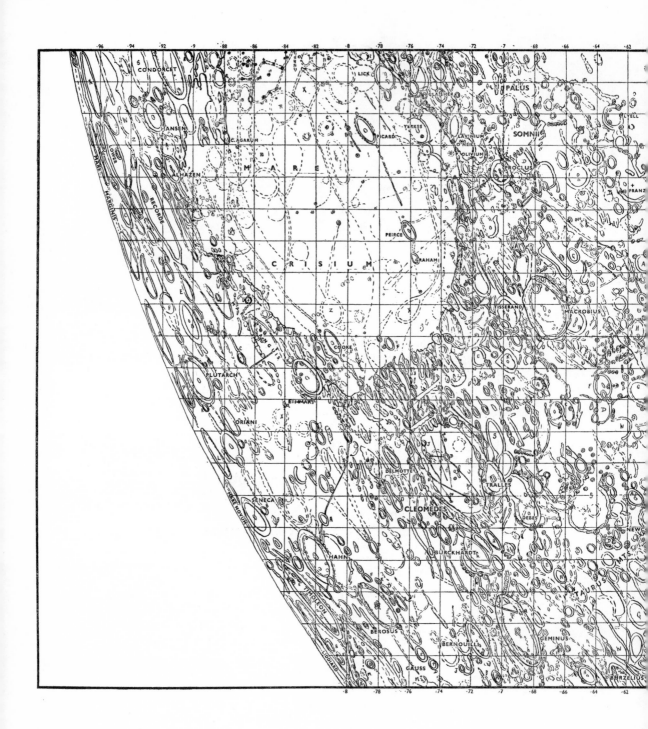

XII

AGARUM, PROM, +878 +258. A cape, projecting into the Mare Crisium on the south-west. On the summit, which is broad, are two craters and some shallow depressions. There are several peaks, and the highest, on the west, rises 11,000 feet above the level of the dark plain. On the west of Agarum is a wide bay, on the surface of which is an ancient ring. From the extremity of the cape a ridge runs northwards, following the contour of the 'coast-line', and there is another a short distance to the east. At the extreme end of the cape, and high above the Mare, is a minute craterlet which would make a magnificent vantage-point to survey the glorious outline of the 'coast', gleaming white in the sunshine and presenting a strong contrast with the dark, almost level plain far below. On several occasions, a mist-like appearance has been witnessed near Agarum, especially when the Mare is bisected by the terminator under sunrise illumination. Wilkins has seen a similar effect in the bay to the west. Neison says that the maximum brightness of Agarum is eight degrees, on a scale of 0 for shadow and 10 for pure white.

ALHAZEN, +914 +275 [Arab mathematician, A.D. 987-1038]. A small ringed-plain close to the western border of the Mare Crisium, with terraced walls and a central mountain on the floor, which also contains some lesser hills. South of Alhazen is an obscure ring, A, connecting it with Hansen. On the west is a large ring with low walls, now called Recorde, and there are others nearer the limb. This is not the object originally called Alhazen by Schröter, which appears to have been a low-lying tract to the west of a prominent mountain mass on the western border of the Mare. Schröter described this as having a dark floor, and it is possible that its hue has changed since his time.

ANGUIS, MARE, +830 +330 to +870 +430. The 'Serpent Sea'. A long, valley-like depression close to Mare Crisium, and described under that heading.

BERNOUILLI, +716 +571 [after two Dutch brothers: Jacques, 1654-1705, and Jean, 1667-1748. Both mathematicians.] A fine crater, 25 miles in diameter, with lofty walls, rising 13,000 feet on the west and 11,000 feet on the east. On the floor are two hills, not shown by Mädler, Neison or Elger. Schmidt and Andĕl show one hill. To the west is a low ring, while there are three hills on the inner east and a craterlet on the northern portion of the floor. On the outer west are several old rings, and, beyond, the crater, J. South are other old rings, the east wall of one being an extension of the south-east wall of Bernouilli itself. North is the crater, B, and other rings.

BEROSUS, +781 +548 [Chaldæan astronomer, circa 250 B.C.]. This large formation has beautifully terraced walls, rising 10,000 feet. On the inner west is a landslip. There are two low hills near the centre. On the north-east crest is a crater, and there is a narrow valley on the south. To the east is a bright plain, and four large craters. These are E, D, A and B, the latter with a central hill. To the north-west is the wall of Gauss. There is a large, low ring on the north-east part of the floor of Berosus, and also evidences of small landslips along the inner west wall in addition to the great one.

BERZELIUS, +622 +597 [Swedish chemist, 1779-1848]. A crater, 24 miles in diameter, with low walls and a low central hill. The floor is dark, and contains a craterlet as well as the central peak. On the west is the crater, H, with a central hill; north is a small crater, E. Between Berzelius and H is a strong mountain ridge, and, on the south, the low rings, R and W. On the south-east is a large low ring, with very fragmentary and broken walls.

BURCKHARDT, +717 +516 [German astronomer, 1773-1825]. A peculiar ring, 35 miles in diameter, on the north-west of Cleomedes, the walls on the west and east being bounded by curved mountain ridges, possibly the remains of once-complete rings which existed prior to the formation of Burckhardt. The walls are lofty, rising 13,000 feet on the east. On the outer north slope are some small craters. On the floor is a nearly central hill, also a crescent-shaped ridge under the west wall and two craterlets on the south-west. Schmidt shows a cleft on the inner east, and another from the centre to the north-west wall, confirmed by Wilkins. On the south-east is the crater A, and west a crater, B; this crater has a craterlet at the northern end of its floor. On the outer west is a peculiar elongated depression, apparently a ring overlapped by Burckhardt. There are craters outside its west wall. There is also a crater-chain on the west.

CLEOMEDES, +730 +460 [Greek astronomer, *circa* 50 B.C.]. A great ring, over 80 miles in diameter, with very massive walls, attaining, on the east, 9,000 feet above the interior, and 8,500 feet on the west. On the south crest is a crater, to the west of which is a narrow pass which widens into a valley running eventually into the Mare Crisium. Some distance to the south of the ringed-plain is a shallow valley, which is roughly parallel to the border. On the east of the crater, C, is a ring from which the wall, here lofty, unbroken and terraced, extends to Tralles, which has intruded slightly upon the interior of Cleomedes. The west wall contains some large depressions near the crest, and midway is a large mass, probably a landslip; the crest of the wall above it extends southwards for some distance. On the inner slopes is a deep ravine.

The interior is distinctly convex, and contains much detail. North-east of the centre is an elongated mountain mass, divided into three peaks. On this mountain Schmidt shows two craterpits, very delicate objects. A little to the north-west is a craterlet and, on the south, the crater, B, with a smaller under the west wall, and between them a low ring. South of B is a craterlet, with another on the floor close to the south slope. There are other craters on the south-west. Near the north inner slope is a group of craters, of which the pair A, on the west are the deepest; east of the pair is a large shallow ring

194

with a craterlet on its north and another on the west. To the west and south Goodacre found craterlets.

Molesworth found a system of clefts on the floor, one of which, running from A to the west slope, is not difficult, and appears as a white line under high illumination. Other clefts found by Molesworth run from the central mountain to the crater B, and also to the north-east wall; traverse the low ring to the west of B; one runs north from the crater under the west wall. Wilkins has confirmed several of these clefts, but they are at all times very delicate objects. There is also a low ring on the east, discovered by Wilkins, and a craterlet two diameters of B to the south-west, with another on the north-east.

The crater group of which A is a member was first seen by Schröter, who thought that the crater A was formed during the epoch of his observations, since he sometimes saw, especially in the early part of his career, its site occupied by a mountain ridge. A similar appearance has since been seen by other observers, Wilkins among them. There is no doubt that these apparent changes are due solely to the varying angle of illumination.

Outside the west wall is a crater, E, with a central hill, and west of this is a large mountain mass, with a smaller to the south. On the north of this mountain is a double crater, while outside the east wall is a large plateau bearing craters on its summit, divided by valleys and separated from the crest of Cleomedes by a broad glacis, arranged in terraces. West of Cleomedes is a large and bright plain. The crater E is now called Delmotte.

CONDORCET, +917 +211 [French mathematician, 1743-94]. A large ring, 45 miles in diameter, to the south-west of the Mare Crisium. The floor is convex, while the walls, which are terraced, rise 8,000 feet. Schmidt shows a craterlet on the floor at the foot of the inner south wall. On the floor is some faint detail; apparently a faint central hill, a craterlet on the south-west and a cleft running from west to south-east at the southern end. This cleft, which was first noted by Wilkins, has been seen by Lenham, 29 February 1952, and again by Wilkins and Moore on 3 October 1952, with the 25-inch 'Newall' refractor at Cambridge. Lenham has also detected the following: Some ridges on the eastern portion, and a pit on the south-east slope. H. Hill has found a minute craterlet close to the inner south, and a terrace on the west. The crater, B, between Condorcet and Hansen, he has noted as a hill; he also records two depressions on the outer west.

COOKE, +810 +382 [English amateur astronomer, 1886-   ]. This crater was for- *Eimmart C* merly known as Eimmart C, and is situated on the north-western portion of the Mare Crisium. It is 14 miles in diameter, but the walls are very low, so that it is only well seen under low illumination. The floor is of the same tint as the surrounding plain, and there is a small central hill. From the north wall a ridge connects Cooke with a small mountain mass near the border of the 'sea'. West is the partial ring, B, open on the north, and with a small crater adjoining it on the south. North of B are three craters in a line. On the south is a faintly marked buried ring, Z, and some 60 miles to the east the crater F, with two smaller craters on its west.

CRISIUM, MARE, +816 +287. The 'Sea of Crises'. One of the smaller of the lunar 'seas', but probably the most interesting, and the most beautiful in the telescope. In fact, the Mare presents a charming picture unique among the lunar formations. It is visible to the naked eye as a small dark oval spot. Although it is elliptical in shape, with the major axis from east to west, it appears, owing to foreshortening, as a strongly oval spot, with the greatest extension from north to south. Its dark grey surface, slightly tinged with green, especially at Full, is very deeply depressed in comparison with the bright mountainous surface outside. The area is 66,000 sq. miles, or 1/94th of the entire visible surface. Neison considered it as the deepest of all the 'seas', and is probably correct. In the crescent it is the first prominent spot to be revealed, for the same reason it is the first spot to disappear after Full. A day or two after Full is the best time for observation.

From the south-west border a strongly marked promontory, the Cape Agarum, intrudes upon the surface. The highest peak in this region rises 11,000 feet. West of Agarum is the deep bay extending to the north-east of Condorcet. From Agarum, a long ridge runs concentric with the somewhat low and indefinite western border of the Mare, as far as the ring Cooke. Midway along its course this ridge passes a little to the east of some isolated hills, which in their turn lie a little to the east of a mountain mass on the Mare. The border at this point consists of a chain of crater-like depressions. From the isolated hills the ridge increases in altitude as it runs to the north.

The western border from this point is well marked, with several high peaks and mountain masses. Under a high light a long and narrow valley-like depression, the Mare Anguis, lines the outer border to Eimmart, conspicuous as a dark, contorted streak.

On the north the border consists of a broad, gently sloping plateau, divided by wide passes, the whole sloping upwards to the high ground south and south-east of Cleomedes. From this point the eastern border is well marked, with peaks rising over 13,000 feet, but one peak to the south-east of Picard rises 15,600 feet. The east border is divided by narrow valleys, to a peak west of which, on the open plain, are several small but, in part, lofty mountains, "islands as it were" (Webb).

Midway along the east border is a narrow pass leading into a ruined ring, F, with a small central hill on which is a summit craterlet. The southern promontory of this ring is called the Prom. Lavinium and the northern cape Olivium. From the former the border is lofty and continuous towards the south, with some craters on the crest, and ends on the far south in a bold headland. West of this is a strong mountain mass, a, projecting on to the Mare.

The southern border was defined by Neison as a most interesting coast-line, consisting of detached mountain masses of roughly triangular shape, separated by narrow winding valleys which extend for many miles into the hilly southern highlands. On a mountain mass, Beta, on the south-west, is the ring Azout (Section XI), east of which is a wide valley, V, and farther east, two sharp promontories, the intervening bay rapidly narrowing on the south. Between these two mountain arms is a low ring, found by Goodacre.

5a, 5b, 5c. Region from Pontanus to the South Pole, as photographed by Lyle T. Johnson in 1954 under three different conditions of illumination

6b. The Mare Crisium. Photograph by E. A. Whitaker, Greenwich Observatory

6a. The Limb Region of Mare Smythii. Photograph by E. A. Whitaker, Greenwich Observatory

The surface of the Mare Crisium is by no means uniform in tint. Under a high light a greenish hue has been noticed, with many minute bright spots and delicate white lines. These, together with the wonderful fan-like rays emanating from Proclus, make the north-east portion appreciably lighter than the rest of the surface.

The largest ringed-plain on the Mare is Picard, with bright walls, rising 5,000 feet above the depressed floor on which is a small central hill. In contact with the south wall of this 21-mile crater is a minute craterlet. About 40 miles to the west is a large but very shallow depression with a central craterlet, first noted by Gaudibert; the whole appearing as a white spot. Invisible at sunrise it makes its appearance when the solar altitude reaches 15 degrees and increases in size until just before Full, after which it decreases again. It also sometimes decreases in size during the progress of a lunar eclipse. Thornton (1953: 18-inch reflector) has found that this feature is actually a low dome crowned by a minute, deep pit, so that it bears a striking resemblance to the modern Linné. East of Picard is a long ridge, very variable in altitude and concentric with the border, curving west and ending in a large, very shallow spoon-shaped ring, evidently a partly-buried crater-ring.

Beyond this ridge, and east of Picard, is an obscure ring, Yerkes, its western wall having disappeared; on the interior is a low central mound. Small and shallow rings extend north of it to the mountain border of the Mare. South of Yerkes are a craterlet, a low ring and another obscure ring, Lick, with a large central hill traversed by cross clefts. Between Picard and Lick are three short clefts, found by Molesworth in 1896, the only clefts but one yet discovered on the surface of the plain.

After Picard the second largest ringed-plain is Peirce, to the north, and 10 miles in diameter, with steep, bright walls rising to a thin crest 7,000 feet above the interior, on which is a small central hill and a minute craterlet on the inner south-west, found by Schmidt and rarely seen. It is in every sense, a 'test object'.

On the south-western portion of the Mare is a peculiar trapezium, formed of ridges, with craterlets on their crests or flanks. This diamond-shaped feature was first traced in its entirety by Barker, and there are some craterlets on its interior. A curved ridge connects its eastern corner with the mountain border of the Mare, and immediately east of this ridge, which is low, Wilkins discovered a cleft of corresponding contour, deep and sharp where it issues forth from the mountains, with a lofty mountain on either side, but gradually becoming very delicate as it approaches the 'trapezium'. It was discovered, 4 October 1952, with the 30-inch reflector belonging to Dr. W. H. Steavenson. Altogether about eighty objects have been found on the surface. Hill shows forty in a drawing (B.A.A. Memoirs, 36, 3); Baum, Moore, Hutchings and Barker have detected others. In a chart based on observations made with a 6-inch refractor (B.A.A. Journal: 59, 150–1949), Moore records seventy-seven objects in an area shown as practically blank by Schmidt and Goodacre, which has led to the suggestion of some alterations in the region. West of the trapezium is a smaller replica of it, also with craterlets on its banks, discovered by Barker; this is an extremely difficult object.

Down the centre of the Mare extends a longitudinal ridge, ending, on the south, at the trapezium.

Near the north-west border is Cooke, and from its north wall runs a short but strongly marked mountain ridge. A long ridge also runs to the east of Peirce and Graham, ending on the north in a peculiar lagoon-like, very shallow, depression, an old and now almost completely buried ring.

Scattered over the surface of the Mare are several craterlets and numerous low ridges. Several of these ridges appear as arcs of circles, doubtless the relics of buried rings, described and figured by C. F. O. Smith. Several observers, including Schröter, have detected occasional obscurations or changes; Schröter noted 'changes' in aspect amongst the group of isolated mountains near the east border which changes he ascribed to the effects of a lunar atmosphere of limited extent.

The Mare Crisium was shown on some of the photographs taken by the Russian vehicle Lunik III in October 1959. At this time the rocket was between 30,000 and 40,000 miles on the far side of the Moon. The outline of the Mare is quite unmistakable, and comparison of the Lunik pictures with those obtained from Earth is very significant.

DEBES, +686 +480 [German cartographer, 1840-1923]. A ring to the north-east of Tralles, formed by the fusion of two rings, with hills and ridges on the interior and craterlets near the centre. The east wall is of 'hour-glass' shape. On the outer east is a crater, while on the north are small craters and hills. Of the craters the most prominent are E and F. Just outside the north-west wall of Debes is a small mountain, with a larger mass on its north-west.

DELMOTTE, +772 +456 [French selenographer, 1876-   ]. A small ring to the west of Cleomedes, with a central ridge and low walls. On the west is a mountain mass, Gamma, with another, Beta, on the south. On the south-east are many hills rather than mountains. A narrow plain separates Delmotte from the west wall of Cleomedes. On the north is another ring about three-quarters the size of Delmotte.

EIMMART, +826 +406 [German amateur astronomer, 1638-1705]. A ringed-plain about 25 miles in diameter, with lofty, peak-sprinkled walls, rising 10,000 feet on the east and broken on the west by a small crater. On the floor is a small central peak, also some mounds and a craterlet under the south-west rim. East of Eimmart is a ridge bordering the Mare Crisium, and beyond is the Mare itself. South is the narrow plain of the Mare Anguis, and north, on the border of a hilly district, are two craters, A and B. West of Eimmart Wilkins has seen a short cleft which cuts through a mountain ridge.

FRANZ, +617 +285 [German astronomer, 1847-1913]. A large but low-rimmed and imperfect formation on the eastern border of the Palus Somnii, with a wide gap in its south wall. To the west is the crater, B, while on the south-west a wide valley runs to Lyell.

GAUSS, +789 +592 [German mathematician, 1777-1855]. One of the largest of the mountain walled-plains, 110 miles in diameter with lofty walls. Schröter styled it 'Mercurius Falsus' and he drew it in his *Selenotopographische Fragmente*, Vol. 2, T. LVIII and T. LXXI. This sketch shows a central and other hills, a crater under the south-west wall and a pit on the east.

At the south the walls are continued for some distance, bordering a wide valley. Elger shows this partly filled with hillocks; he also shows a mountain mass on the interior of Gauss opposite the entrance to the valley. The east wall is crowned with little peaks and is terraced on the inner slopes; those on the north being especially prominent. The inner west slope is broad, with some evidences of landslips, and is broken by a large crater, A. On the floor of Gauss is a fine central mountain, and a little to the east of it is a large, shallow crater, B. A delicate ridge extends south from the central peak to another shallow crater. Between this and the south-west wall is a smaller ring with very white walls, but of no great height. To the north of the central peak are some isolated hillocks, part of a discontinuous ridge. One of these consists of two curved parts of a discontinuous ridge. Moore (12½-inch reflector, 1 January 1953) noted that the central peak and longitudinal ridge enclose, in part, a darker area, to the west, which seems to be an old ring occupying nearly half the total floor of Gauss. One of the ridges consists of two curved fragments, relics of an ancient ring. North-east of Gauss is a mountain. On the north is a large enclosure, while on the north-west, and close to the limb, is the ring Paluzie, with the great ring Liddiard beyond.

On the inner west slope is a large abutting ring, shown in a beautiful drawing by Elger, 20 October 1888. Arthur has seen three craterlets on the west wall and one on the floor; all the craters are shallow.

The central mountain ridge expands, in the centre, into a considerable peak and, on the north, it divides at a small crater. There is still much work to be done before our knowledge of Gauss and its neighbourhood is complete.

GEMINUS, +690 +565 [Greek astronomer, *circa* 70 B.C.]. A beautiful crater, 55 miles in diameter, with broad, richly-terraced walls, rising 16,000 feet on the west and 12,000 feet on the east and descending in a gentle slope to the interior, which lies 15,000 feet below the western crest (on which is a small crater). In the centre of the crater is a rounded hill with a craterlet on its summit; this was omitted by Schmidt. North of it is a craterlet, omitted by Goodacre. On the southern part is a craterpit, while on the east is a low ridge. A ravine crosses the floor near the south end and there is another on the north. The ravine or cleft on the south continues beyond the walls, and can be traced as far as the crater Burckhardt.

Geminus is surrounded by hills and craters. A fine craterlet-chain runs to the south-east, and is bordered by a ridge on the east. On the south-west are the two craters, C and D, while on the north-west is the crater K, a peculiar and very low-walled enclosure.

Bordering the north-east wall is a crater-row, while on the south-east are a low ring and the craters, E, R and J, with many smaller rings. The hills here form part of the Taurus Mountains. Along the outer east glacis is a chain of shallow depressions.

GLAISHER, +740 +228 [English meteorologist, 1809-1903]. A ring within the mountainous border on the south-east of the Mare Crisium, and 10 miles in diameter. On the south is a larger ring with a craterlet on its south. This ring is connected by a ridge to the well-known depression south of the Prom. Lavinium. East of the ridge stretches the golden-coloured Palus Somnii.

GRAHAM, +751 +331 [nineteenth-century English astronomer]. This crater was formerly known as Peirce A, and is described under that heading. (In the I.A.U. list, Graham was referred to as Peirce B.)

HAHN, +820 + 518 [German astronomer, 1741-1805]. A fine regular ring, 45 miles in diameter, on the far west of Cleomedes, with bright, peak-sprinkled walls, lowest on the west, the formation appearing breached when on the evening terminator. The inner slopes are faintly terraced, while on the interior is a central mountain of considerable length. On the outer north wall is a pair of craters, on the south a shallow depression from which a chain of irregular depressions tends south-south-east. On the south-east is a crater, A. From this a delicate cleft runs towards Hahn. To the west, and close to the limb is a large walled-plain, formerly marked A, but now known as Timoleon. This presents many points of resemblance to Gauss, and contains craters and a discontinuous central ridge.

HANSEN, +926 +242 [Danish astronomer, 1795-1874]. A small but perfect ring to the north-west of Condorcet, separated from Alhazen by a low ring. The inner slopes are terraced, and on the floor is a low central hill, also some mounds. On the south-west is the bright crater, A, and south-east the larger crater, B. On the south is a large, low-walled crater, S, while on the east lies the border of the Mare Crisium. To the west are some large but low rings; of these Recorde W and Z are the most prominent.

INCOGNITO, MARE. The 'Unknown Sea'. Invisible at mean libration. A plain on the further hemisphere, the extreme border of which is only just visible under most favourable conditions of libration. It lies to the west of Gauss. To the south is a crater, G, and also the ring Liddiard. Light rays converge to a point west of it, suggesting a ray-crater which is for ever concealed. It was discovered by Wilkins.

LAVINIUM, PROM., +734 +259. The southern cape of a little bay on the eastern border of the Mare Crisium, really the remains of an old ring, with a breach in its western wall. On the summit of the cape is a craterlet. To the south is an elongated depression.

LICK, +774 +220 [American millionaire and founder of the Lick Observatory, 1796-

1876]. The remains of a ring, almost submerged beneath the surface of the Mare Crisium, and abutting on the south-eastern border, which has slightly intruded upon Lick. There is a crater on its north rim, and some very low mounds on the interior which has evidently been overwhelmed by the once-plastic matter which now forms the surface of the 'sea'. Lick is 21 miles in diameter. Between Lick and Picard is a short cleft, while to the west of it is the relic of a very low ring. Between Lick and Yerkes is another low ring, with a craterlet on its western rim.

LIDDIARD, +810 +584 [English electrical engineer, 1894-   ]. A great walled-plain, 100 miles in diameter, with a mountain in the centre. Peaks on the walls sometimes appear in profile on the limb. The inner slopes are terraced, with evidences of landslips in places. At the outer south end is a small crater and a curved ridge running towards Seneca. West is a plain, called the Mare Incognito and wholly situated on the normally averted hemisphere; east is the ring Paluzie, and south-east Timoleon. Lenham has found a prominent small crater between Liddiard and Paluzie. It is on the limb at mean libration but can only be fully seen under extreme libration of the north-western limb. Between it and Timoleon is a crater, and there are two craters, H and K, close to the wall of Gauss.

LOWER, +950 +269 [English selenographer, circa 1610]. A crater, 50 miles in diameter, near the limb, and with walls of moderate height. On the floor is a crater at the east end. To the south is the large ring, X, and west the craters, F and G.

LYELL, +629 +241 [Scottish geologist, 1797-1875]. An old ring on the eastern border of the Palus Somnii, and south of Franz. There is a gap in its south-east wall, with a crater on either side, while on the interior are three hills near the western wall. Some distance to the south-west is the crater A. Lyell is about 26 miles in diameter.

MACROBIUS, +674 +363 [Greek grammarian, circa A.D. 400]. This beautiful walled-plain is easily found at Full, owing to the brightness of the walls. It is 42 miles in diameter, with terraced walls rising 13,000 feet on the west and not much inferior on the east, on the crest of which is the crater, A. This is also bright at Full. At the foot of the wall below A is a row of hillocks. The inner slopes are everywhere terraced; on the west large masses have slid down to the interior, on which is a compound, double-peaked central mountain, and several hills to its north. On the inner south is a large but very shallow ring, and on the inner south-west a curved ridge, probably the remains of another old ring. On the north-west the crest of the wall is broken, and here is a pass which leads into a valley. A ravine runs along the outer west wall and is bordered by the crater Tisserand, with a crater on its west wall. North is the crater F. Several irregular depressions exist to the north-east, while on the east are many craters, depressions and ridges. These fill the space between Maraldi and Römer. The floor is occasionally very dark.

MARGINIS, MARE. +943 +152. 'Border Sea'. A plain on the west limb of the Moon, extending from Neper northwards, thus south-west of the Mare Crisium and described by W. H. Pickering in 1892. It has been drawn by L. F. Ball in the B.A.A. Journal (47, 7), and is also shown on many lunar photographs. The surface is rather light in tint, with a number of extensive landslips and evidences of inundation and erosion both on the surface the eastern border. Several large ruined rings can be traced on the surface and, close to it and the limb, is a very considerable ringed-plain with a dark floor and many little peaks on its walls, particularly the eastern. The Mare extends into the farther hemisphere, only the tips of three peaks, north-west of Neper, and some inconsiderable swellings being visible. From the ringed-plain above mentioned, a ridge runs southwards, towards three small but tolerably bright craters to the north of Neper. On the east a similar ridge extends from the outer north glacis of Neper to a landswell within the largest enclosure on the plain; the walls of this ring being very fragmentary and altogether wanting on both the north and the south. West of Neper the plain terminates in the highlands bordering this ringed-plain. On the north is no definite boundary, and here a lofty, discontinuous ridge traverses the surface. Wilkins has seen two deep bays and a crater-chain on the extreme west.

NEWCOMB, +603 +495 [Canadian-American astronomer, 1835-1909]. A fine crater, 32 miles in diameter, with lofty walls, rising 12,000 feet and finely terraced on the inner slopes. On the south crest is a crater, H, while on the outer south-west are two rings, J and C. To the west of the latter is a mountain. On the west is a large obscure ring, P, open on the south. On the southern headland is a very brilliant crater, A, one of the light-surrounded objects and the centre of a minor ray system. North are several rings, the largest being F. On the interior of Newcomb is a central mountain, also craterlets; there is a low hill on the northern portion.

NOVUM, MARE. Limb, + 435. 'New Sea'. A small plain on the limb at mean libration, to the north-west of Plutarch.

OLIVIUM, PROM., +730 +258. The northern cape of the small bay on the eastern border of the Mare Crisium; it has a craterlet on its summit. It and the neighbouring promontory, Lavinium, make an interesting pair.

ORIANI, +876 +435 [Italian astronomer, 1752-1832]. An irregular ring composed of two rings in contact, the dividing wall having disappeared. The southern component contains a crater, another on the crest and a crater-chain running south. This feature was described by Goodacre as a valley. Outside the east wall is a hill of some height.

PEIRCE, +761 +313 [American mathematician, 1809-80]. The second largest crater on the Mare Crisium, 12 miles in diameter, with bright walls rising 7,000 feet. On the interior is a small central hill, also a craterlet on the inner south-west. On the north is the smaller and deeper crater, Graham, formerly Peirce A, which is connected to Peirce by a low ridge. Peirce and Graham sometimes are not distinguishable near First Quarter.

PICARD, +789 +251, [French astronomer, 1620-82]. The largest crater on the surface of the Mare Crisium, 21 miles in diameter, with bright walls, rising 8,000 feet above the floor, on which is a central hill. West are two craterlets, and farther west a white spot, with a central craterpit. This is the curious object described with Mare Crisium. On the south-east are two crossed clefts, to the east of which is the crater, A, on the rim of an old ring. North is a larger obscure ring, the walls of which are low on the west and from which curved ridges, portions of once-complete rings, connect it with the crater, E. Still further north are some isolated hills. Here Wilkins found a crater-cone. On the south are two low rings. The area is crossed by the light rays from Proclus under high illumination.

PLUTARCH, +897 +408 [Greek biographer, A.D. 46-120]. A great ring, 40 miles in diameter, with terraced walls, a central mountain, and two small craters on the south wall. On the outer south-west is another crater. West is the crater B with a smaller, D, on its north. The crater C lies on the south-east. On the limb to the north-west is the small, dark plain called Mare Novum.

PROCLUS, +702 +277 [Greek mathematician, A.D. 410-485]. A brilliant object with narrow walls, and the centre of a ray system. These rays extend chiefly to the west, where some of them cross the surface of the Mare Crisium. Owing to the brightness of the interior, details are difficult to see. Proclus is 18 miles in diameter, and the walls are steep, rising 8,000 feet. They are circular on the west, have a break on the south-east and a distinct crater on the eastern crest. On the floor is a central elevation, doubted by Neison and Elger but seen by Col. Watson, Wilkins and Moore. Schmidt shows what appears to be a curved ridge with two craterlets on the crest; this Goodacre described as a longitudinal cleft. Elger mentions the crater on the crest of the east wall, and this is shown by Schmidt, as well as a ring-like object on the floor under the west wall. The latter was omitted by Elger. It has been seen by Goodacre and Wilkins. Abutting on the north wall is a small partial ring, open on the north and with a craterlet on either side of the gap. East is a low ring, with linear walls and craterlets on the south wall; west is a crater, and beyond a partial ring which lies on the outer slope of the well-known partial formation lying on the eastern border of the Mare Crisium. There is some object to the east of the centre of the floor. With Dr. Steavenson's 30-inch reflector Wilkins found, 5 October 1952, three minute craterlets on the west and south inner slopes. At the same time the central elevation was distinctly seen.

Thornton discovered bright bands on the inner west slope, which may be due to breaks in the walls. They seem to be bordered by dusky bands of a similar nature to those in Aristarchus and other formations. These dusky streaks have been confirmed by Brown, Wilkinson and Moore.

Of the light rays radiating from Proclus, the brightest and the most conspicuous runs north-east; others cross the Mare to Picard and Peirce. There are also many short rays tending south, the whole being bright at Full. Proclus sometimes appears distinctly yellow, noted by Barker. The bright bands on the inner crest, first clearly traced by Thornton, were observed by F. Sargent as far back as 1911.

RECORDE, +925 +308 [Welsh scientist, 1510-58]. A ring, fully 80 miles in diameter, to the west of the Mare Crisium, with a crater on the floor at the southern end and a smaller on the south-east wall. On the south is a valley formed by the fusion of old rings, W and Z. To the west are the craters A and C, with ridges and other rings. East is a fine crater-row, and numerous ridges running to the border of the Mare Crisium.

SENECA, +860 +493 [Roman statesman and orator, 3 B.C.-A.D. 65]. A ringed-plain, with a large crater on its northern wall from which a ridge runs northwards. There is also a smaller crater on the crest of the east wall. On the floor is a central hill of little height; neither are the walls of much altitude. To the west is a large, low ring, and east a bright plain which extends to Hahn.

SOMNII, PALUS, +670 +250. 'Marsh of Sleep.' A well-defined area, described by Neison as golden-brown in tint and visible under any illumination. It is also easily found from its situation, which is to the south-east of the Mare Crisium. The surface is very uneven, full of little hills, craters and the remains of ancient rings. Many partially destroyed craters will be noted around its margin; of these Lyell and Franz are the most prominent. The Marsh is best defined on the east, where it borders the Mare Tranquillitatis. Barker found that the colour was subject to variation. The surface resembles a low plateau, and there are some evidences that more than one flow of liquid or plastic matter flowed over this portion of the Moon in the early days of its formation.

TIMOLEON, +823 +545 [Greek general and statesman, *circa* 337 B.C.]. A great ring very near the limb, to the north-west of Hahn. It is fully 80 miles in diameter, with walls bearing peaks of at least 10,000 feet in altitude, and bears a general resemblance to Gauss. On the vast interior are craters, ridges and many hills. Of the craters, the largest lies on the west, and there are at least four craters to the south of it. On the northern part of the floor is another crater, F, while one of the hills lies almost exactly in the centre and thus constitutes a central hill. On the outer west is a small crater.

TISSERAND, +689 +367 [French astronomer, 1845-96]. A ring to the west of Macrobius, with a crater on its north wall and at least four hills on its interior. To the north-west are the craters C and D, while on the north is the crater, F, beyond which is a very peculiar square-shaped formation, K.

TRALLES, +706 +469 [German physicist, 1763-1822]. A very deep but abnormal ringed-plain, 28 miles in diameter, intruding on the north-east of the ring of Cleomedes.

The walls, which exhibit traces of terraces, rise 13,700 feet on the east above the very depressed floor, on which is a most remarkable compound central elevation. This consists of three parallel elongated crater-cones, very shallow, with ravines between them. They are evidently volcanic products. The interior terraces are especially noteworthy on the west, where there is a peculiar ear-shaped projection, seen by Goodacre, 1901. This feature casts a shadow when the rest of the floor is free. Close to the east wall, and slightly encroaching on the outer slope, is a curious double formation, Debes, and to the south a small crater, B. A cleft cuts through the south-west wall of Tralles and can be traced on to the interior of Cleomedes. This was discovered by Goodacre in 1898.

YERKES, +755 +250 [American financier and patron of astronomy, 1837-1905]. This object is the relic of a once-complete ring on the surface of the Mare Crisium, to the east of Picard. It is now in a ruinous condition; the wall is well marked except on the west, facing the broad expanse of the 'sea', where it is very 'ghostly'. On the interior is a low central hill, and a craterlet to the north of it. On the south is a very low-rimmed ring, and to the north a smaller but similar formation. Of the latter only the east wall is of any height. Still farther to the north is a similar, but larger, partial ring ending in a deep little crater, E. From the north-west of Yerkes a long ridge runs northwards, following the contour of the Mare and ending, on the north, in a shallow lagoon-like enclosure, X. To the west of Yerkes is a minute hillock, also two clefts; farther west is Picard.

XIII

This section consists of a small area of the north-west limb. It is crowded with ringed plains, the most important of which is the great enclosure Messala. All the formations are affected by libration, and many of them are difficult to observe on account of their unfavourable position.

There are no Mare surfaces in the section, but there is a bright plain, and several clefts have been detected in connection with Messala.

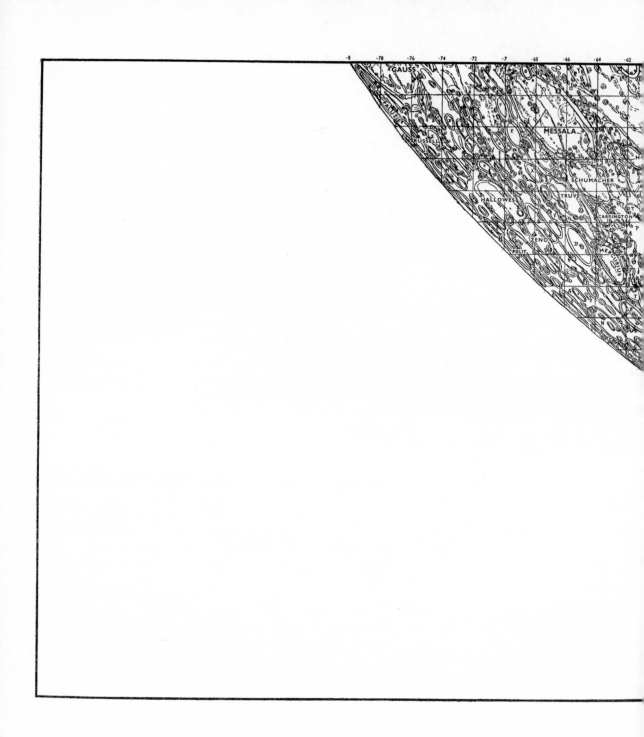

XIII

CARRINGTON, +636 +694 [English astronomer, 1826-75]. A small ringed-plain, with low walls, and three craters on the northern outer glacis. On the east is a ridge-bounded enclosure, S, while between Carrington and Endymion is a plain which has been called 'Mare Horologii' on some recent charts.

GAUSS. Part of Gauss appears in this Section, but a larger part lies in Section XII.

HALLOWES, +710 +690 [English selenographer]. A large enclosure, with low walls broken on the south. The north wall has been destroyed by the intrusions of the ring Zeno and other craters. There is a peak of some altitude on Hallowes' east wall and a craterlet-row under the south-east wall, while the western wall is disturbed by four craterlets. There is a discontinuous ridge down the centre of the floor.

HOOKE, +616 +658 [English scientist, 1635-1703]. A regular ring-plain, with low walls contracted on the south. The floor is level, apart from a craterlet on the north and two very low mounds on the south. To the west is a crater, D, bright at Full Moon. East of Hooke lie the remains of once-complete and prominent formations, while a chain made up of three craterlets lies under the outer south wall.

MERCURIUS, +629 +726 [Mythical]. A fine ringed-plain 25 miles in diameter, with a low central peak and evidences of landslips on the south, east and west. There are craters on the east wall, one of which, A, is of some size. To the west of Mercurius is the ring, D, containing two craters and two hills; on the east is an ancient ring, P. North of Mercurius lies E, on the interior of which is a strong ridge concentric with the west wall and containing two craterlets. Between Mercurius and the limb are several formations, all difficult to examine owing to their unfavourable position on the disk.

MESSALA, +674 +632 [Jewish-Arab astronomer, *circa* A.D. 815]. A great mountain-walled plain oblong in form, measuring 72 miles from end to end. The walls, which are generally low, contain several peaks, one of which—according to Neison—rises to 3,580 feet, the height of Snowdon (Messala Beta). The walls are much broken, and terraced on the inner slopes, while the outer glacis is gentle. A large crater, B, lies on the crest at the point where the south and east walls meet; other craters, J and K, crown the extremities of the north wall. Outside the west wall is a rugged region, found by Wilkins to be traversed by a cleft which runs on to the floor of Messala and joins another cleft. This latter cleft is continued to the south wall, and was first noted by Straker and Elger.

On the south-west portion of the floor a group of four large craters was recorded by

Schmidt, but Müller and Goodacre drew them as hills; Goodacre also found a cleft running to the south wall. Between two of the clefts are two craterlets. On the east wall of Messala, Elger drew a low ring, partially overlaid by the wall of Messala and containing three hills, with a short gap in its western rim; but we have never seen it clearly defined.

South of this feature, on the floor of Messala, lie a craterlet and two little hills; north is a crater, and also a partial ring.

A row of three craters extends from the north wall of Messala, and the wall itself has been seen breached by Dr. S. M. Green, who also detected a buried ring on the south-east portion of the interior. A drawing by this talented and lamented observer appears in the 10th Memoir of the B.A.A. Lunar Section.

In addition to the above-mentioned details, the interior of Messala has a weathered appearance, as though subjected to erosive action in the past. Strangely enough, Schröter shows very little detail in the area, and Schmidt was the first to produce a detailed chart. Our map is based upon the best available photographs, as well as personal drawings, and shows the complexity of the walls and the mass of detail between Messala and the limb. The formation would well repay further study with powerful telescopes. The north wall is common with the south wall of Schumacher.

PALUZÍE, +770 +635 [contemporary Spanish selenographer]. A great ring very close to the limb, near Gauss. It has high walls, but its position makes it hard to examine. Its northern floor is disturbed by a small, deep crater, Russell.

POLIT, +692 +720 [Spanish physicist, 1880-   ]. A crater to the west of Hallowes, and close to the limb, formerly known as Hallowes H. To the west of it is another ring, B.

RUSSELL, +758 +645 [nineteenth-century English painter and amateur astronomer]. A deep crater 10 miles in diameter, described with Paluzie.

SCHUMACHER, +645 +673 [Danish astronomer, 1780-1850]. A smooth ring 25 miles in diameter, with crater-broken walls. On the otherwise featureless floor can be traced two slight landslips and the remains of a partial ring. On the east wall is a large crater, A, with a rim of very irregular height. Between Schumacher and Hooke is a crater, L.

STRUVE, +662 +685 [German astronomer, 1793-1864]. A small ring, containing a central peak. Struve is remarkable for its situation on a dark patch; it can thus be recognized under any conditions of illumination.

ZENO, +678 +708 [Cypriot scientist, 340-264 B.C.]. A large ring, intruding upon Hallowes. The floor is generally very smooth, though there is a crater on the inner north and another some way south of the centre. Between Zeno and the limb are several rings, one of which, H, is of some size. Zeno itself is about 27 miles in diameter.

XIV

This section, which includes the north-north-west limb, contains some objects of great interest. Of the walled plains, the most conspicuous are Atlas and its companion Hercules, both worthy of close study, and the dark-floored Endymion, which can be readily identified under any conditions of lighting. Less prominent, but not less interesting features are the semi-ruined bay Gärtner; Cepheus, where certain features are suspected of variation; Bürg, with its fine associated cleft system; and the ray-crater Thales. Near Thales, too, are some faint rays which seem to come from over the limb, and must therefore emanate from a crater on the permanently averted part of the Moon.

There are several Mare surfaces included in the section—the whole of the Lacus Mortis and most of the Lacus Somniorum, as well as the western end of the Mare Frigoris and a smaller, completely enclosed plain close to the limb, known as Mare Humboldtianum—Humboldt's Sea

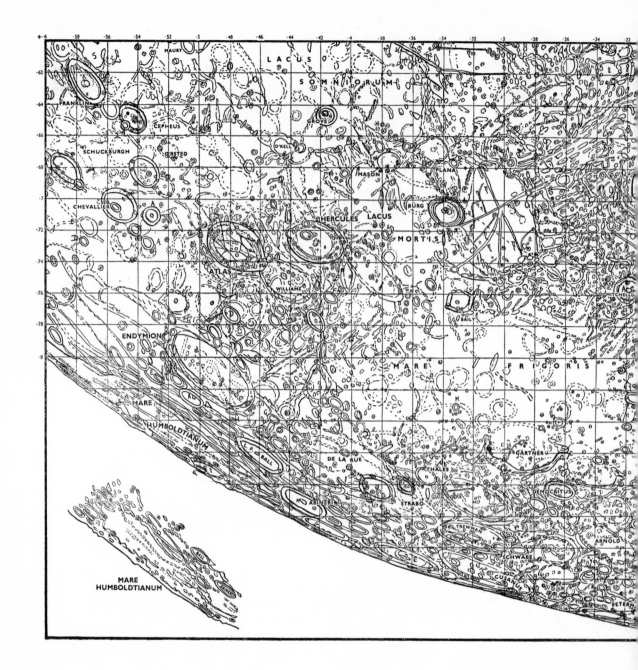

MARE
HUMBOLDTIANUM

XIV

ABINERI, +430 −891 [contemporary English selenographer]. This is a large ring to the north of De La Rue and was formerly known as Strabo A. There are three small craters on the outer south slope, and a large crater, G, on the north-west. Abineri lies just beyond the north end of the Mare Humboldtianum, and is about 35 miles in diameter.

ARNOLD, +231 +919 [German amateur astronomer, 1650-95]. Although this formation is 50 miles across it is ill-defined; the walls are very low, and wanting in places on the south, where there is a low ring. There is another on the north, and craters on the north wall. The floor is dark, and contains a crater on the south-west, several craterlets and some hills. To the north is the crater, A, with rows of craterlets on its interior. The crater C contains ridges, while J is very dark. On the west are some old rings and hillocks.

ATLAS, +481 +727 [Mythical]. This prominent object forms, with its companion, Hercules, a fine pair of craters. Atlas is 55 miles in diameter, with terraced walls rising 10,000 feet on the east, 9,000 feet on the west and 11,000 feet on the north. On the west is a small crater, and the outer slope here contains a chain of depressions. On the eastern slope is a valley, while there are craterlets on both the north and south crests. On the interior, which is bright, is a group of six hills at the centre, the relic of an old ring. One of these hills is higher than the rest, and might be regarded as a central peak. It is, however, very small and rises abruptly from the floor to a sharp summit, seen by Wilkins, 5 October 1952, with the 30-inch reflector belonging to Dr. W. H. Steavenson. The most remarkable objects are the craterlets, connected by clefts, and three prominent dark, variable spots, with interior craterlets. The largest are at the south-east and the north, and are connected by clefts, called 'river-beds' by Pickering. Reese, U.S.A., has seen the indications of the former existence of an inner ring, fragments of which are still visible on the west and east. Wilkins has found eleven certain clefts on the floor, one cutting through the south-east wall. On the north-east is a low ring, and west the deep crater, A, with a central mountain. Under high illumination many objects on the floor glitter in a remarkable manner.

BAILY, +328 +763 [English amateur astronomer, 1774-1844]. A formation 20 miles in diameter, with very low walls, broken by a gap on the south, while there is a crater on the crest of the north wall. On the floor and north of the centre is a crater. To the south-west is the deep crater, A. To the east is a low plateau with craters on its surface.

BALL, L. F. +466 +859 [contemporary English selenographer]. This is a large and tolerably deep ring, about 40 miles in diameter, on the east border of the Mare

Humboldtianum. On the interior is a central mountain, and also a hill at the north end.

BÜRG, +334 +708 [Austrian astronomer, 1766-1834]. This crater is 28 miles in diameter, with walls rising 6,100 feet above a strongly concave floor on which is a large and double central mountain bearing a summit craterlet. The inner slopes are terraced. On the north wall is a crater, and another on the south-west. On the inner west is a minute craterlet, while on the eastern portion of the floor is a ridge concentric with the wall. Bürg stands on the western edge of a small, dark plain which is crossed by many clefts. One of the most prominent runs from the north-east wall across the plain to its east rampart, and continues beyond through the mountainous region to the west of Eudoxus. Along the centre of the plain is another prominent cleft, from north to south. The other clefts are more difficult to detect, and reference should be made to the map. Three in particular radiate from a node in the centre. In addition to the clefts are hills and some craterlets. South of Bürg are hills and craterlets, and a craterlet-chain on the south-west border of the plain. To the west is an old ring, of which only the west wall now remains, while on the north is the dark Lacus Mortis. Goodacre gives a drawing of Bürg and the surroundings in the Memoirs of the British Astronomical Association, 32, 2. Some of the chief clefts can be seen in small instruments. Lenham has seen nine with only 3¼-inches aperture.

CEPHEUS, +544 +648 [Mythical King]. A crater 28 miles in diameter, with walls of 9,000 feet altitude. A bright crater, A, breaks the crest on the north-west. Molesworth drew a central craterpit, but Schmidt shows this as a hill. Wilkins has found a low hill a little south of the centre. To the south is an ancient ring, and there are others on the north, some very imperfect. Between Cepheus and Franklin is a low ring, while on the south-east are some little craters and low rings.

CHEVALLIER, +552 +704 [English mathematician, 1794-1873]. This formation has low walls and a deep crater on the interior. To the west is one of the numerous examples of old rings found in this region, while on the north is a bright crater, A, the centre of a minor ray system. To the east is the deep crater, Atlas A.

CUSANUS, +293 +950 [German mathematician, 1401-64]. A crater 30 miles in diameter, but with low walls, destroyed in places by the intrusion of craters. The floor is smooth. Between it and the limb is a large ring. On the west Cusanus intrudes upon a large enclosure with craters and ridges on its interior. On the surface to the east are a mountain and a crater-chain, while there are four craters close together on the south wall. Some faint rays appear over the limb near Cusanus, undoubtedly coming from a ray-crater on the averted hemisphere.

DE LA RUE, +400 +860 [English astronomer, 1815-89]. A large but little more than ridge-bordered enclosure, and irregular, with low walls, discontinuous in places. On the interior are some craters and ridges. Both on the south and the west are the remains of old rings. To the north-east is Strabo; north-west, Ball; and north, the crater Abineri. On the south the wall is very broken, and opens into two low-rimmed enclosures.

DEMOCRITUS, +267 +885 [Greek philosopher, 460-360 B.C.]. A very deep, some-what shell-shaped ring, pointed on the north with a central hill and some mounds on the floor. On the south is an old ring, on the south rim of which is the distinct crater, B. To the south-east is a small mountain. On the north-west is a crater with two smaller craters on the east; this crater stands on the south rim of a once-complete enclosure. Democritus is the deepest crater in this region, and is always easily found.

ENDYMION, +492 +803. [Mythical]. A great crater, 78 miles in diameter, with lofty, peak-surmounted walls, rising 15,000 feet on the west and still higher on the north. The floor is dark, which makes the formation easy to detect under any illumination. In general the floor is remarkably smooth, but there is some delicate detail. This consists of white spots, a light streak, and a few craterlets and hills, or cones. Debes and Anděl depicted a central hill, and some observers, including Lenham, three craterlets in a line on the northern portion. Wilkins, however, does not confirm this. On 5 October 1952, with power 300, on the 30-inch reflector belonging to Dr. W. H. Steavenson, the for-mation being close to the evening terminator and about a third of the floor already in shadow, Wilkins distinctly saw a faint whitish streak near the centre, but placed some-what diagonally. At its eastern end was a minute white spot. On the southern portion are a distinct craterlet, three mounds, also probably craterlets, and a landslip from the south-eastern wall. North of the whitish streak, which may be a low ridge, although it cast no shadow, are three delicate craterlets, while on the west, along the foot of the inner slope, is a delicate cleft, running to a craterpit almost in the centre of this portion of the slope. This cleft had been seen previously in his own 15¼-inch, but with this instrument its true nature was undecided. There is also a craterlet at the northern end of the floor. D. W. G. Arthur found a valley on the outer north-east wall, ending on the north in two confluent irregular depressions. Endymion has overlapped an older and large ring, a portion of which can be seen on the west and north-west. Beyond this mountain ridge is the Mare Humboldtianum.

FRANKLIN, +576 +627 [American statesman and scientist, 1706-90]. A fine crater, 34 miles in diameter, with walls rising 8,000 feet in some places and finely terraced on the inner slopes. On the floor is a central hill, which is connected to the south wall by a ridge. On the inner north slope are two craterlets. There are also some dark spots, sus-pected of being variable in tint, and also suspected clefts on the interior. To the north are several partly-buried rings; south-east, craters; and south an ancient ring, S. West are some isolated hills. Just outside the east wall is the small crater, A, while a crater-chain traverses the surface on the outer west.

GALLE, +213 +827 [German astronomer, 1812-1910]. A small crater to the north-west of Aristoteles, and on the Mare Frigoris. On the floor is a craterlet on the east, and there is another on the south wall. Abutting on the outer north is another craterlet. To the south is the small but bright crater, A, and on the north the crater C.

GÄRTNER, +290 +855 [German geologist, 1750-1813]. A fine example of a formation portion of which has been greatly reduced by erosive forces in the past. It lies on the northern coast-line of the Mare Frigoris, and while the northern portion is still well marked, the southern wall is now marked by a very low ridge barely detectable. Of the remaining portion of the wall, the western end is a lofty promontory; west of it is the relic of a smaller but once-perfect ring and west of this are two small craters. On the floor of Gärtner is a craterlet, D, with two pits on its east, and there are some craterlets along the northern part of the floor close to the wall. Moore (20 April 1953: Meudon 33-inch refractor) independently detected two clefts near D, which had been discovered previously by E. A. Whitaker at Greenwich. On the site of the former south wall is a small crater with a larger to the south-east and three hills between them. East is the very similar partial ring described under Democritus. On the outer north are two craters, several low rings and the large low-walled formation to the east of Thales. South-east of Gärtner is a prominent crater, C, in which Moore, in 1953, discovered a central peak.

GROVE, +415 +647 [Welsh physicist, 1811-96]. A crater, 15 miles in diameter, with walls rising 7,000 feet on the west above the floor on which are three hills, one almost central but of no great height. Moore (20 April 1953: Meudon 33-inch refractor) found an old ring on the floor, and an irregular west crest, but failed to find the three hills (see special drawing). To the south is the Lacus Somniorum, and some low ridges run from the walls across this plain. Immediately to the south is an old ring, and on the east is a peculiar arrangement of hills forming a diamond-shaped enclosure. To the north-east are the mountainous highlands of Mason and Plana.

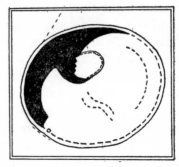

GROVE

20 April 1953, 20h. 33-inch
20 m., O.G. (Meudon)
× 520, Patrick Moore

HERCULES, +434 +728 [Mythical]. This crater is the companion to Atlas, the two formations forming a pair of nearly equal-sized craters. It is 45 miles in diameter, with broad, finely-terraced walls rising 11,000 feet. On the inner west are a ravine, some landslips, and craters on the north. On the west a crater has intruded, and there is another on the south just below the crest. On the depressed interior is a deep crater, D, with some little peaks on its south-eastern rim, and two hills on the floor close to the inner north wall. On the northern portion of Hercules, Arthur Mee drew a curved ridge and two nearly central craterlets. The inner east slope is very broad and contains some hills and pits; there is a craterlet on the west slope close to the floor. There are some light spots on the floor. To the east is the dark Lacus Mortis, and abutting on the wall a

216

low ring. Due north is the crater, F, and farther north the deep, centrally peaked crater A, numerous rings and ridges.

HUMBOLDTIANUM, MARE, +496 +864 to +591 +800 [German explorer, 1769-1859]. 'Humboldt's Sea'. A plain on the north-west limb of the Moon, containing much detail, although Goodacre shows nothing. The west border contains peaks rising 16,000 feet and sometimes visible in profile. There is a bay on the far west, in all probability the remains of an old ring. On the interior of the Mare, Wilkins and Abineri have found several objects. There is a long meridional ridge in the centre, to the west of which is a small crater. From a crater on the south wall a chain of four craterlets runs northwards. To the west of this, and close under the wall, is a dark, cleft-like marking. North of the craterlet-chain are four small craters equally spaced from east to west. On the north-east wall is a low ancient ring. On the western portion are three domes, and there are two ridges concentric with the south-west wall. At the north end of the central ridge are two craterlets, and there is a low ring close under the east wall. There are also two hills on the south, two craterlets near the south-east wall, four hills to the east of the craterlet-chain and two hills to the west of the four craters already mentioned. Abineri has found twenty craters or craterlets on the surface; the positions of most features still await accurate determination.

MASON, +374 +675 [English astronomer, 1730-87]. A crater, 15 miles in diameter, with walls low on the north, where is a gap. In this gap are two craterlets, and there is a ridge on the east concentric with the wall. Moore, using Dr. W. H. Steavenson's 30-inch reflector at Cambridge, on 26 September 1953, found a ridge on the west floor, and two craterlets under the inner east wall. The wall is very broad on the south, and here is a crater, also two craterlets. To the west is what appears to be the western wall of a former ring, and on this broad rugged region are some craters. Between Mason and Plana is a small crater.

MAURY, +510 +603 [American geographer, 1806-73]. A bright and deep ring, 12 miles in diameter, the node of four ridges, and with a low central hill. To the east is an old ring.

MITCHELL, +222 +758 [American woman astronomer, 1818-89]. This was formerly called Aristoteles A, and lies on the west of that great formation. It is deep and with a central hill, with two hillocks on the east of it and a craterlet on the south. Adjoining on the south-east is a low ring, containing two craterlets and some hills. South of this old ring is a cleft, ending on the south-west in a small crater. North, on the border of the Mare Frigoris, are some ridges, craterlets and craterlet-chains. There is also a short bent cleft. West are numerous hillocks and curved ridges. To the south-west are many low-rimmed formations extending to the small plain to the east of Bürg.

MORTIS, LACUS, +280 +680 to +410 +770. The 'Lake of Death'. A small dark plain to the east of Hercules, with Bürg on the east and Mason on the south. On the surface are craters, chiefly on the western portion, and some obscure rings of which X, to the north of Bürg, is the most prominent.

ŒRSTED, +538 +682 [Danish physicist, 1777-1851]. A low-walled ring 25 miles in diameter, with a crater to the north of the centre and two craterlets. On the east is a still more obscure ring, while to the south are two small craters. Abutting on the south wall is a low ring. On the west are six shallow depressions, filling up the space to Cepheus and Shuckburgh.

O'KELL, +445 +750. [English amateur astronomer, 1861-1947]. A large low ring adjoining Atlas on the north-east, and nearly as large. There is a hill nearly in the centre, some hillocks, ridges and craterlets within the encircling walls. To the north-east is the deep crater A, with a central peak; east is the crater F, together with many hills and craterlets, while on the north-west, beyond some old rings, is the crater D. A short cleft runs from the north wall of D to a depression, one of several flanking Endymion on the south. (On the map the name 'Williams' is given where O'Kell should be placed.)

PETERMANN, +250 +962 [German geographer, 1822-78]. A large but very discontinuous formation to the north of Arnold, and close to the limb. On the north-west portion of the interior is a large crater, and both the east and west walls are marked by rows of craters.

PLANA, +348 +672 [Italian astronomer, 1781-1864]. A crater, 24 miles in diameter, with low and broken walls, and a break on the north, where the narrow wall contains two craterlets. On the otherwise smooth floor is a central hill, found by Moore, using Dr. Steavenson's 30-inch reflector in 1953, to be double; also a craterlet and two low ridges on the west. The floor is slightly convex. The south wall is prolonged southwards as a fine mountain ridge, gradually contracting, and with craters and peaks. On the east and far south of this feature two fine clefts run for a short distance to the north-east. South of these there is a remarkable cleft system, beginning on the west near Daniell, and with branches in places. The chief cleft can be traced to the foothills on the west of Eudoxus. To the north-east of Plana is the small crater, C, while north a craterlet-chain runs towards Bürg. East are three craterlets in a line and numerous hills forming the border of the cleft-traversed plain east of Bürg. On the west a high and hilly region connects Plana with Mason. West of the great mountain arm from the south wall are some isolated, often curved elevations; portions of the walls of once-complete rings.

SCHWABE, +301 +907 [German astronomer, 1789-1875]. A small but deep crater to the south of Cusanus, with a large, low ring to the east and the crater Trewman on the west. North are hills and craterlets.

SHUCKBURGH, +587 +681 [English astronomer, 1751-1804]. A somewhat square enclosure, with low walls bearing a crater on the inner north-west. There are other craters on the north wall, and a minute craterlet. The floor appears to be quite free from detail. Müller found a cleft to the north-east, visible with a 3½-inch refractor.

SOMNIORUM, LACUS, +410 +610. The 'Lake of Dreams'. This romantically named area is really a bay on the northern side of the Mare Serenitatis. On its surface are small craters, hills and a cleft cutting through a low ring to the south of the great mountain arm from Plana. This cleft has already been described under Plana. Everywhere on the surface of the Lacus are the faintly traceable remains of once-prominent rings, doubtless overwhelmed when the material forming the present surface was fluid.

STRABO, +384 +882 [Greek historian and geographer, 55 B.C.-A.D. 24]. A crater 32 miles in diameter, with walls somewhat broken but bearing some high peaks; and the centre of a small minor ray system. The floor appears quite smooth. Strabo lies on the north-east wall of De La Rue, here mere ridges, and the crater is partly surrounded, on the east, by an outer concentric row of hills. To the north-west is Abineri, with craters between it and Strabo. Due north is a large ring, beyond a mountain mass of some height. South are a few ridges, and then the open Mare Frigoris.

THALES, +364 +881 [Ionian philosopher, 624-547 B.C.]. A crater near Strabo, and the centre of a ray system. On the interior is a small central hill, and there is a small mountain just outside the east wall. A ridge connects Thales with De La Rue; east is a large ring, with very low walls and a group of four hills in the centre of the floor. It also contains three craterlets on the west and three hills on the east. North is Strabo A, and the west wall of Trewman. In 1892, Barnard once saw Thales filled with 'pale luminous haze', though all surrounding details were sharp and normal.

TREWMAN, +321 +919 [Contemporary English electronic specialist]. This object has been named by Wilkins, and is shown, in outline, by Goodacre. It is a fine ring to the north-west of Gärtner, and has many craters on its interior. The west wall is low and broken by craters; farther west are some long, shallow valleys running north-west to south-east. There are three craters beyond; the middle crater is Thales B. On the south wall are three craters, and one on the east. The latter is Schwabe F. On the north-east rim is a peculiarly shaped depression. The north wall is, in part, well marked, but farther west is occupied by a group of craters near Strabo C. On the interior of Trewman is a small but bright central hill. This hill lies on the south rim of a very low ring, within which are two craterlets. To the west of this ring is a smaller but similar object. On the southern portion of Trewman are some small craters, while from the western border some delicate ridges run on to the floor.

WILLIAMS, +449 +665 An irregular formation to the north-west of Grove and south of Hercules. It has a wide gap in its eastern rampart, and a smooth floor. Abutting on the south-west is a low ring, and there are some shallow craters on the north-west. (See note under 'O'Kell'.)

XV

This section includes one of the most interesting regions on the lunar surface. We see here such well-known objects as Aristoteles, Eudoxus, Plato, Cassini, the mountain ranges of the Alps and Caucasus, and the North Polar district.

The southern portion is largely occupied by the broad expanse of the Mare Imbrium, and on its surface are the bright little mountains of Pico, Piton and the Teneriffe Range.

Plato is the most important formation on the map, and is one of the best-observed spots on the Moon's surface.

This section should be used in conjunction with the special Polar Projection Chart and the Library Maps, whenever reference is desired to formations which are close to the limb and cannot be well shown on the mean libration chart.

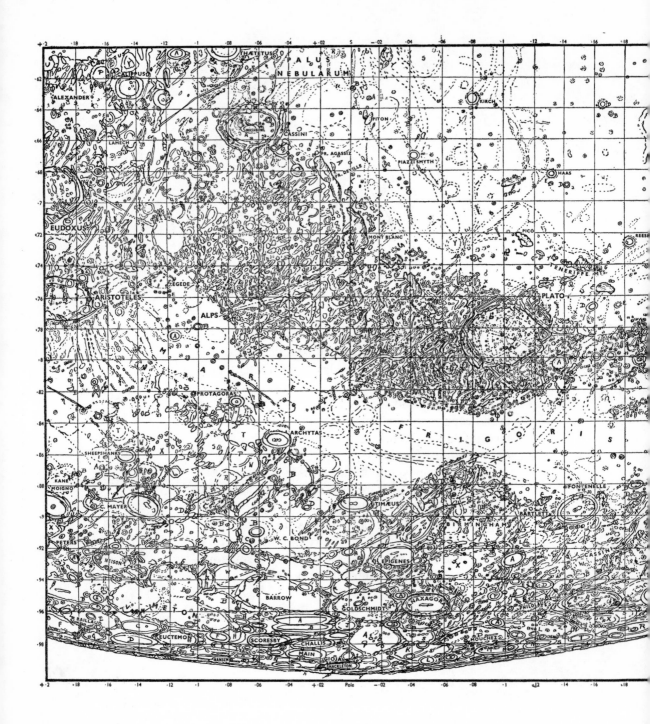

XV

AGASSIZ, PROMONTORIUM, +020 +672 [Swiss naturalist, 1807-73]. Agassiz is a cape on the extreme border of the Alps, between Cassini and Mont Blanc. Close to its foot, and on the plain, is a craterlet. The mountainous mass rises abruptly above the cape to a height of 7,650 feet. On the west are the remains of an old ring, and beyond it a most extraordinary object—a small crater, the north part of which has been covered by a plateau, possibly due to a lava flow.

ALEXANDER, +180 +645 [Greek general, 356-323 B.C.]. A ring 60 miles across, with many signs of erosion in the past. The walls are low—mere hills, on the west—and the floor is dark with ridges, hills and small craters. A high mountain exists on the north wall, while on the eastern part of the rampart are projections enclosing shallow rings. There are several landslips from the rampart, which is here somewhat pointed. The largest of these landslips is crescent-shaped, and includes two craterlets.

ALPINE VALLEY. This, one of the finest valleys on the lunar surface, is a great gorge, which cuts through the mighty chain of the Alps for a distance of 80 miles. It begins on the west at a low ring on the edge of a low plateau, is flanked by lofty hills, and widens, with spurs jutting out in places; it is also crossed by a cleft. Farther east, craterpits line the southern side, and the valley is then partly blocked by a mountain; beyond this is a still higher mountain, which towers 12,000 feet. The valley then opens into an amphitheatre, and this is almost blocked on the east by the lofty peaks of the Alpine range, flanking the Mare Imbrium. Pickering found a cleft running down the centre, and intersecting some minute pits. This great valley was first drawn by Bianchini. Haas has found a dark area near the south-east end, variable in intensity. Wilkins found that Pickering's cleft is nearer the south than the north side, while Barker has detected a second and parallel cleft. There is a very dark area on the south.

ALPS. A range of bright mountains, curving along the border of the Mare Imbrium from Plato to Cassini. The chief peaks rise abruptly from the dark plain. Just south of the great valley is a massive mountain mass called Mont Blanc, rising 11,800 feet. Of the other peaks, one on the south rises 8,000 feet, with a 6,000-feet peak north of it; a peak north of Cassini rises 6,000 feet, and one north-east of it 7,600 feet, while to the west of Plato there is a peak of 12,000 feet. The ground rises gradually on the west, and here are many little hills, not exceeding 500 feet in height; farther east, however, the hills are higher. Schröter noted a light spot near Mont Blanc, on the dark side, in 1788; it was recovered by Grover in 1865. Emley has found a remarkable variable light area in the hinterland between Cassini and the Valley. This region is covered with rows of little hills having a pronounced south-east to north-west orientation. As the sun rises higher, a small area near the centre becomes much brighter than its surroundings. This bright area contains several low mounds. Another low hill near by also brightens, but remains misty and ill defined. Two light-streaks resolve, under a low sun, into several low mounds, while ridges enclose a crateriform depression which is breached on the north.

ANAXAGORAS, —050 +959 [Greek philosopher, 500-428 B.C.]. A very bright crater 32 miles in diameter, the centre of a bright ray system. It has steep terraced walls, rising 10,000 feet above the floor, on which is a bright central mountain of altitude 1,000 feet. On the south crest is a crater, and there is another on the inner north-east. There is also a crater on the north-west of the floor. Abutting on the south wall is the crater A. Anaxagoras overlaps an old ring on the north, and this old crater is full of hills, with craterlets and craters. In its turn this ring overlaps another, with a central crater and some hills. Just east of Anaxagoras is a mountain mass, from which a valley, V, runs to the south-east. On the limb at extreme libration, north of Anaxagoras, is a large ring, K, about 45 miles in diameter, with a crater 15 miles in diameter on its north crest, another 10 miles in diameter on the north-west crest, and a more indefinite crater 11 miles in diameter on its south crest.

ARCHYTAS, + 046 +855 [Greek philosopher, 428-347 B.C.]. A bright little crater, 21 miles in diameter, on the north border of the Mare Frigoris. Its walls rise 5,000 feet above the floor, which contains a central mountain with three peaks. To the east is a mountain, and south-west Protagoras, also with a low central hill. Between Protagoras and Archytas are two low rings, of which only the north walls remain. On the north are other old rings, from which wide valleys run north-west. There is a crater on the outer, terraced north slope, while on the south is a low-rimmed ring with a cleft on its south. On the west a low ridge runs to three craterlets.

ARISTOTELES, +191 +768 [great Greek philosopher, 383-322 B.C.]. A majestic walled-plain 60 miles across, with magnificent ravine-divided and finely-terraced walls rising in considerable peaks, the highest 11,000 feet. On the floor are many hills, one group being nearly central and with the remains of an old ring to the west of it, and crossed by a craterlet-chain found by Webb and confirmed by Gaudibert. On the west wall a deep crater, Mitchell, abuts; and to the south of this is an old ring. On the north, and on the border of the Mare Frigoris, are a short crater-rill and innumerable craterlets.

Aristoteles is especially remarkable for the magnificent rows of hillocks which radiate from its walls, especially on the north-east. They are of but little height, but so numerous that for a short time, under a low sun, they appear as thickly-crowded points of light amid the still-extensive shadow. They were well drawn by Mädler in the 'Mappa Selenographica', and described in detail by Webb in the *Intellectual Observer*, Vol. IX. Several lunar photographs, including Paris XXXV and Mt. Wilson, show these remarkable hillock rows.

From the east wall, near the peak *n*, which rises 10,700 feet, begins a group of bright and, in part, lofty mountains, stretching as far as Egede. Other mountain masses extend to the north-east of Eudoxus.

BAILLAUD, +155 +960 [French astronomer, 1848-1934]. A large but ill-defined ring to the north-west of Meton. It has crater-bearing walls, and a central crater on the floor, while the west wall has been destroyed by a large crater. To the north is the crater, G, and east the two large rings, C and D, with smooth floors.

BARROW, +045 +949 [English mathematician, 1630-77]. A splendid telescopic object, 45 miles in diameter, with broken walls, bearing a crater on the south-west. On the floor is a crater south-east of the centre. On the south-east wall is the crater, A, and east of it a little peak. Another peak lies on the south-west wall, and beyond this part of the wall is the enclosure, W. South of Barrow is a large enclosure with broken walls, and common with W. C. Bond on the south. Outside the north wall are two large and prominent craters, A and B, while west of A is the small ring, C, which has slightly deformed the wall at this point.

BARTLETT, −120 +900 [contemporary American selenographer]. This is the name given to a ridge-bordered area west of Fontenelle, and on the north boundary of the Mare Frigoris. It is not a conspicuous object, and can scarcely be called a definite formation at all, but is most interesting on account of the suggested changes which have taken place.

Where Bartlett lies to-day, Beer and Mädler, and later Neison, drew a strongly-marked, artificial-looking square. In the words of the Rev. T. W. Webb, in his famous *Celestial Objects*: 'There is a nearly square enclosure foreshortened into a lozenge, whose rampart-like boundaries throw the observer into the highest astonishment.' Neison's description is as follows: 'West of Fontenelle, Mädler discovered a very peculiar formation, from its regularity and perfect form one of those strange objects that seem as though they were the work of Selenites, though from its vastness alone seems to be natural and not artificial. . . . A perfect square, enclosed by long straight walls about 65 miles in length, 1 in breadth, and from 250 to 3,000 feet in height. The highest side is in the north-west. . . . Before the chief wall, at Zeta, is a regular cross. The north-east side is lower, and in one or two places somewhat interrupted, and its height somewhat irregular, the small peak, Delta, being 1,300 feet. The south-east wall is a very uniform straight wall of considerable steepness; and finally, the south-west border is described by Mädler as a broad light streak, but under very favourable conditions a long, nearly straight ridge . . . 200 feet high. Within the quadrangle are two rows of low peaks, and south of the cross Zeta is another one, not mentioned by Mädler.'

This seems definite enough. Yet, as Dr. J. J. Bartlett pointed out in 1950, the 'Square' of Mädler and Neison no longer exists at all. The south-east wall described as 'uniform and straight' has gone; nothing remains of the artificial aspect, and the modern area is nothing more than a rough region partly enclosed by ridges.

Moore investigated the problem, following some interesting correspondence with Bartlett, Barcroft and Haas (in the course of which he suggested the renaming of the 'Square' after Bartlett), and found a photograph taken by Draper in 1863, showing the 'Square' as it is to-day. Yet Neison's book, published in 1876, still describes the Square as striking and artificial-looking; this seems to show that he had not observed it carefully, and had merely taken and amplified the description given by Mädler. Luckily, one of Schröter's drawings of the area escaped the destruction at Lilienthal; it was made in 1809, and shows the 'Square' in its modern form, a prominent mountain mass which Mädler and Neison misplaced also being correctly drawn.

The evidence, therefore, is decidedly against any change. It seems certain that Mädler made an error, and that Neison copied it. Experiments made by Moore seem to give a possible solution; the area was examined first with a 3-inch refractor (not much smaller than Mädler's instrument), and then with the 12½-inch reflector. In the 3-inch there was a decided impression of a Square, probably because the 'interior' is slightly darker than the surrounding country; in the 12½-inch the true character was revealed. The fact that Schröter did not fall into the same trap as Mädler is probably because his telescope, though not so good, was larger.

Moore obtained a good view with the 33-inch Meudon refractor in 1953, and the drawing (given here) was checked by Wilkins. Epsilon, the mountain mass displaced by Mädler but not by Schröter, is crowned by two peaks; the 'south wall' is barely traceable, but includes a double peak, B, and a pair of peaks, C. South of C are several large hills, and a curved ridge which seems to be a ruined crater. The pair of craterlets, D,

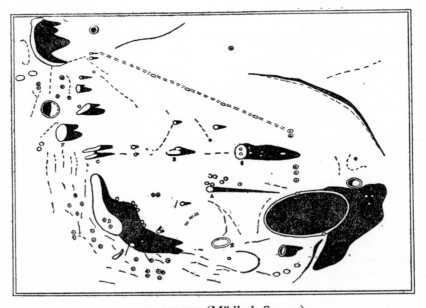

BARTLETT (Mädler's Square)
22 April 1953, 33 inch O.G. (Meudon Observatory), Patrick Moore

lies on the 'west wall', the only remaining rampart of any height; the north wall is absent, marked only by a few low ridges and a very low-walled ring, E. On the floor of Bartlett there are several hills and two craterlets; one of the hills, A, casts a curiously long shadow at times, as is shown on the drawing.

The 'crosses' recorded by Mädler and Neison remain a mystery. Webb failed to find the main one, but added that Birmingham, a celebrated Irish astronomer, had been more successful; more recently, indications of crosses have been seen by Dr. Bartlett and other American observers. No crosses were visible when the Meudon drawing was made, but they may have been masked by shadow. The area will more than repay further study.

BIRMINGHAM, −080 +900 [Irish selenographer, 1829-84]. This is a very large ridge-bordered plain, with a nearly central crater, B, and south of it many hills and a cleft. On the west portion are a fine straight cleft, and some low rings; the east side contains craters, low ridges and a short craterlet-chain. The south wall is very complex on the outer slopes, with numerous craters and mountain masses culminating in a steep peak near Timæus, 4,500 feet high, while on the south-east are two lofty peaks. The eastern border is broken in places, especially on the north. To the north-east is the fine crater, A, and to the west the low ring, X, and the elliptical depression, P.

BLANC, MONT, 000 +710. This is the highest peak of the western Lunar Alps, and may easily be found, a little south of the exit of the Alpine Valley. It rises 12,000 feet, though Schröter made it 14,000 feet, and there is a lower peak on the south, rising 6,500 feet above the dark surface of the Mare Imbrium. On the open plain are some small and much lower hills, islands as it were; while on the west are numerous little mountains, decreasing in altitude but increasing in number towards the west. Schröter in 1789, and later Grover in 1865, both saw a bright light speck close to Mont Blanc, while the region was still unilluminated.

BOND, W. C. +030 +910 [American astronomer, 1789-1859]. A very large ridge-bordered plain, with low walls and a wall crater, A, 7 miles in diameter. The vast floor is crossed by rows of hills in a general north-west to south-east direction, while there are craters on the north, old rings along the east border and another on the south near Timæus. On the west portion is the crater B, with a smaller, C, on its north. The west wall is very angular, and on the south-west is a large oblong depression divided into two by a ridge. This opens into the large enclosure, Archytas B. The south wall is wanting at one spot, west of which is the half of an old ring. On this part of the floor is the small but distinct crater, D. East of the gap just mentioned is Timæus, with a cleft cutting through its west wall. North of Timæus, and on the interior of Bond, is a very low-rimmed ring, full of hillocks and some craterlets. Between Birmingham and Barrow is another long enclosure with fragmentary walls.

CALIPPUS, +142 +627 [Greek astronomer, *circa* 330 B.C.]. This formation is somewhat deformed, being decidedly oval from east to west, as though it had been subjected to pressure in the past. It is 19 miles in diameter, and there are hills on the interior, the highest being a little south of the centre. On the east is a curved mountain arm, the relic of an old ring, and rising 13,000 feet above the plain at its foot. To the north-east, near a low ring, is a great mountain, its lofty summit rising over 18,000 feet; the highest in the Caucasus range, and very prominent under low illumination. On the west is the broken and discontinuous border of Alexander, and with only one peak of any note; south is the peculiar, low, triangular object, Y.

CASSINI, +062 +647 [Italian astronomer, 1625-1712]. A beautiful and peculiar object 36 miles in diameter, with broad and very complex walls, in part double, but with a narrow crest—the whole exhibiting a polygonal outline. The chief peaks are 4,000 feet on the west, but only 1,500 feet on the east, while on the north they are only 800 feet. On the floor is a bright crater, A, 8 miles in diameter, within which the Authors discovered, on 3 April 1952, with the great 33-inch Meudon refractor, a white, very shallow crater within which is a most minute central pit, the whole strongly resembling a 'Washbowl', and named accordingly. There was also a ridge and a hillock on the eastern side

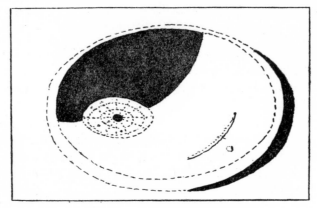

CASSINI A and THE WASHBOWL
H. P. Wilkins

of A. Besides A, the floor of Cassini contains a smaller crater, B, three hills between A and B, and some hills arranged in a semicircle on the west, possibly the remains of a once-complete ring. There are also three curved ridges to the south-west of A, a craterlet between A and the north wall, a hill or crater-cone between B and the east wall, and more curved ridges. To the north of Cassini is a small mountain mass, a crater to the north-east and a depression on the east; also a lofty mountain ridge, prominent at sunrise. Using a 12½-inch reflector, on 24 November 1952, Moore noted indications of a very shallow ring abutting on the south wall of Cassini, detectable only by a slight change in the surface hue. Cassini was omitted from the maps of Hevelius and Riccioli.

CASSINI, J. J., −150 +920 [son of the above astronomer, following him as Director of the Paris Observatory, 1677-1756]. This is nothing more than a large ridge-bounded plain, with a fairly well-marked western wall, rising in one peak as high as 5,000 feet; the other portions are, however, much lower. On the interior are a large but obviously ancient ring, numerous hills, ridges, and a cleft. On the west is the deep crater Birmingham A, and north of it the two smaller craters, E and F, with the larger crater, D. Two craterlet-chains run from D on to the floor of Cassini, and there is a larger chain connected with A. The eastern wall is very broken; in parts it is represented by nothing more than parallel rows of hills and some enclosed but shallow depressions. Of these, P is the most easily seen. South of Cassini is Fontenelle, and three craterlets just outside its north wall. The south-east wall is even more vague than the eastern, and its site can only be traced by some ridges, mixed with small craters and little hillocks, all of little importance.

CHALLIS, +029 +983 [English astronomer, 1803-62]. A crater 35 miles in diameter, with a smooth floor. There is a crater on the north-east wall, and another on the inner south slope. Where Challis joins Main the wall is very low, and is marked by two hills. Challis lies close under the north-east wall of the much more distinct formation, Scoresby. Moore has found two distinct hills on the south-east glacis, and another, with an oval base, some 20 miles to the south. From Challis a long, low ridge runs almost as far as Anaxagoras.

DEVILLE, PROMONTORIUM, +010 +682 [French geologist, 1814-76]. A mountain mass south of Mont Blanc, and thus in the main crest of the Lunar Alps. The highest point rises 8,500 feet.

EGEDE, +126 +746 [Danish missionary, 1686-1758]. A most peculiar object—a diamond-shaped formation with low, broken walls, rising at their highest, a small peak on the west wall, only 400 feet, and with a dark floor on which Molesworth found some craterlets. There is, however, a delicate cleft, or fault, crossing the interior from west to east, but rarely visible.

EPIGENES, —035 +922 [Greek astronomer, circa 300 B.C.]. A 30-mile diameter crater, with broad walls and craters on both the north and south-west crests. The floor contains several hills, the most prominent being west of the centre. West of this hill is a low-rimmed crater-ring. The outer north wall is lined by craters, while on the north-west is the ring, B, with the peak, Y, on its west. To the west, beyond a ridge, is the fine crater A, while on the east are many craterlets and hills, and also the large but shallow ring X.

ESQUIVEL (invisible at mean libration) [Spanish geographer, circa 1550]. A fine ring, situated on the averted hemisphere beyond Nansen. It has bright walls, and is about 20 miles in diameter.

EUCTEMON, +122 +972 [Greek astronomer, circa 432 B.C.]. A great ringed-plain with lofty walls, rising 10,000 feet on the east but lower on the west, where are many peaks. On the floor is a craterlet under the south wall, and there is another on the north.

Between Euctemon and the limb are lofty mountains, the most prominent being Nansen Beta, which rises 11,000 feet. Gamma is also high, rising 8,000 feet. On the south is Meton.

EUDOXUS, +202 +699 [Greek astronomer (friend of Plato), 408-355 B.C.]. A great crater 40 miles in diameter, with very lofty walls, 11,000 feet on the west, though lower on the east. On the outer north slope are crater-rows, while on the interior are numerous hills, especially on the north-east. On the southern portion of the floor is a circular arrangement of hills, probably an old ring. There is a pass in the south wall. On the outer west is an ancient ring, while to the south is very hilly country which extends towards the east, the mountains becoming higher and rising in two peaks on the south-east to 7,000 feet. One lofty hill is cut through by a cleft, which is crossed by another; there is also a cleft on the north. Haas found the sunrise shadow darker than that within Aristoteles, and this is confirmed by some photographs.

FONTENELLE, −145 +893 [French astronomer, 1657-1757]. This crater is 23 miles in diameter, with narrow but bright walls on the south, where are two gaps, but broad on the east. Wilkins has seen the walls almost as brilliant as Aristarchus, with the 33-inch Meudon refractor. On the floor are a central crater, a pair of craterlets near the south inner slope, ridges, and a ravine on the north. From the north wall a ridge runs north-west bearing a crater on its summit, while to the south is a small mountain, rising 3,000 feet and situated on the edge of an old ring. There is another low-rimmed ring on the north, while to the east is the very distinct crater, B, with a smaller one on the north.

GIOJA, +004 +993 [Italian explorer, circa 1302]. A crater 26 miles in diameter, close to the North Pole; it disturbs the south-east wall of the large enclosure, Shackleton, and the wall is prolonged on the west, forming Shackleton's south rampart. The latitude of the formation is 83° 14′ North, and until Shackleton was named it was regarded as the polar formation.

Gioja is not perfectly round, as the north wall is somewhat distorted, bearing a craterlet. There is another craterlet on the southern outer glacis, and three more on the eastern outer slopes. A central mountain has been recorded on the floor, but Moore, who has often looked for it, has yet to see it with any certainty. It must be very low.

East of Gioja is a craterlet, with another, minute craterlet south-east of it; and to the north-east is an incomplete ring about 12 miles in diameter, containing a small craterlet. A ridge runs south-eastwards from Gioja, roughly parallel to that running from Challis towards Anaxagoras.

Wilkins has measured the heights of the following peaks, which are shown on the Polar Projection Chart: Gioja (1) 9,000 feet; (2) 8,000 feet; (3 and 4) each 3,500 feet; Gamma 7,000 feet (long. 174° 47′, lat. 86° 44′ North); Alpha 9,500 feet; Beta (1) 8,800 feet; Beta 8,000 feet.

GOLDSCHMIDT, −015 +960 [German astronomer, 1802-66]. A large ring, but with broken walls, especially low on the south, and with a crater on the east. On the floor is a small crater just to the west of the centre; also hills and numerous craterlets. Some are shown by Schmidt, but many others were found by Goodacre, Fauth and Barker. To the north is a low ring.

HAAS, −131 +681 [contemporary American selenographer]. A small but conspicuous crater, 9 miles in diameter, in the Mare Imbrium, to the south of Plato. To the north-east is the crater, D, with a smaller due north, while south is the craterlet, F. On the west is a little isolated mountain, Beta, rising 4,000 feet, although Schmidt makes it 6,000 feet. There are many craterlets and ridges in the neighbourhood.

KANE, +193 +892 [American explorer, 1820-57]. A low-rimmed ring to the south of Moigno, with craters, B and F, to the south and others on the walls. There is little detail on the floor, apart from some craterpits.

KIRCH, −076 +632 [German astronomer, 1639-1710]. A bright crater, with low walls; it is 7 miles in diameter, with a craterlet on the outer south slope and several on the south-east. To the south-east is the smaller crater, F. From Kirch, a long ridge winds across the Mare Imbrium.

LAMÈCH, +167 +679 [French selenographer, 1894-   ]. A most peculiar object to the north of Calippus, being, to all appearances, two halves of a crater which have drifted apart, so that a wide gap now intervenes. East of it is a mountain mass, and north-east a very lofty mountain ridge, while on the south, beyond a dark plain, is the great mountain, Calippus Alpha, rising to nearly 19,000 feet.

MAIN, +028 +988 [English astronomer, 1808-78]. This crater is 30 miles in diameter, and is overlapped by Challis. Owing to its position near the North Pole it is not easy to observe, but it is shown on some photographs. To the north are two large rings close to the limb, Shackleton and Shackleton A; the latter formation has the distinction of being the most northerly formation on the Moon, since the actual Pole lies on the interior.

MAYER, C. +134 +893 [German mathematician, 1719-83]. A crater 25 miles in diameter, with a central hill. To the east are two old rings, while on the south is a large low ring full of small craters. On the south-west is a large enclosure with low walls, and to the north-west parallel rows of hillocks run towards Peters.

METON, +104 +957 [Greek astronomer, *circa* 432 B.C.]. This is one of the very largest enclosed plains on the Moon's surface, being over 100 miles long and still further extended on the south by a great bay, really the portion of a ruined ring. There is another bay on the south-west. On the vast interior, which is of a light grey colour and in general smooth, is a small mountain close to the north rampart. Wilkins, with the 33-inch O.G., found a cleft from the mountain mass M on the N. wall towards the centre of the floor. There are also some ridges tending to an east-west direction, but all very low; and a few craterlets can be detected here and there. Between Meton and Barrow is a ring with high wall peaks, except on the north, and with three craterlets on the floor.

MOIGNO, +190 +914 [French Jesuit mathematician, 1804-84]. This crater, 20 miles in diameter, has a dark floor, with a crater on the north-east. Beyond the outer north-east glacis is a crater-chain.

MOUCHEZ, −080 +985 [French astronomer, 1821-92]. A large ring to the north-east of Anaxagoras, and near the limb at mean libration. On the floor are at least twelve craterlets, some ridges, and a low-rimmed ring. According to Arthur, the summit of the east wall is in +1160 +9765, and the most prominent craterlet on the eastern portion of the floor +1265 +9744. To the south-east is the smaller crater, A, with the even smaller, J, on its east wall, while the north-east wall is deformed by the intrusion of a crater which lies on the south wall of the ring M, containing craters and hills. To the north-west is a large ring, K, bearing craters on its walls. Just outside the south-west wall of Mouchez is a mountain of some altitude, and there is a smaller hill on the east.

NANSEN, +085 +980 [Norwegian explorer, 1861-1930]. A large ring to the east of Main, situated in 80° North latitude. It is in part shown on the Paris Atlas, L II, and the Belgian Atlas, XXXV. Nansen is about 70 miles in diameter, and made up of three formations that have coalesced; remnants of the former dividing walls can be traced in places. The southern component, marked Euctemon J on the I.A.U. Map, with a diameter of 37 miles, overlaps another ring, A, on the south. Of A, only the south wall now remains. The floor of Nansen is fairly smooth. At the peak Beta the wall rises to 11,000 feet, and at Gamma to 8,000 feet. Just south of the latter peak is the bright crater, Sacco, 19 miles in diameter.

Between Nansen and the limb is a low-walled enclosure, and beyond it lies the fine bright ring Esquivel. There are also indications of two walled-plains on the farther hemisphere. The south walls of these are occasionally visible in extreme libration.

This region was first studied in detail by Moore, and depicted in the B.A.A. Journal, Vol. 61, No. 7.

NEISON, +150 +925 [English selenographer, 1851-1938]. A small ringed-plain on the north-north-west of C. Mayer, with low walls and a smooth floor, except close to the walls, where there are many little craterlets, the largest being on the west. To the west is the crater A, and another to the south. Meton lies on the north-east.

PEARY, +030 +999 [American explorer, 1856-1920]. A deep crater very near the North Pole, being in 87° North latitude. It has a central peak. It lies to the west of Shackleton, and is 15 miles in diameter. Peary is prominent under low illumination, and is best seen after Full, but is at all times difficult to observe owing to its situation. For this reason, it does not appear on the older maps. On the south is a bright craterlet, A, the most easterly of three. There are also several hillocks, and some pits. The three craterlets really lie on the inner south slope of Nansen. On the north are hillocks and ridges, which are connected to, and are in part a portion of, the farther wall of Shackleton A, the ring within which is the actual Pole. Farther to the north, and on the other side, are several hills and ridges.

PETERS, +185 +928 [German astronomer, 1806-80]. This small ring lies north of Moigno, and has a craterlet on its floor. Between it and Moigno is the ring, X, and south-west the crater A, some craterlets and hills. To the north-east is a fine and lofty mountain, Beta, and the crater B.

PHILOLAUS, −165 +949 [Greek philosopher, *circa* 480 B.C.]. A crater 46 miles in diameter, with terraced walls rising 12,000 feet above a floor upon which are many irregularities, the two highest being south of the centre. Near the north-east wall is a ridge, and a craterlet-chain runs along the outer west wall, continuing far north to a ring which contains two prominent craters. There is a large landslip on the west. At the foot of the inner south-east wall there is a hillock, and there is another on the north-east. It has been reported that the shadow shows a slight brownish cast. Philolaus overlaps an ancient ring on the east.

PIAZZI SMYTH, −042 +667 [Astronomer Royal for Scotland, 1819-1900]. Although only 6 miles in diameter, this little crater is a conspicuous object, owing to its bright walls, which rise 3,500 feet above the floor. On the east is a ridge, with a craterlet to the south. There is a small hill on the north, and north-west a hill with a pit on its south.

PICO, −106 +717. An isolated white mountain, south of Plato, and rising 8,000 feet at the highest of its three peaks. Crevasses run down the slopes, and there are craterlets at its base. Pico remains bright at all times; at sunrise Haas found that the brightest part is apparently detached to the north-east. As the solar altitude increases, the plain to the west and north-west brightens, and then looks like part of the mountain. Later this area darkens again, and the point to the north-east joins the main mass, but separates again towards sunset. From these apparent variations, the shape and extent of Pico vary from time to time, and Pickering considered that the variable spots on the mountain were due to patches of snow. He also traced what he called a 'snow-storm' extending south from the north-east end and visible between co-longitude 65 and 110; this appearance was, in part, confirmed by Rawstron in 1933-4. An ideal picture of Pico was given by Nasmyth.

About 36 miles to the south is a lower, isolated mountain, 4,000 feet high, and with a little hill on its south-east. This peak has a shallow summit crater.

PITON, −012 +652. Another bright mountain, similar to Pico, and 7,000 feet high, isolated on the surface of the Mare Imbrium. The mountain appears double and has a craterlet on its summit, shown on both the Mt. Wilson and Pic-du-Midi photographs. To the south are two craters, and beyond these are three low hills, possibly the remains of an ancient ring. Gruithuisen suspected changes in the appearance of Piton, and this was confirmed by Pickering, who ascribed them to clouds or the deposits of hoar-frost.

Martz, in America, noted a sinuous bright streak from near the north base of Piton to the north of Piazzi Smyth, probably a ridge.

PLATO, −100 +782 [greatest Greek philosopher, 427-347 B.C.]. A beautiful walled-plain familiar to every observer, and situated in the bright mountainous region separating the Maria Imbrium and Frigoris. The floor, which is 60 miles in diameter, is of a dark steel-grey tint, in strong contrast to the bright surrounding walls, and the formation is distinctly visible under any illumination. At Full, Plato appears as an oval dusky spot.

The interior, one of the most critically and best observed regions on the Moon, is remarkably smooth and level, and is evidently the congealed surface of once-fluid lava. Under low illumination it is crossed by the steeple-like shadows cast by the peaks on the walls, which rise over 7,000 feet above the interior, and twice the average height of the rampart. A little to the west of the centre is a white and conspicuous cratercone, 2 miles in diameter, with a bowl-shaped interior; on the north-east is a pair of cones smaller than the first, the more northerly of these being three-quarters the diameter of its neigh-

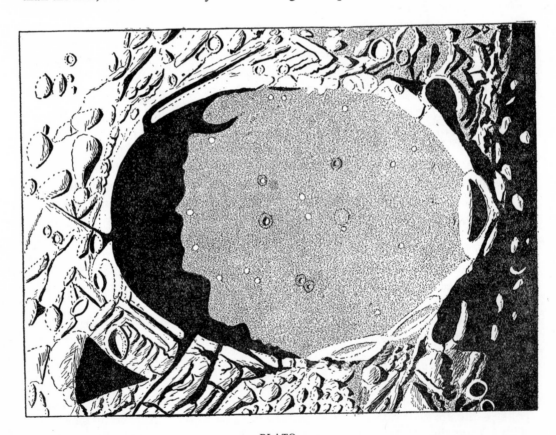

PLATO

3 April 1952, 21h. 30m. × 460, 33-inch Meudon Refractor, H. P. Wilkins

bour. Another cratercone lies to the south-east, and yet another on the east. There are also a large number of light spots, some of which probably have craterpits inside, too small for detection; Pickering found seventy spots in all. In addition to the cones and spots, there is a complex system of faint light streaks, only visible when the Sun has attained some altitude, and fully developed at local noon.

Mädler drew four little specks in the 'Mappa Selenographica', Gruithuisen seven; while others were gradually discovered by Challis, Dobie, Pratt, Gledhill, Dawes and Knott. Both cratercones and spots were carefully studied by Elger, Gledhill and Pratt (1869-71), and the results were summarized by Birt. Changes were inferred in relative intensity and visibility, and again by Elger, Allison, Gray and Stanley Williams (1880-82). Williams in particular carefully studied the floor, although his instrumental equipment was only a 6½-inch reflector. Changes were strongly suspected from a comparison of the two series of observations, and two fine shaded drawings, typical of the period, appeared in Neison's *Moon*, 1876.

The American observer, Prof. W. H. Pickering, resurveyed the floor in 1892 and subsequent years, as did Molesworth in 1896. Pickering, in 1904, described the floor as 'one of the most continuously active volcanic regions on the Moon'.

Since then the interior has been carefully and systematically observed, and in 1920 Dr. W. H. Steavenson noted several spots with the 28-inch Greenwich refractor, but only five were ever seen as cratercones or craterlets.

Wilkins has observed the interior, every lunation, since 1936, with apertures of 6 to 15 inches, and noted apparent changes in intensity and visibility among the spots and streaks. Goodacre, Elger and others recorded the occasional concealing of known floor detail, apparently by vapour of some sort. Thornton, 9 October 1945, 11h. 23½m., noted a bright flash on the floor close to the west wall, as though the surface had been struck by a meteor; Birt noted flashes of light playing over the floor. Klein, Neison and Pratt noted the appearance of some fog-like veil on several occasions, and Webb records parallel beams of light over the floor at sunrise, seen long before by Bianchini.

One of the best views ever obtained of Plato was probably that enjoyed by the Authors on 3 April 1952, with the great 33-inch Meudon refractor. On this occasion four perfectly clear and indeed glaring cratercones were seen, with interior shadows, but no trace of any shadows on the outer slopes, thus proving the slight elevation above the level of the floor. Twenty-one light spots were also charted, one surrounded by a light area, while three streaks were seen in the north-east quarter.

The system of light streaks develops as the Sun's altitude increases, and also apparently varies in different lunations. Some of the streaks seem to be merely extensions of those emanating from Anaxagoras across the dark Mare Frigoris; others connect the spots, while a prominent triangular patch, the 'Sector', extends from a diffuse light area to the east of the nearly central cone to the south-east wall.

The walls are divided into distinct sections; on the south are some small landslips; on the east a large mass has become detached and now intrudes on the floor, leaving a triangular cavity filled with shadow at sunrise.

The inner north-east slope is broad, and contains two shallow, elliptical depressions; further west the wall consists of separate mountain masses. A prominent valley issues from the south-west wall, and runs south-east, gradually narrowing, to the remains of a large ruined ring due south of Plato and on the Mare Imbrium. The bright mountain Pico stands on its southern rim.

The environs of Plato are rough, and consist of a mass of little hills, craterlets and a low plateau, divided by valleys; some winding clefts can at times be detected. On the north-east is the deep crater, A, with numerous smaller craters around and a remarkable group to the east. West of Plato are two double craters, many hills and little bright mountains, the outlying heights of the Lunar Alps, which end at Plato.

The highlands of Plato narrow at the crater A, and the cape Plato Phi, rises 1,500 feet above the dark Mare, which is only 55 miles across to the opposite, 4,500-feet high cape, Timæus Gamma; hence, as Neison remarks, the two are in sight of each other.

The enormous amount of detail on the surface surrounding Plato defies description, and recourse should be had to the map. None of the hills are of any especial height except at the end of the main Alpine chain, where we meet with peaks of 15,000 feet altitude. The rugged mountainous region east of Plato, and south of A, contains peaks up to 4,500 feet, but farther east the detail consists almost entirely of craters and crater-pits, often in chains, the whole forming one of the most interesting regions on the Moon.

For many years the floor of Plato was considered to darken as the Sun's altitude increased, and R. A. Proctor was, probably, the first to question the reality of this variation, which at first sight seems perfectly clear even in a small instrument. We, however, believe the reverse to be true, and that the apparent darkening at local noon or beyond is due to contrast with the bright surrounding walls, which brighten up considerably more than the area which they enclose. That the floor *does* brighten is evident when we consider how the light streaks then appear, and how many of the spots, in particular one near a small ruined ring abutting on the west wall, often loom larger under high illumination. Haas considers the floor to be darkest near the border, but this is, at least partly, due to contrast with the brilliant wall nearby, and does not indicate any considerable convexity of floor. Indeed the entire area, apart from the shadows, appeared equally illuminated when examined with the 33-inch refractor, and there was also no sign of the fault reported by earlier observers as crossing the floor from north-west to the south-east; neither was there any indication of the cleft shown by some observers as crossing the floor diagonally from the middle of the western wall to a valley on the north-north-west.

The shaded drawing of this magnificent lunar formation was made under excellent conditions with the great telescope, and may be relied upon as depicting, with accuracy, the relative sizes and intensities of the cratercones, spots and streaks visible under that particular angle of illumination.

PROTAGORAS, +072 +828 [Greek philosopher, 481-411 B.C.]. A small crater with a central hill, situated on the north border of the Mare Frigoris and south-west of Archytas. On the east is a smaller crater, B, and south a cleft, which ends, on the west, in three craterlets. North are obscure rings and isolated hills.

REESE, —182 +724 [contemporary American selenographer]. A small bright crater, 9 miles in diameter, east of Pico. A craterlet, A, lies to the north-west, between Reese and the Teneriffe Mountains.

RHODES, —101 +990 A crater on the limb north of Philolaus, entirely on the farther hemisphere and therefore excessively difficult to examine. A similar but slightly smaller crater, Rhodes A, adjoins it to the east.

SACCO, +075 +985 [Contemporary Spanish astronomer.] This was formerly known as Scoresby A, and is a fine, regular, bright-walled crater, 19 miles in diameter, to the north-west of Scoresby and just outside Nansen.

SCORESBY, +052 +978 [English explorer, 1789-1857]. This crater is 36 miles in diameter, and is deep, with a twin-peaked central hill and terraced walls. On 10 October 1948 Arthur found a crater on the floor between the central hill and the north hill, two craters on the south wall, and another on the north-eastern rim. Moore has found a crater on the outer south and a hill on the inner north-west, with another hill on the outer north-east. To the north, and close to the wall, is a hill, and beyond it two minute spots. Due north are three small craters and a hillock, while to the north-west is the deep crater Sacco, with a hill on its outer north slope and a craterlet to the east. The wall of Nansen lies north of Sacco, with a peak rising 8,000 feet. West is the imperfect formation Nansen A.

SHACKLETON, +014 +996 [English Polar explorer, 1874-1922]. A large ring north of Main, with the crater Gioja, on its south wall. North of it is another ring, A, within which lies the North Pole. The west wall of Shackleton is massive, but it is lower on the east, and here is an incomplete crater, C. On the floor are three minor ridges and some low hills. On the south wall, and west of Gioja, is a small crater (lettered B in Moore's chart), with two little peaks to the east and three hillocks just beyond the wall on the south-west. On the north-east, where it joins A, there is a grand peak rising 9,000 feet, and at this point the wall divides, enclosing a small plain, like a 'pocket' on the wall. West of this peak are several wall-peaks, though of inferior altitude, and at the west end a craterlet and a peak, Delta, rising 8,000 feet. Immediately to the west is Peary. There is a lofty peak, Beta, on the farther wall of A, and beyond the Pole, thus on the farther hemisphere. Still farther on this hemisphere are hills, and a crater, C. These features are mapped in the special Polar Projection Chart. These mountains so near to the Pole are bathed in perpetual sunlight.

SHEEPSHANKS, +150 +859 [woman benefactor to astronomy, 1789-1876]. A crater on the north border of the Mare Frigoris, and to the south-west of Mayer C. On the north-west is the crater A, and on both north and south are old rings.

TENERIFFE MOUNTAINS, −150 +740. A bright mountain range east of Plato, and on the Mare Imbrium. Two of the mountains on the north are prominent, and farther east is another, rising 8,000 feet. This mountain marks the wall of a large, ancient ring on the south-east of Plato. To the south-west lie two lower groups, with two hills between them and Pico. All these mountains are remarkably bright, and appear brilliant when close to the terminator.

THEÆTETUS, +084 +602 [Greek philosopher (friend of Plato), *circa* 380 B.C.]. A bright crater 16 miles in diameter, with walls rising 7,000 feet above the depressed floor. On 21 April 1953 Moore, using the 33-inch Meudon refractor, recorded a low but fairly bright central hill, at once confirmed by Wilkins and by Bertaud. The floor is depressed 5,000 feet below the outer surface. On the north a chain of hills, from which a cleft runs north-west, crosses the Palus Nebularum. To the west is a valley, and beyond this valley rises a lofty mountain, as well as a bright crater, A. On the north the hills are so arranged as to suggest the remains of an ancient ring. There are indications of a still larger ring between it and the south glacis of Cassini. In 1902 the French astronomer, Charbonneaux, using the 33-inch Meudon refractor, saw what he described as an 'unmistakable white cloud' form close to Theætetus; and on 24 December 1952 Moore, using his $12\frac{1}{2}$-inch reflector, saw a hazy line of light crossing the shadow-filled interior.

TIMÆUS, − 004 +890 [Italian philosopher, *circa* 400 B.C.]. This bright crater is 22 miles in diameter, and lies on the north border of the Mare Frigoris. On the floor is a double central hill, and there is a craterlet on the south-west wall. Timæus is the centre of a minor ray system.

TROUVELOT, +066 +758 [French astronomer, 1827-95]. A small crater $5\frac{1}{2}$ miles in diameter in the Alpine highlands, south of the Alpine Valley, and surrounded by hills and craterlets.

VÄISÄLÄ, −180 +990 (invisible at mean libration) [contemporary Finnish astronomer]. Väisälä is so badly placed on the lunar disk that it can only be seen under favourable conditions of libration, and so far only the Authors appear to have drawn it in any detail. It lies eastwards along the limb from Shackleton, and is a fine formation almost 50 miles in diameter; the outer eastern glacis is disturbed by another prominent crater, A.

South of Väisälä lies a low-walled ring, 15 miles in diameter, and to the north-west is a crater, D. Väisälä itself seems to have a comparatively smooth floor, on which Moore has suspected an axial ridge; there are also slight indications that the formation is made up of the fusion of two old plains, and there is certainly the wreck of an old ring abutting on the north. This formation will repay further study.

WASHBOWL, THE. +065 +649. This curious little formation lies inside Cassini A, and has been described with it. In small telescopes it looks like a mountain, a large aperture is necessary to detect its true nature.

XVI

This section contains one of the finest of all lunar features, the Sinus Iridum, a great bay of the vast Mare Imbrium. Of the craters, Pythagoras, by its great size, lofty walls and interesting details, easily stands foremost. Other notable objects are the lofty peaks of the Jura Mountains, flanking the Sinus Iridum, and the great rings Babbage, South, Anaximander and Œnopides.

A large portion is occupied by the dark plains of the Maria Imbrium and Frigoris, with, in the far east, the Sinus Roris.

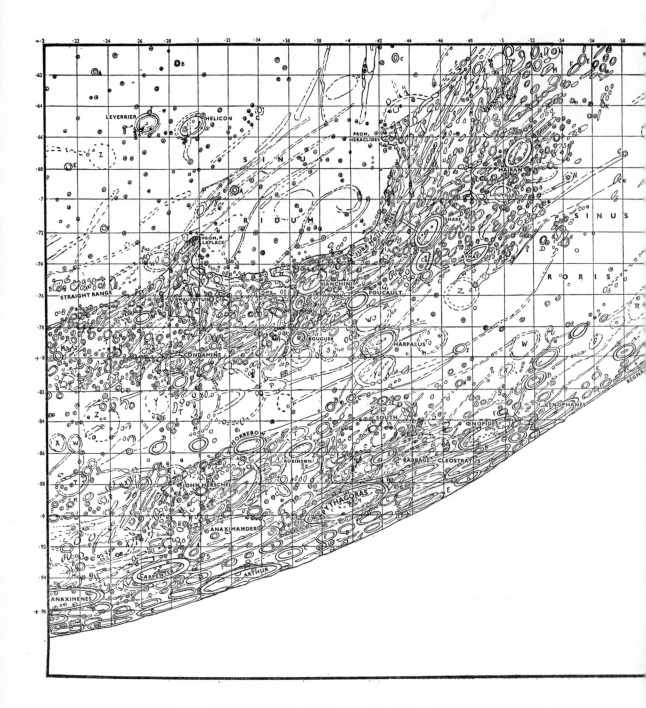

XVI

ANAXIMANDER, —313 +914 [Greek philosopher, 611-547 B.C.]. A fine formation, 54 miles in diameter, with walls rising 6,500 feet on the west but 9,800 feet on the south-west. There is a crater on the south-east crest, and another on the south just beyond the crest. On the interior are two craters on the western portion; of these one, A, is deep, and there are other small craters and some ridges. Anaximander overlaps an older ring, S, on the north. This has a high peak, Gamma, on the east, and north of this a crater-chain runs to Pythagoras. To the north and near the limb is a large crater, formerly A but now called Arthur. On the northern portion of the floor of Anaximander is a short cleft.

ANAXIMENES, —211 +953 [Greek philosopher, 585-528 B.C.]. A great ring, 65 miles in diameter, with walls rising 8,000 feet on the east but lower elsewhere. On the floor are some craters at the foot of the inner slopes. North is a crater, A, with lofty peak-sprinkled walls. Anaximenes overlaps an older ring, P, on the north-east. The floor of Anaximenes is smooth, apart from the craters near the inner slopes, and is rather dark in tint. On the north and south there are wall peaks of 3,200 feet altitude. South is the relic of a large old ring.

ARTHUR, —323 +940 [contemporary English amateur astronomer]. This object was formerly known as Anaximander C (I.A.U. Map, 1935). It is a great walled-plain on

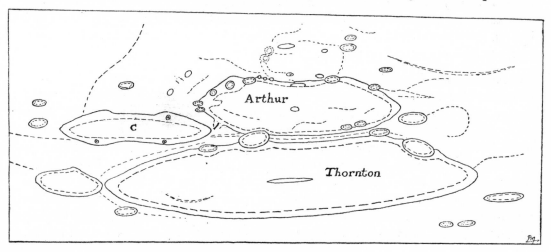

ARTHUR AND THORNTON

Chart by Patrick Moore, from observations made 1950-1952: 8½-inch Reflector; 12½-inch Reflector; 33-inch O.G.

the north-east limb, just visible under conditions of mean libration. The diameter is estimated at 60 miles by Moore, who first mapped it in detail with the 33-inch Meudon refractor, 1952, but this value is only rough. Accurately shown in the 300-inch map, but either omitted or misplaced in all other maps. The walls are of very considerable height. The south wall is distorted, and there are indications of an old ring abutting on it, though the 'walls' of this now consist only of discontinuous ridges and mounds.

The south-east wall is interrupted by a large craterlet and an even larger one lies on the outer glacis of the north-east wall. Two more break the north wall, but the most conspicuous of the wall-craters is that in the north-west, connected by a ridge to the crater, Arthur C. The west wall is broad, though not exceptionally lofty, and on the inner slope of it is a leaf-shaped table land. There is evidence of terracing all round.

The floor contains a central mountain of some height, and several ridges.

To the north-west lies Arthur C, a well-formed ring some 30 miles in diameter, very difficult to examine in detail owing to its extreme foreshortening, and closely north of Arthur is an even greater formation, now called Thornton.

AYMAT, −485 +731 [Spanish astronomer]. A crater 12 miles in diameter, lying north-east of Sharp. It is somewhat pear-shaped, and has a central peak. North of Aymat is a very old ring, Z.

BABBAGE, −430 +860 [English mathematician, 1792-1871]. This is not a true crater, but is due to the fusion of two large rings. South of the centre of the southern component is a deep crater, A, with a smaller to the north-east, from which a slight ridge runs south-east, and is sometimes to be seen as a bright line amid the shadow. On the south crest is a row of little peaks, some craterlets on the outer slope and a partial ring, S. This is really on the floor of South, the formation adjoining Babbage on the south. The east wall is tolerably high. The northern component contains some ridges and small craters. Pythagoras lies close to the north-west, and was much misplaced by Goodacre. North is the ring, F, and on the mean libration limb a double formation, A and E.

BIANCHINI, −372 +752 [Italian astronomer, 1662-1729]. A fine crater 25 miles in diameter, near the crest of the Jura Mountains, the range which borders the Sinus Iridum. Bianchini has high, polygonal walls, a central mountain on the floor and a crater on the north, and another on the inner south. To the north-west are ancient rings, while on the south-west a valley runs to the Sinus Iridum. A ridge crosses the floor of Bianchini with a shorter ridge near the west wall, probably a landslide. To the north-west is a peculiar crater with a remarkable crater-chain on its east, running past the west wall of Bianchini. The peak Beta, on the south wall, rises 7,400 feet, but on the west the wall is higher, and here a peak rises 8,500 feet above the floor. The wall is lower on the south-west, and between it and the border of the Sinus Iridum are several craters.

BOUGUER, −357 +790 [French hydrographer, 1698-1758]. This crater is 15 miles in diameter, and is on the border of the Mare Frigoris. It has a central craterlet, and a portion of a concentric ring on the eastern part of the floor. On the west is a crater-chain, on the east rim of a very low, large depression, A, which is crossed by low ridges. To the north are three craters and another old ring, L, while south are many craters. On the east are small hills which encircle Bouguer, and to the north-west, beyond L, is a group of five little hills closely grouped together. On the Mare to the north-east is an old ring, S.

CARPENTER, —273 +936 [English astronomer, 1840-99]. A fine and regular ring, adjoining Anaximander on the north-west. It has a central mountain, with a pit to the south, and a ridge to the east wall. On the inner south is a craterlet, and there are also two craterlets on the southern portion of the floor. Carpenter overlaps an older ring on the west. Between it and the limb are many rings of which Arthur, D, G and J are the most prominent. There is a small mountain immediately to the west of Carpenter.

CLEOSTRATUS, —478 +872 [Greek poet-astronomer, *circa* 500 B.C.]. A crater with steep, narrow walls and a smooth floor. To the east is a crater with a dark interior. Wilkins has seen a long ridge on the interior of Cleostratus and two hills on the inner north, possibly landslips. North are two craters close to the limb T. There is a lofty peak on the north-east wall and to the south of Cleostratus a long ridge running in the direction of Xenophanes.

CONDAMINE, —281 +803 [French physicist, 1701-74]. A crater on the southern border of the Mare Frigoris, 30 miles in diameter with walls rising 4,000 feet in places. There is a craterlet on the north-west crest and a pass in the north wall, which gives access into a low ring. On the floor are some craterlets and hills. To the north-east is the crater, A, to the east of which are three elongated rings abutting upon a pair of craters from which a crater-rill runs south. On the west is a very interesting region, extending to Plato and consisting of a plateau with many little hills, numerous craters and craterlets. Many of these craterlets are arranged in chains; there are also some old rings. An old ring, G, lies on the outer north-west slope, and has a minute central hill and three craterlets on its north-west rim. To the north of the crater A is a hill, T, on the Mare Frigoris; also the four craters E, F, M and B. To the east of Condamine is the crater D, while the south-east wall is prolonged and evidently marks the site of an ancient ring. To the south is the bright peak, Beta.

FOUCAULT, —408 +770 [French physicist, 1819-68]. This crater, which lies on the south border of the Mare Frigoris and marks the boundary of the narrowest portion of the Sinus Iridum highlands, is 10 miles in diameter, and has a central hill, according to Goodacre; though this is not shown on the 1919 Mt. Wilson photograph. There appears to be a craterlet on the western portion of the floor. To the south-east is a mountain of some height; north is the obscure ring, W, occupying the space between Foucault and Harpalus.

FRIGORIS, MARE, +420 +760 to —420 +900. The 'Sea of Cold'. A large though foreshortened dark plain in the northern part of the disk, and lying between the highlands of Aristoteles, Plato and the Alps on the south; defined by Archytas, Timæus and

Fontenelle on the north. With low powers it appears as a narrow dusky streak across the northern portion of the Moon. The narrowest portion, only 44 miles, lies between the two capes, Timæus Gamma and Plato Phi, which are in sight from each other.

HARPALUS, —416 +795 [Greek astronomer, *circa* 460 B.C.]. A deep crater, 22 miles in diameter, with lofty walls rising no less than 16,000 feet on the east. On the floor is a hill a little south of the centre, a small crater under the north wall and a very low ring on the inner west. Abutting on the west wall are the remains of two craters. Moore found, 1952, two hills on the north-east part of the interior and also suspected a low ridge concentric with the north wall. An old ring, 17 miles in diameter, abuts on the north wall; this is traceable only as its floor is slightly darker than the surrounding country. On the outer south is a very low ring, and north-east are some low hills. Harpalus is the centre of a minor ray system.

HELICON, —298 +648 [Greek mathematician, *circa* 400 B.C.]. A crater, 13 miles in diameter and the companion to Leverrier. It is of very considerable depth, 5,000 feet, and has a central crater and a craterlet on the south-east portion of the floor. The most remarkable feature, however, is a curved ridge which crosses the floor to a crater, B, on the open plain to the south. Fauth showed a double central crater and a crater on the inner south, a hill on the west and a concentric ridge on the west, but omitted Gaudibert's two hills on the east. There are many craterlets on the surrounding portion of the Mare Imbrium.

The floor of Helicon is not level but drops considerably from west to east, and the east wall shows definite signs of terracing. Moore, using an 8½-inch reflector, on 18 March 1951, noted a craterlike depression in the west wall.

HERACLIDES, PROM., —418 +656 [Greek astronomer, 388-310 B.C.]. The east promontory of the Sinus Iridum, rising 4,000 feet above the plain. Cassini first detected here the outline of a female head, that of the 'Moon Maiden', only visible under certain conditions of lighting. This appearance has since been confirmed by others but is very rarely to be seen. Moore has found a large, obscure ring between Heraclides and Delisle. The east and west walls of this obscure ring are tolerably prominent ridges, and appear on some photographs, but the other portions are very low.

HERSCHEL, J., —305 +885 [English astronomer, son of Sir W. Herschel, 1792-1871]. This is nothing more than a vast ridge-bordered portion of the surface, about 90 miles across, with a lofty mountain on its western border. On the vast interior are numerous hills, craters and ridges, many marking the sites of ancient rings. The southern wall is marked by craters in places; the largest crater on the interior is nearly central. On the north-west portion is an old ring, K, on the west rim of which is the crater, H. The south-west part contains many craterlets, some in chains; here the wall is very broken and reduced to isolated fragments. There are several craters on the south-east portion, while on the north-east is a long, but not deep, cleft, some hills and ridges. A fine view was obtained by Moore on 24 April 1953, with the 33-inch Meudon refractor, and over eighty objects were charted on the floor. The drawing, which was checked at the time by Wilkins, is reproduced here.

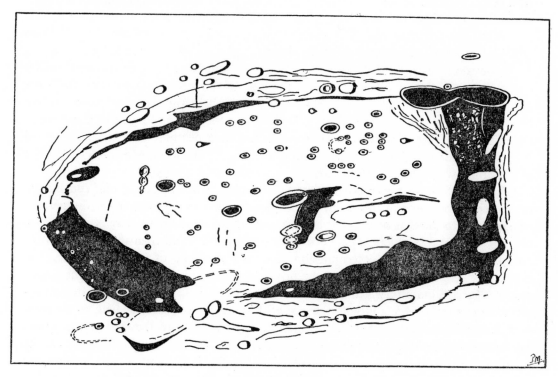

JOHN HERSCHEL

24 April 1953, 21h. 33-inch O.G. (Meudon) × 560, Patrick Moore

HORREBOW, −339 +854 [Danish astronomer, 1679-1764]. This crater lies to the south-east of Herschel and overlaps an older ring, A, on the west. The walls are terraced and there is a crater on the inner east. North-east is the small crater, B, while to the south-west and on the Mare Frigoris is the fine crater group of B, *f*, E and M, with craterlets, hills and the small mountain, T. East is the crater, T with a broken west wall.

IRIDUM, SINUS, --375 +710. The 'Bay of Rainbows'. This is one of the finest of all lunar landscapes, and forms a great bay of the Mare Imbrium. It is roughly semicircular, and what may have once been a southern border has almost entirely disappeared; now there are merely low ridges in its place and these disappear soon after sunrise.

From the Mare the surface of the Bay gradually falls in a regular slope to 2,000 feet below the level of the Mare on the south. The bordering range, now called the Jura Mountains, is very rugged and contains numerous peaks, rather low on the west and east but of great height in the more central portions. A great mountain near Sharp rises at least 20,000 feet, and to the east of it is another somewhat lower pinnacle. On the surface of the Sinus is the crater A, which stands on the site of an old ring. A itself is on a raised plateau. Along the western border are many isolated hills and much débris, evidently fallen from the bordering crest; scattered over the surface are many minute craterlets. The principal craterlets and the ridges are shown on the map. Under high illumination some white rings probably indicate the sites of buried craters.

The western cape, Laplace, rises over 8,000 feet and has two large and two smaller craterlets on its plateau-like summit. On the west of this promontory is clear evidence of an old ring with a central peak. Here and there valleys run from the plain into the highlands; the largest is that west of Bianchini. On the east and north of Cape Hera-clides is a small ring of which the western part has disappeared. Moore found a ruined ring to the south of Heraclides and the bright crater, C. Herschel, which lies on the site of its former wall. On the interior are four craterlets and a ridge.

The bordering crest is of great interest. Beginning with Laplace, it first runs north, then swerves east; and at this point a delicate cleft runs to the plain from Maupertuis. Immediately to the east of the cleft are two craters, while the plain here is dotted with hills, like gigantic boulders. There are some other craters and then the valley west of Sharp. This has a rounded termination, evidently the relic of an ancient ring. The mountains here are of great height, the principal crest peak being Delta, to the south-east of Sharp. Soon afterwards the crest begins to turn south with small craters at intervals, and a lofty ridge a little to the east of the actual crest; of these heights the great peak Sharp Delta rises 20,000 feet, overshadowing the rings to the west of the crater. The mountains now begin to become less crowded, and the bordering crest lowers to the somewhat scattered group around Heraclides. On the hinterland of this portion are many lofty peaks, some nearly 15,000 feet in altitude but gradually falling off towards Mairan. On the far south-east the most prominent mass is M, south-west of Mairan. South of it is the crater A, with E to the south-west, on the border of the Mare Imbrium. Many of the peaks are not easily measurable owing to their position.

JURA MOUNTAINS, —400 +735. The great mountain range bordering the Sinus Iridum, and already described under that heading.

LAPLACE, PROM. —300 +725 [Great French mathematician, 1749-1827]. The western headland of the Sinus Iridum, rising 9,000 feet above the Sinus and 7,200 feet above the Mare Imbrium. There is a row of four craterlets on the summit and a larger crater on the north, together with smaller and shallow depressions, also a ridge. To the west is an old ring, with two craterlets on its western rim.

LEVERRIER, —268 +647 [French mathematician, 1811-77]. A companion crater to Helicon, 11 miles in diameter, with a wall rising 1,500 feet above the Mare, and with a floor depressed 4,500 feet below the level of the surrounding plain. It has a low central hill and a crater on the inner north, and two more hills on the inner south. There is a small crater on the southern crest. From the terraced walls a ridge projects on to the

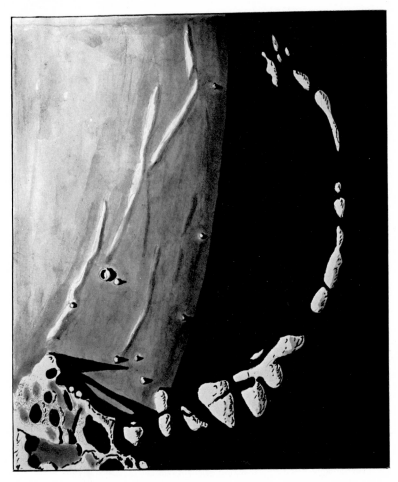

7a. The Sinus Iridum at Lunar Sunrise. Drawing by
H. P. Wilkins

7b. The North-East Limb, showing Pythagoras. Photograph taken at the
Pic du Midi Observatory

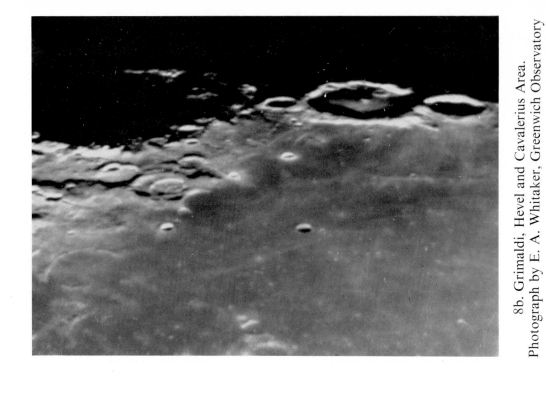

8b. Grimaldi, Hevel and Cavalerius Area.
Photograph by E. A. Whitaker, Greenwich Observatory

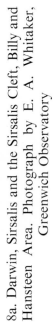

8a. Darwin, Sirsalis and the Sirsalis Cleft, Billy and
Hansteen Area. Photograph by E. A. Whitaker,
Greenwich Observatory

floor. To the outside are many mounds and craterlets. Leverrier is very dark under low illumination, and sometimes difficult to trace at Full. A ridge runs south from the wall. To the south, among numerous craterlets, are the two small craters A and B.

LOUVILLE, —513 +692 [French mathematician, 1671-1732]. A triangular and dusky area with shallow craters on its rim. It lies to the north of Mairan, from which it is separated by some ridges and many craterlets. To the west is a somewhat similar formation, with many craterlets on the interior. East are craterlets and a few ridges, rapidly declining in altitude as the Sinus Roris is approached. The highest of the many hills near Louville rises 5,000 feet. From the north wall a ridge runs, in a serpentine curve, to the crater Sharp A. On the Sinus Roris, to the north-east, is a remarkable arrangement of hillocks and craters. Of the latter D and K are the largest. Between this group and the border of the Sinus is a fine, long cleft.

MAIRAN, —514 +664 [French scientist, 1678-1771]. A fine crater 25 miles in diameter, with lofty walls, rising 15,000 feet above the floor on the west, but somewhat lower on the east, and with a crater on the south crest. There is a valley on the inner south wall, and three craterlets on the inner east, while a low ridge crosses the floor. It is very doubtful whether there is a central mountain. From the south wall a craterlet-chain runs to the south-east, and there is a curve of small craters on the outer east. Farther east is a low, partial ring, S, and north of this a craterlet situated on a small bright area. On the west and north-west are many hills; also lofty mountains, some over 15,000 feet in altitude. Farther towards Sharp are peaks of 20,000 feet.

MAUPERTUIS, —303 +756 [French mathematician, 1698-1759]. An irregular formation, about 20 miles in diameter, to the north of Cape Laplace. It is almost too complex for easy description. There is a gap in the south rampart opening into a valley, V, which runs to the Sinus Iridum. On the north is a pass into a ruined ring. On the interior is a ridge, also some low hills and depressions. West, beyond some craterlets and hills, is the deep and bright crater A, with a smaller, C, on the south-west, and a still smaller crater beyond, near the border of the Mare Imbrium. To the north-west is a plain traversed by a row of craters and extending to Condamine. Eastwards is a confused jumble of craters, ridges and mountains, while on the south-east is the mountainous border of the Sinus Iridum.

ŒNOPIDES, —489 +838 [Greek geometer, 500-430 B.C.]. A great ring 42 miles in diameter, near the limb, with somewhat irregular walls, bearing a crater on the south-east crest, some gaps on the south and craterlets in places. On the interior are two craterlets near the west wall, a hill near the east wall and two pits close under the inner south wall. To the east is A, within which Moore found a low central hill, 8 April 1952, with the 33-inch Meudon refractor. The crater A is joined on its west wall to a large, shallow enclosure. To the south-east of A are two lofty hills, and A itself seems to have broken into a larger ring whose east wall now alone remains, looking usually like a simple ridge.

247

PYTHAGORAS, —397 +894 [Ionian-Greek philosopher, *circa* 500 B.C.]. One of the greatest of all the lunar rings, but close to the limb. It is 75 miles in diameter, with magnificently terraced walls, towering 17,000 feet in places at peaks which stand out boldly. On the floor is a fine multiple central mountain group, the highest peak of which rises 5,000 feet. Moore discovered, 7 April 1952, with the 33-inch Meudon refractor, a summit craterlet on this peak, confirmed by Wilkins with the same giant telescope. There are some low hills on the interior. The north wall is but little elevated above the outer level, and the inner slope here is full of depressions. On the inner north-west are two craters, another on the south crest, and one on the inner south, also two craterlets on the north. Along the inner east slope are large landslips, while there is a narrow cleft close to the north-east crest. A fine craterlet-chain runs towards Anaximander. To the north are some large craters, E and D being the deepest, while on the east is the crater F, on the outer slope of Babbage.

RÉGNAULT, —586 +810 [French physicist and chemist, 1810-78]. A small crater close to the limb, with a larger crater, B, containing a central hill, on the south, and two others, E and D, to the west.

ROBINSON, —370 +858 [Irish astronomer, 1792-1882]. A small crater with a craterlet on its west, and terraced walls. The floor is smooth. On the south is a low ring, T; east are two craters on the west border of South, while to the north are some lofty mountains and some old rings.

RORIS, SINUS. The 'Bay of Dew'. This is really a bay on the far east of the Mare Frigoris, or alternatively, it might be regarded as a northern extension of the vast Oceanus Procellarum. The centre is in —530 +720. On its surface are some low ridges and the peculiar formation Rümker (Section XVII). It extends almost to the limb at mean libration, only the narrow mountainous regions of Gerard and Lavoisier separating the dark grey plain from the limb. There are some low rings here and there and a few isolated hills, none of any great height.

SHARP, —451 +716 [English astronomer, 1651-1742]. A deep crater, 22 miles in diameter, with a crater on the inner north-east. On the floor is a small central mountain, some mounds and a ridge from the west. There are indications of terracing on the inner east slope. On the north is the crater, C, with three craterlets on its interior and with its east wall replaced by a crater-valley. North of C is a small crater. West of C are numerous craterlets and ridges, and from the west glacis of Sharp, C. F. O. Smith found, 21 March 1948, a valley running westwards. To the north-east is the large crater, Aymat. All around Sharp are lofty mountains, the highest 20,000 feet in altitude, lying on the east, although many peaks here are nearly as lofty. The hills are lower on the west, and here is the relic of an ancient ring, of which only the west rim now remains.

SOUTH, —412 +842 [English astronomer, 1785-1867]. A large enclosure, with low and broken walls, highest on the east and with little peaks at intervals. The interior is very rough, and there is a crater near the centre. On the eastern portion is a large, ancient ring, while on the west are two obvious craters, and south a row of small craters. There are also numerous ridges crossing the interior. On the northern part is the low ring, S. There is a crater-chain on the north-west border, where the wall is very discontinuous.

STRAIGHT RANGE, —203 +748 to —244 +748. A long and narrow range of little mountains, extending for 40 miles and situated 100 miles east of Plato on the surface of the Mare Imbrium. The peaks on the east and the west rise very abruptly from the dark Mare, and being bright present a striking appearance, although the highest peaks rise only 6,000 feet. There are lower hills between these greater heights. The brightest of the peaks is situated midway along the range; but the mountains are not as brilliant as Pico or Piton.

THORNTON (invisible at mean libration) [contemporary English selenographer]. Really situated on the averted hemisphere, and north of Arthur. It is difficult to examine owing to its position, but is of great depth and of considerable size. There is an elongated central mountain and also several hills, confined to the eastern portion of the floor. The south-east wall is slightly distorted. To the north-east of Thornton are indications of another great ring, and two small craters. Moore found a curved ridge on the floor, 22 April 1952, with an 8½-inch reflector.

XENOPHANES, —535 +838 [Ionian Greek philosopher, 570-478 B.C.]. A fine ring near the limb, east of Cleostratus and Œnopides. Neison says that it is as deep as Pythagoras, and has a diameter of 185 miles; this would make Xenophanes the largest true walled-plain on the Moon, but as a matter of fact the real diameter is only about 67 miles, so that Neison's value, as given, is either a wild overestimate or a misprint.

Xenophanes has lofty walls, and a massive, elongated central mountain. Observing, 25 July 1953, with Wilkins' 15¼-inch reflector, the Authors detected a summit craterlet on the exact centre of the mountain mass. There is a ruined ring on the inner east floor, and a crater on the floor just under the east wall. The walls are crowned by high peaks, and several craterlets.

South of Xenophanes is a crater, K; further south still, on the Mare Frigoris, other craters, of considerable size and depth. Between Xenophanes and Régnault are several craters, two of which, E and D, are deep; there are also two considerable craters, D and A, on the north-west, near Cleostratus.

There are several rings between Xenophanes and the limb at maximum libration, some of which are large and deep; but the whole area is difficult to study, owing to its unfavourable position, and our knowledge of the environs of Xenophanes is still far from complete.

XVII

This section includes a small portion of the north-east limb, and is chiefly occupied by the Sinus Roris, really a part of the Oceanus Procellarum. About fifty craters are shown on the map, the majority of them in no way prominent. Of the principal objects, Repsold, Gerard and Rümker present features of interest, the latter being possibly a 'Wargentin type' of formation.

Under favourable conditions of libration, several craters and other objects can be seen beyond Gerard and the mean-libration limb generally. These lie on the normally averted hemisphere.

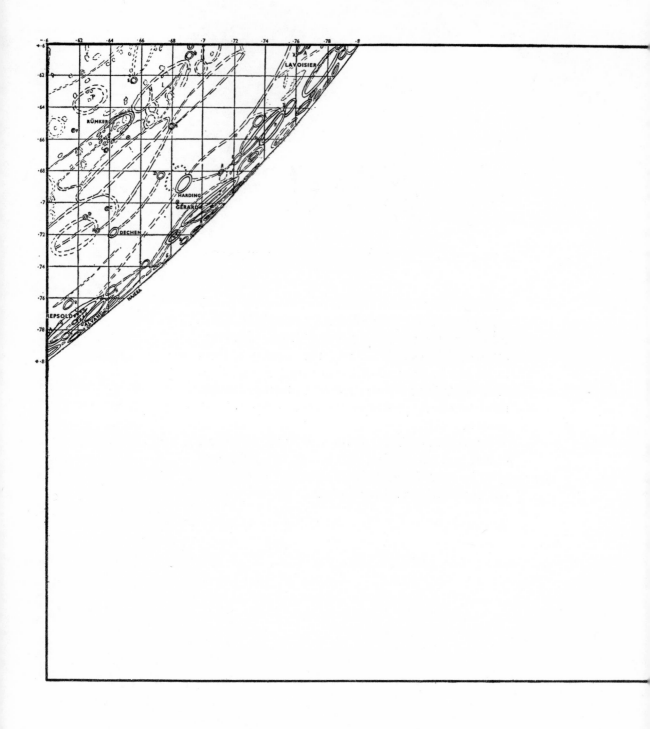

XVII

DECHEN, −643 +719 [German geologist, 1800-89]. A crater 7 miles in diameter, situated on a long ridge from Repsold to Harding D. On the west are three craters, A, B and C.

GALVANI, −630 +768 [Italian physicist, 1737-98]. A small crater close to Repsold, and described under that heading.

GERARD, −705 +700 [Scottish explorer, 1792-1839]. A ringed-plain 50 miles in diameter, with a long ridge running down the centre of the floor. At the northern end of this ridge Schmidt shows a crater. On the inner west slope are a hillock and a craterlet. Outside on the west is a hillock, a, and on the east a crater and a low ring. On the south are the craters E, F and P; between E and F is a low ridge, while from F a ridge runs to the crater Lavoisier S. This is on the limb at mean libration.

HARDING, −688 +688 [German astronomer, 1765-1834]. A distinct crater, 14 miles in diameter, with low walls, from which ridges run south-west to the craters B, R and D. The latter has a low twin-peaked central hill, and a deep crater, E, on its north wall. South of D is a 'ghost' crater, and north-west of this a white spot. Harding itself has intruded upon a 'ghost' ring. The hill at −681 +676 is seen to be surrounded by a white nimbus, under high light.

LAVOISIER, −776 +617 [French chemist, 1743-94]. A crater 40 miles in diameter, with a smooth floor apart from a ridge close to, and concentric with, the west wall. To the west is the crater A, the walls of which are very brilliant when on the morning terminator. On the outer north is a hill, Gamma. Between Lavoisier and A are some ruined rings.

NAJERÁ (invisible at mean libration) [Spanish scientist, *circa* 1650]. A crater some 40 miles in diameter, very close to the limb and not far from Galvani, therefore extremely difficult to examine. It appears to be regular in shape, and so far no detail has been detected on the floor. Between Najerá and the limb, at maximum libration, are several craters—one of which, P, is of considerable size—and some mountain ridges.

REPSOLD, −618 +775 [German optician, 1771-1830]. A large mountain-ringed plain 70 miles across, with a peak, Alpha, on the south wall. Schmidt found two craters and some long ridges on the interior. With a 12½-inch reflector, Wilkins found four craterlets close to the south wall, three hills near the north wall, and a central ridge. On the north are several rings, and of these the largest, Galvani, is 20 miles in diameter. There is also a ring with a central peak. On the limb opposite the south end of Repsold is a peak,

Beta, and on the limb near here is the large formation, Najerá, wholly on the averted hemisphere.

RÜMKER, —643 +653 [German astronomer, 1788-1862]. Rümker, Neison's 'Harding K', is a peculiar formation, really a plateau. It is 30 miles across, and was shown by Goodacre as a ruined ring, which it certainly does resemble under some conditions of lighting. The highest portion rises only 200 feet, and there is a peak nearly in the centre, as well as several isolated hills to the north-west. To the west are white spots, and on the east two craterlets, A and B, while to the south-west lie an isolated mountain and some white spots, probably the sites of buried rings. Rümker is steepest on the east, where it terminates in a ridge; on the south, however, the slope is very gentle. From the south wall a delicate dark line, possibly a cleft, can sometimes be traced. On the south is a minute craterlet, D, and also a white spot, X, bright at Full. To the west is a craterlet, F.

XVIII

This section is occupied by the broad expanse of the vast Oceanus Procellarum, the largest of the great grey surfaces. It includes the high-light of the Moon, the brightest of all the formations, Aristarchus; and here, too, can be found Herodotus, the great serpentine valley known generally as 'Schröter's Valley', and numerous fine clefts and domes in the disturbed and hilly district to the north. Certainly, this is one of the most interesting of all the lunar regions.

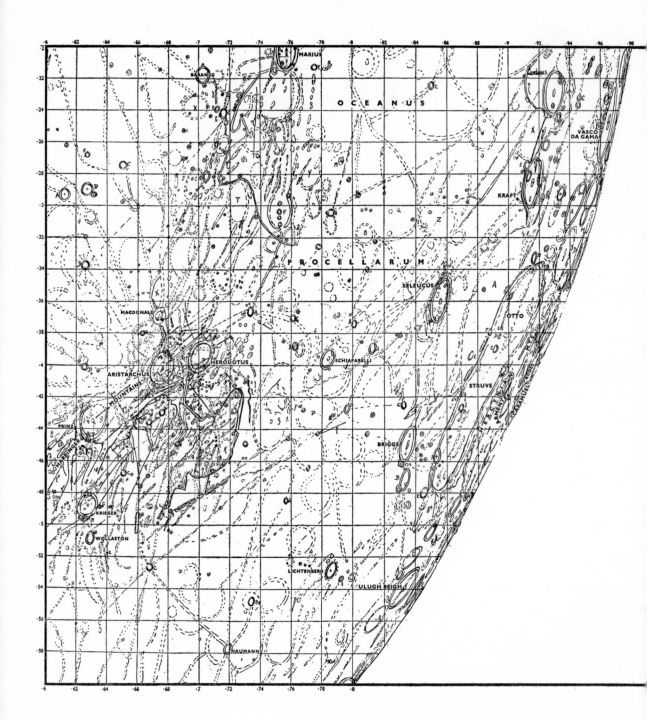

XVIII

ARISTARCHUS, −676 +402 [Greek astronomer, 310-230 B.C.]. This is the high-light of the Moon, being the most brilliant object on the lunar surface. At Full it is so bright as to dazzle the eye and confuse the details; it is even bright when earthlit, and easily seen in a small glass. From its striking visibility when on the dark portion of the crescent Moon, as seen in his 6½-inch reflector, Sir W. Herschel considered it to be an active volcano—an idea long since abandoned.

The massive, terraced walls, 29 miles from crest to crest, are not circular, but of a decidedly polygonal contour, especially on the east—though the departure from a regular curve is much exaggerated in the drawings of many observers. The west wall is terraced on the inner slope; at the south end is a small shallow pit, just below the crest, from which a deep ravine runs along the slope eastwards, with a hillock midway along it. Below this are further terraces.

Aristarchus stands on a rocky plateau, and its walls rise 2,000 feet above the general surface level. The south end of the plateau is bounded by curved ridges, evidently the remains of ancient rings whose south walls have been eroded down to the level of the plain. Beyond these is a ring, MacDonald, with low walls and a craterlet on its floor close to the north rim. This craterlet has been omitted from all previous maps.

Neison shows a craterlet on the crest of the south wall; Goodacre represents it as a hill; actually it appears to be the shallow pit mentioned above. On the floor is a long, narrow central mountain, 1,000 feet high, on the summit of which is a craterpit; this craterpit, originally suspected by Wilkins, was distinctly seen by him on 7 April 1952, with the Meudon refractor, and at once confirmed by Moore with the same telescope. It is very small, but not a difficult object with so large an aperture. There is a low hill to the north of the central mountain, and another on the south-west; Burrell has found some more low hills along the inner east slope.

The now-famous radial dark bands, extending up the east and other walls, are generally supposed to have been first recorded by Phillips in 1868, though as a matter of fact a drawing made by Lord Rosse five years earlier shows them distinctly. They were not mentioned by Mädler, Schmidt or Neison (though all three paid considerable atten-tion to Aristarchus), and little attention was paid to them until the present century. Barker, who has thoroughly investigated their history, considers that they have defin-itely increased in visibility during the last fifty years or so. It is true that to-day they cannot possibly be overlooked, and several are conspicuous even with a 3-inch refractor. There are at least nine bands, extending up the east, south and north walls, possibly up the west wall also. They appear to develop as the Sun rises over them; Favarger has seen brilliant star-like points on the bright regions between them, confirmed in part by

R   257

Baum and Moore, to whom, however, they were merely 'bright patches'. The bands do not seem to originate at the central elevation, but some distance away from it; they have been said to consist of a darkish streak with a lighter area to either side, but Wilkins, at Meudon, detected 'fine structure' in them, which appearance was confirmed by Moore. At their fullest development the bands to the eastern wall seem to cross the crest and extend on to the outer surface.

The outer north slope is very broad and rocky. Traversing this hilly ground, Burrell found two delicate clefts, confirmed by Barker. Beyond this is a large triangular plateau, separated from the north slope by a fan-shaped valley traversed by two clefts, one of which is fairly prominent and joins a fine valley-cleft running along the foot of the slope on the west. Wilkins has also noted a fine ravine running the entire length of the west glacis. Many fine and delicate clefts run from Aristarchus towards the Harbinger Mountains, only visible under favourable conditions. In a drawing dated 25 February 1934 Burrell showed two bent clefts winding south from the south wall, and also a cleft from the east wall towards Herodotus. On 9 January 1941 Wilkins discovered three clefts running eastwards and slightly north from the east wall to the terminator; the most northerly of them joined the coarser valley-cleft traversing the valley between Aristarchus and the plateau to the north. At the foot of the east wall is a small rimless depression, crossed by a cleft.

Aristarchus is a ray centre. Most of the rays tend south and south-west, and are much fainter than the gleaming crater-ring of Aristarchus itself; they join and intermingle with rays emanating from Kepler and Copernicus.

ARMENTER, −898 +426 [Spanish solar physicist, 1886-   ]. A crater east of Otto Struve and the Hercynian Mountains. There are two craters on its south wall; the diameter is about 12 miles. North of Armenter are two craters and a mountain; east a crater, D, which lies on the averted hemisphere.

BARANGE, −702 + 218 [Spanish astronomer]. A conspicuous crater 9 miles in diameter, north-west of Marius, and formerly known as Marius A. To the north is a larger 'ghost' ring, X.

BRIGGS, −835 +445 [English mathematician, 1556-1630]. A crater 33 miles in diameter, lying on the open plain not far from Otto Struve. There is a mountain mass at the extreme northern point of the wall, and farther north a considerable crater, B, with a smaller crater on its west. Ridges run from the north and south walls of Briggs; the floor appears to be fairly level, apart from a long, discontinuous mountain ridge.

CARAMUEL, −907 +423 [Spanish scientist (Archbishop of Otranto), 1606-82]. A large ring on the averted hemisphere, 105 miles in diameter; there is a central crater, and smaller craters on the west wall. Caramuel is excessively difficult to examine, and further observations of it are needed before it can be drawn with real accuracy. The formation was first discovered by the Authors, and has since been photographed by E. A. Whitaker, who has produced the best chart of it so far available.

CARDANUS, —928 +229 [Italian mathematician, 1501-76]. A prominent ringed-plain 32 miles in diameter, with walls rising to 4,000 feet above the interior which contains a central mountain and many craterlets. There is also a small crater midway between the central hill and the north wall. A deep ravine runs along the outer western slope, while the interior slopes are terraced. Close to the north-west wall is a partial ring; north-east lie two craters, and farther east two craters with their walls in contact. On the south are several rings, and on the south-east a deep crater, A, on the interior of which is a central hill. From the south wall of A, Molesworth found a cleft running south for about 50 miles (it is, in part, a crater-chain), and this runs into a much longer cleft running east to west, also found by Molesworth. This latter cleft passes some small craters, beginning at a crater on the east and ending at a hill on the west. Goodacre found a continuation to the north-west wall of Cardanus.

HARBINGER MOUNTAINS, —590 +450. A small bright mountain group near Aristarchus, with peaks rising 3,000 feet to the east, and to a greater altitude in the north-west; the highest peak attains nearly 8,000 feet. The most important formations in the area are the incomplete ring, Prinz, and the crater, Krieger. There are many clefts in the region, and, near Prinz, some interesting domes, described under that heading.

HERCYNIAN MOUNTAINS, —895 +415. A lofty mountain range near the limb, east of Otto Struve. Neison gives the height as 3,800 feet, but this is an under-estimate, and on the north there are summits rising to at least 7,000 feet. There are indications that two parallel mountain chains exist, one forming in part the eastern border of Otto Struve and the other in the region of the great ring, Caramuel, with very rough, hilly ground between.

HERODOTUS, —701 +394 [Greek historian, 484-408 B.C.]. The companion crater to Aristarchus. It is 23 miles in diameter, and the darkness of its interior is in striking contrast to its brilliant neighbour. The rather narrow walls rise about 4,000 feet, and are widest on the west and south, where spurs enclose what must originally have been a large crater-ring now almost levelled by erosion. West of the centre of this old ring is a mountain mass, with a summit craterlet discovered by Wilkins; to the east of this mountain is a cleft, and just outside the east of the ancient ring a longer cleft, running on to the open plain to the south.

The walls of Herodotus, although irregular outside, are nearly circular on the inner crest. There are two small craters on the south-west crest, and on the north is another craterlet, which has been shown as a simple break by some observers. A shallow valley runs from the south glacis of Aristarchus along the outer south-west wall of Herodotus.

On the southern portion of the floor is a white streak running east to west; this has been seen as a circle by Thornton and C. F. O. Smith. There is a small crater on the inner north-east, and north of this Moore, with the Meudon 33-inch refractor, recorded two hillocks and some low ridges. In the extreme north Schröter's Valley enters Herodotus; and outside the west wall, close to the entrance-point of the Valley, is a very old

259

ring, whose walls have been so damaged that they are now barely traceable. On 22 March 1948 Thornton, using his 18-inch reflector, found a cleft on the northern part of the floor of Herodotus.

KRAFFT, —915 +285 [Russian astronomer, 1743-1814]. A crater 30 miles in diameter, with a central mountain; there is a crater on the south-west, and some hills on the north. On the outer south slope is a small crater, from which a cleft runs to Cardanus; east of this cleft is a second cleft, cutting through the south wall and on to the interior. East of Krafft are some craters and ridges.

Wilkins examined Krafft at Meudon on 8 April 1952, and found the following new features: a hill or cratercone at the southern end of the floor, a crater-row on the inner east, and two delicate craterpits near the east crest.

KRIEGER, —627 +484 [German astronomer, 1865-1902]. A small crater south of Wollaston, and formerly known as Wollaston B. The walls are of some altitude; a peak on the west rises nearly 2,000 feet, and there is a higher peak, attaining 2,700 feet, on the north wall. There is a craterlet on the west wall, and on the north wall is the crater B, with a smaller crater on its north-west. The floor includes a feeble central mountain.

Krieger is associated with an interesting system of clefts. From B, a cleft, η^2, runs north-westwards, parallel to another cleft farther north, η^3, ending at a low ring, S, adjoining Krieger on the west. Outside to the east is a small crater, C, from which a cleft, η^7, runs south-westwards. Another cleft, η^8, runs from the south wall, while between η^7 and η^8 is a long cleft, η^6. South are hills and craterlets, with fine clefts running in the direction of Prinz.

LICHTENBERG, —785 +527 [German physicist, 1742-99]. A small crater 12 miles in diameter, on the open plain, west of Ulugh Beigh. Some way north of it lies an old ring, open and imperfect; and on the east are some craterlets and ridges, forming the wall of a large obscure ring close to Ulugh Beigh. Barcroft has found a dark area immediately west of Lichtenberg, independently confirmed by Moore; this is evidently an old ring whose walls have been levelled. Moore has also observed a peak on the east wall of Lichtenberg.

Lichtenberg is a minor ray centre, the rays being displayed chiefly on the north and east; under high light it appears as an ill-defined, whitish nimbus. Between 1830 and 1840 Mädler on several occasions noted a reddish tint on the surface closely west, and this was recovered in 1940 by Barcroft. It has also been seen by Haas, and on 21 January 1952 R. M. Baum observed a reddish glow in the area, due probably to the solar rays striking some unusual surface component at a particular angle.

MacDONALD, —675 +369 [English amateur astronomer]. A small ring south of Aristarchus, with broad walls; the floor contains a low central hill, and a crater north of it. There are two craterlets on the east. South of MacDonald is a large, ridge-bounded enclosure, X, and to the north is a ridge, flanked on either side by craterpits, running towards Aristarchus and forming part of the boundary of another low ring, also lettered X. To the north-east are delicate craterpit-chains and fine clefts.

MARIUS, —758 +206 [German astronomer, 1570-1624]. An interesting crater 26 miles in diameter, with walls rising to 4,000 feet above the interior. There is a small break on the south, and on the south-west the wall is disturbed by a crater, A, shown by Schröter, and very distinct, although Neison, curiously, missed it. On the outer north-west is a mountain, from which a ravine runs along the slope to a pair of craters on the south-west. There are also craters on the south, east and north outer slopes, ridges on the east, and craterlets and craters to the west, as well as some old rings to the north and south. Krieger noted a long serpentine cleft, starting from some hills near the northern wall of Marius and running half-way to Herodotus; it had ben partly seen by Schmidt, and has since been glimpsed by Gaudibert, Müller, Goodacre and Wilkins, but it is at all times a very difficult object. The surface traversed by this cleft contains several craters and numerous hills, few of any altitude, and little superior in brightness to the general surface of the plain.

Beer and Mädler recorded no floor detail inside Marius, but a crater in the north-west, close to the wall, was detected by the keen-eyed Gruithuisen and rediscovered by Webb in 1864. This is now a comparatively easy object. Schröter announced the discovery of a low, convex central elevation, and this, too, is not hard to see. Further detail was added by Elger and Molesworth, and on 2 January 1901 Scriven Bolton, with a $4\frac{1}{8}$-inch refractor, saw a low longitudinal ridge, also a triangular dark patch extending from the central hill to the east wall; both these features were confirmed by Goodacre on 1 April 1901. Further observations by Bolton between 1901 and 1903 disclosed a system of bright streaks on the interior, variable in brightness during each lunation and most conspicuous about the time of Full.

On 7 April 1952 Wilkins had an excellent view of Marius with the 33-inch Meudon refractor, and recorded some new detail. The central hill was plain, with a white crater-let on the north-west part of the floor, an old ring on the south-west, a very low ridge near to and concentric with the west wall, two spindle-shaped objects on the floor of the inner north-east slope, a shallow depression on the north-east inner slope, and seven hills or white spots. Bolton's ridge, however, could not be found, and its existence must therefore he regarded as dubious.

NAUMANN, —719 +578 [German geologist, 1797-1873]. A bright crater in the Oceanus Procellarum, some distance north-west of Lichtenberg. Many low ridges radiate from it as a node.

OCEANUS, PROCELLARUM, The 'Ocean of Storms'. —600 —100 to —900 +350. The largest of all the great dark plains, with an area of about two million square miles, and with many obscure rings, hills, craters and ridges on its surface. This great expanse is lighter in tone than the Mare Humorum or the Mare Imbrium, and is rendered still lighter by the Copernican and Keplerian light streaks which cross its surface. It is bordered on the south by the bright mountainous region between Sirsalis and the Mare Humorum. On the north it opens into the Sinus Roris, by which it communicates with the Mare Frigoris. There is no true western border between it and the Mare Imbrium, while on the east the boundary can be traced by the bright mountainous strip, broad on the south but narrowing on the north, past Ulugh Beigh and Vasco da Gama, thence to Lavoisier and the Sinus Roris. The Oceanus extends from Section XVIII on to Sections XIX, V and VI.

PRINZ, −630 +435 [German astronomer, 1857-1910]. An incomplete ring in the Harbinger Mountains, open to the south, with craterlets in its north wall, and some hills and a delicate cleft on its interior. The drawings of the area by Krieger and Fauth differ considerably, but recent delineations made by Dr. S. R. B. Cooke, D. C. Brown and K. W. Abineri are much more reliable. Inside Prinz are two domes, and Abineri has noted five craterlets on the north wall; also three hills, from one of which a cleft issues, turning first east and then north. West of this cleft are two domes, with a delicate craterpit-chain and a cleft separating them. On the eastern dome are a double craterlet, a shallow pointed depression, and a hillock; on the western dome, two craterlets. Another cleft runs northwards from three pits on its west, and still farther west is a craterlet from which yet another cleft begins, running north and then west. To the west of this last cleft are some isolated hills of the Harbinger range, and a short cleft, near Prinz's north-west wall. It will be seen that the whole area is highly complex.

RODÉS, −910 +404 [Spanish astronomer, 1881-1939]. A small ringed-plain to the south of Caramuel.

SCHIAPARELLI, −784 +396 [Italian astronomer, 1835-1910]. A distinct ring-plain 16 miles in diameter, with walls rising 3,000 feet above an interior which contains a central hill. The wall is broadest on the north; there is a slight break in the north-east wall, and a white mound on the inner west slope. A light streak runs south-eastwards, past the south wall, so that the formation can be readily identified at Full. Just outside the west wall of Schiaparelli is a shallow craterlet, and to the south a large, low ring.

SCHRÖTER'S VALLEY, −700 +428. This remarkable feature was the first of the valley-clefts to be detected (though it is true that Hevelius recorded some objects that may well be clefts). It was discovered by Schröter in 1787 and is generally named after him, although the crater allotted to Schröter lies far away (Section I).

    For some years there was much discussion as to whether the Valley started inside Herodotus, or outside the north wall. Moore's observation with the 33-inch refractor at Meudon, on 7 April 1952, indicates that the former is the case. The Valley then cuts through a large round-topped hill, surmounted by a massive cliff and, as a narrow cleft, enters a lagoon-like enclosure, which Dr. Steavenson aptly christened the Cobra-Head. This is evidently made up of at least two old craters fused together, as is shown on the drawing; in the larger component there is even the remnant of a central hill, as well as a short cleft and a mound; there is also a minute break in the east wall, previously un-recorded. South-east of the Cobra-Head lie a ridge, two hills, and two very delicate clefts that probably connect up with the main system.

The Valley then runs north, turns north-east and then south-east, with three bends, swerves south-eastwards, and passes, as a fine cleft, round the south of a plateau; turns north, and finally ends at a mountain mass. (Krieger made it continue south-eastwards, but in this he was certainly mistaken.) Dr. A. F. O'D. Alexander, observing with the 24-inch refractor at the Pic-du-Midi, observed many minute sinuosities along the Valley.

On 30 March 1950 Wilkins found a delicate cleft connecting the Cobra-Head with the chief bend, and this has been confirmed by Thornton and Abineri. A more obvious prolongation was discovered by Goodacre in 1901; this cuts through the mountain ridge on the high ground east of Herodotus, and bends sharply northwards, running along the foot of the ridge. Slightly east of this is another cleft, first seen by Schmidt. Thornton has recently found three others.

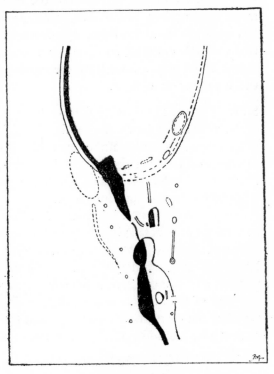

THE COBRA HEAD

7 April 1952, 22h., 33-inch O.G. (Observatory of Meudon) × 420, Patrick Moore

The Valley in its windings partly encloses a darkish area to the south of it, possibly an old ring. In this is a hill, surrounded by five peaks, and east of the hill Pickering found seven tiny craterlets which he thought subject to periodic ob-scurations by whitish cloud or mist. Gruithuisen and Klein noted an occasional greenish hue in the area, and on 10 February 1949 Thornton, with his 18-inch reflector, noticed 'what seemed to be a diffused patch of thin smoke or vapour, apparently originating from the east side of the Valley near the Cobra-Head, where the landslip is, and spread over the edge on to the plain for a short distance. Every detail of the Valley was per-fectly clear and distinct except where this patch occurred, but there the definition was poor and very blurred.' Schröter's Valley is, indeed, one of the most interesting forma-tions on the entire Moon.

SELEUCUS, —856 +360 [Babylonian philosopher, *circa* 150 B.C.]. A fine crater 32 miles in diameter, with terraced walls rising to 10,000 feet above a greatly depressed floor, on which stands a central mountain. The inner north slope is very broad, with two shallow depressions. The outer slopes rise very little above the level of the surrounding country. There are some small peaks on the west wall, and on 11 December 1951 R. M. Baum recorded two peaks on the north-east crest and two smaller ones on the north-west crest. According to Lenham, the interior slopes exhibit dusky bands; but these await confirmation, and Moore, using his 12½-inch reflector and the Meudon refractor, has been unable to see them. North-west of Seleucus is a crater, A, and between the two a double craterlet, standing on a long ridge which runs to the outer west wall of Seleucus and joins a ridge from the south wall. To the south is an obscure ring, Z, with two craterlets on its floor.

STRUVE, OTTO, −847 +479 to −916 +337 [Russian astronomer, 1819-1905]. A vast enclosed area, evidently the result of the fusion of two ancient rings each about 100 miles across, one south of the other; the dividing wall has been absolutely obliterated. On the west the wall rises about 4,000 feet, disturbed by the crater B and a craterlet north of it; on the east wall are shallow craters, and the east wall itself is really a parallel ridge to the Hercynian Mountains.

On the vast interior, which clearly exhibits the convexity of the lunar globe, Goodacre shows little detail; but Wilkins has seen four large, rather shallow craters near the west wall, two low, whitish ridges extending to the centre from the south wall, a short, low ridge, and a craterlet close to the north wall. There is also a very low central plateau, and a low ring near the south-east wall.

West of Otto Struve is a smaller, ridge-bordered enclosure, A, with walls that are very low but everywhere traceable when the formation is near the terminator; another ancient ring lies north of it, and, to the south-east, a crater with a central mountain.

ULUGH BEIGH, −832 +540 [Mongol prince and astronomer, 1393-1449]. A fine crater 30 miles in diameter, but rather inconveniently near the limb. It has narrow walls, surmounted by little peaks; there are traces of interior terracing, and on the floor is a central mountain, the highest point of a long ridge. To the south are two low rings; east, a ridge and a low ring, and west, a crater with the remains of an ancient enclosure beyond it.

VASCO DA GAMA, −964 +246 [Portuguese navigator, 1469-1524]. A bright crater 50 miles in diameter, close to the limb. There is a crater-chain on the outer western glacis, and four high peaks on the east wall; east, on the farther hemisphere, are craters, and south a crater-chain, near which Wilkins has suspected a cleft. To the west is a shallow enclosure some 35 miles across. Like Ulugh Beigh, Vasco da Gama has a long ridge on its floor, rising to a considerable peak in the centre.

WOLLASTON, −629 +508 [English chemist, 1766-1828]. A bright, 8-mile crater in the foothills of the Harbinger Mountains, north-east of Krieger. To the east lie a chain of five craterlets and a distinct crater, Wollaston C.

XIX

This section of the eastern equatorial portion of the disk contains several large and important formations. Of these Grimaldi with its dark floor, the nearby Riccioli and the ringed plains Hevel, Cavalerius and Sven Hedin are all worthy of the closest attention. The greater part of the area is occupied by the Oceanus Procellarum, and the ringed formations are chiefly concentrated near the limb. In connection with many of the formations will be found delicate systems of clefts.

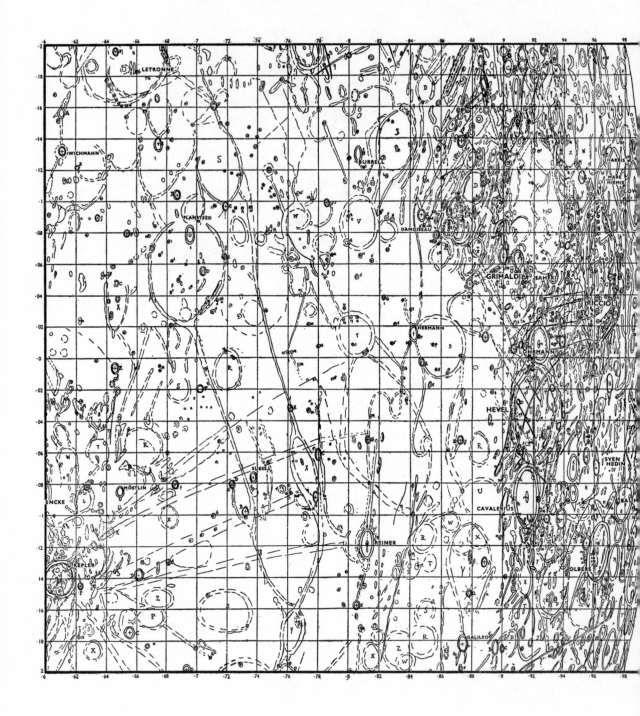

BAUM, −980 +092 [contemporary English selenographer]. An imperfect crater 15 miles in diameter. It lies to the north-east of Sven Hedin, and used to be known as Sven Hedin F. The floor includes several hills. The northern glacis is disturbed by a smaller ring, T.

BOLTON (invisible at mean libration). [English selenographer.] A large central-peaked crater on the farther hemisphere, with a diameter of 40 miles (Moore). There are four small peaks on the west wall, and a rounded mountain rather more than half-way down the outer west glacis. The north walls are extended by a long and massive ridge. On the floor, which is a light grey, brightening under a high sun, is some faint detail in addition to the central mountain. To the east are lofty peaks. A short, straight ridge runs north-west from Bolton. This area was first properly charted by R. M. Baum.

BURRELL, −809 −130 [contemporary English selenographer]. A small but distinct crater between Hansteen and Damoiseau. It is identical with the crater named 'Melloni' by Schmidt, and is in need of attention, as Whitaker has recently (1954) found it much less distinct than is generally supposed. To the east is a large, old ring, S, and south a hill. There are also many craterlets in the immediate surroundings. North-west is a peculiar arrangement of ridges, evidently, in part, the remains of an old and eroded ring, also the mountain mass, M. This has a craterlet on its summit. From the principal old ring on the west a very low ridge connects with the bright little crater, A.

BUSS, −992 −018 [English spectroscopist]. A fine crater to the east of Riccioli, and close to the east limb. On the floor is a crater, A, on the western portion and an old ring on the northern. A crater-chain runs south from Buss and beyond this, on the limb, three peaks are often visible in profile. The north-east wall of Buss is very slightly distorted by an old, shallow ring to the outside.

CAVALERIUS, −916 +089 [Italian mathematician, 1598-1647]. A fine crater 40 miles in diameter, with walls rising 10,000 feet above the floor on which is a central ridge, and another ridge concentric with the inner south wall. There are also two craterlets on the north, and another on the west. To the west of the crater are two craters and some ridges. On the outer east is a little crater, also a hill, M. A cleft from the interior of Hevel touches the outer south-east wall, and then curves north-east. On the east is a small crater, L, while north are three old rings, and east of these the large old ring, W, containing the two craters, E and F. To the north of the partial crater, T, and the ring, W, are three small craters and a long cleft from the south-west of Cardanus to the crater Olbers S. This cleft is crossed by another which, on the south, becomes a crater-chain. It can be traced to near the brilliant crater, F, north of Olbers A.

D'ALEMBERT MOUNTAINS, —070 to —170 [French mathematician, 1717-1783]. A great range of very lofty mountains on the east limb of the Moon, with peaks of 20,000 feet in places, and many lower. To the east of Riccioli are three peaks and a remarkable table-like mountain a little farther to the north. Schröter noted a lofty peak, as high as our Chimborazo, in this region. The delineations of Schröter and Neison are here superior to the maps of Schmidt and Goodacre.

DAMOISEAU, —870 —083 [French astronomer, 1768-1846]. A complex arrange-ment of ridges and rings, the largest ring being 23 miles in diameter with a smaller ring on its interior. This smaller ring contains craterlets and a curved ridge. On its west is a still smaller ring.

A large ring abuts on the south-east; on the north and the west are old rings, while on the south-west is a large, imperfect and eroded ring, S, with a hill, M, on its floor.

The largest ring associated with Damoiseau contains the smaller craters, 5, 6, 7 and 8, and the craterlet, 4, on the south rim. On the west rim is a ring, 1, with a smaller, 2, on the south-west. The intrusive ring, B, is perfect except on the west, where the wall now consists of isolated hills. To the north-west are the craters L and 10. Damoiseau E is bright, and south of it is the mountain, M.

On the south-east is the large ring, D, with four craters on its east wall and a short ridge on the western side of the floor. To the south of D is the crater, F, from which a delicate cleft, Eta, runs towards the mountain, M. To the east is the wall of Grimaldi, and north-east the crater F, and the ridge, M2.

ENCKE. This crater lies partly in this Section and partly in Section VI. It is described in the latter Section.

FLAMSTEED, —696 —078 [English Astronomer Royal, 1646-1720]. This bright crater, 9 miles in diameter, stands on the south rim of a 60-mile-diameter ancient ring, the rim of which is only 150 feet on the south, 1,100 feet on the north-east, its highest point, and appears complete at Full. Inside this great ring are five hills, several craters and landslips on the outer north-east slope, seen by Wilkins, 24 October 1920, and again 23 August 1923. A long ridge runs northwards from the ring.

To the south-west is the crater F, and just east of it a small mountain. On the south is the deep crater, B, and on the east rim the little crater, E. The crater C, on the south-east, lies on the north rim of another large, obscure ring, S, open on the south. The east wall of this ring is prolonged on the south as a low ridge to the crater F.

GALILEO, —874 +182 [Great Italian astronomer, 1564-1642]. A bright crater, 9 miles in diameter, without any notable features. To the north is the crater A, and east the crater B, on a low ring, D. Two ridges run from the north wall, and there is also a long ridge on the west. To the west of this are several obscure rings, X, Z, W, R and S.

S is a large, very low enclosure divided by a ridge and with a crater, A, on the east side of the interior.

GREEN, —011 —100 [English selenographer (died in action), 1920-42]. A large ring with a central hill, near the limb in mean libration. There are three peaks on the east wall and two on the north-west. The floor is a light grey. To the east is a great valley, with a lofty mountain towering above it on the north. There are also the craters G and F, with four smaller on the north. (See B.A.A. Memoirs, 36, 3.) It was first charted by R. M. Baum.

GRIMALDI, —926 —093 [Italian Jesuit astronomer, 1618-63]. A great walled-plain, 120 miles in diameter, with a very dark floor. The walls are discontinuous and consist of a mass of cliffs. On the east they average 4,000 feet in height, with much débris along the inner east slope, and also some peculiar semicircular plateaux. On the west the walls are very broken, with a peak of 9,000 feet on the south-west. At sunrise the northern portion of the east walls appears first, indicating a superior altitude. There is a lower portion half-way along the southern portion of the east wall. Wilkins found two clefts cutting through the south wall, 27 February 1934, with a 12½-inch reflector. The interior is convex, and the generally dark tint does not extend right up to the south wall. On the north-east portion is a bright crater, Saheki (formerly known as B), which is connected by ridges to the north wall. There is also a long ridge from the south wall, part of which is very low. South of Saheki is a low, dark hill. There are also three hills to the east and some old rings, now mere curved ridges, on the south; another ridge near the west wall and one from the south; also two craters near the east wall, according to a drawing by Goodacre in 1901. There is also a craterlet to the south of Saheki, and another on the rim of an old ring under the north-west wall. A peak on the west wall of Grimaldi has four summits, the highest being on the south. From the south wall are many little capes and projecting ridges on to the floor, and separated by narrow valleys. There is also a cleft on the south-east part of the interior.

Haas found the floor greenish at co-longitude 132°-140°. This was confirmed by Pickering.

The first comprehensive chart was that of Goodacre in B.A.A. Memoirs, 10, 2. Wilkins observed some dark, variable spots on the interior, B.A.A. Journal, 51, 4. Some of these appear in Pickering's Photographic Atlas, and Paris 57. Dr. S. M. Green, 24 November 1939, found two minute craterlets on the eastern portion and one on the north, but these are omitted by Arthur in his fine drawing in B.A.A. Memoirs, 36, 3.

The inner east slope abounds in interesting detail, ridges, mounds, mountain masses and craters. Dr. S. R. B. Cooke has noted some 'fault blocks' or arcuate terraces on the inner east slopes, confirmed by Abineri. D. W. G. Arthur has recently secured many accurate measures of the objects within and around Grimaldi. At the south end Franz described a crater at —909 —148, but Blagg and Karl Müller give a crater, K, described by Arthur as a deep, enlarged portion of a crater-valley and not a true crater. This aspect was seen by Wilkins, 27 February 1934, when another valley was noted parallel to the first on the east.

HARRIS, —972 —123 [English engineer, 1906-   ]. A ring, overlapping an older ring, B, on the south-west and with a craterlet on the south end of the floor. North-east is the crater Lowe, and north the Mare Hiemis. On the west wall of B is a craterlet, 15. South is the low ring, D, with another, M, on its south. To the north-west is a very imperfect ring, W, with a minute craterlet, 13, on its east wall. Within W is the crater, 14, with a ridge to the east, both just outside the wall of Riccioli. West of Harris is a group of old rings, S, W, and Z, the latter under the south-east wall of Grimaldi. Here are the two peaks Grimaldi M and Delta. From the north wall of Harris a strong mountain ridge runs northwards and contracts as it proceeds along the outer east of Riccioli. Between Harris and the crater Lowe C is a small hill.

HERMANN, —842 —015 [Swiss mathematician, 1678-1733]. A bright ring, 10 miles in diameter, associated with ridges tending north and south. On the outer east slope is a small crater, with a larger, A, to the north-east; also several more minute craterlets and the little crater, G, on the south-west. On the west is an obscure ring, T, with four craterlets within it, and another, 16, on its north-east rim.

HEVEL, —923 +038 [celebrated Danzig selenographer, 1611-87]. A great crater, 70 miles in diameter, with walls bearing peaks of 6,000 feet on the west, but lower and more broken on the east. The inner slopes are terraced, and there are three craters on the eastern slopes. The interior, which is convex, has a low central hill, with a summit craterpit; a larger hill lies to the north, also hills and many clefts. On the west and east are old rings. On the walls, starting from the south, are two craters connected by a cleft, 6, followed by the craters 3 and F. Through a pass in the west wall a long cleft, 5, passes and runs through the centre of the floor to the south wall. There is a break in the north-west wall through which passes the cleft, 1, running to the crater E, on the west side of the floor. A cleft, 9, connects E with the crater D, close to the west wall. Cleft 1 continues beyond E and curves south-east, cutting cleft 5, thence through the wall and up to the rampart of Riccioli (8). Another cleft, 4, from a small partial ring, X, on the inner south-west, crosses 5 and 8 and ends at a low hill. The mountain, M, is not quite central. To the north-east of M is the bright crater, A.

The west wall is very complex, with ravines and craterlets to the east of the cleft 1. From the outer west wall a cleft, 6, runs north-west to the ring, 19. West is the isolated mountain, M, and several craterlets. Through the south-west wall passes the cleft, 3, nearly as far as Lohrmann A. On the outer east slope are some craters and hills, while north of the crater F a cleft, 15, runs north towards the east wall of Cavalerius. East are the craters F and G, the former shaped like a bean, and north-east is the large crater, K, with a central hill. Between Hevel and Riccioli are many hills and the crater, D.

HIEMIS, MARE, —988 —097. The 'Winter Sea'. A dark area, south of Riccioli and east of Grimaldi, with the craters Harris and B at its south end.

270

INGALLS, −956 +009 [contemporary American astronomer]. A crater, north of Riccioli and formerly known as Riccioli C. It contains a large ring occupying much of its floor on the western side, while Moore found a valley connecting it with Riccioli, and a minute hillock on its floor with the 33-inch Meudon refractor, 8 April 1952. The inner crater contains a high peak on its east wall, and Ingalls itself has a high peak on its north wall. There is a low hill under the inner south-east wall.

KEPLER, −609 +141 [German astronomer, 1571-1630]. A bright crater, the centre of an extensive ray system; 22 miles in diameter, with terraced walls, a narrow valley on the outer west, a central hill and a low ring to it, north. The walls bear peaks rising 10,000 feet, and there is a narrow pass in the north wall. From the south wall is a spur of rock. West are large landswells, and south and south-east old rings. The rays from Kepler come right up to the walls and in this respect differ from those associated with Tycho. Haas found a dark area on the northern portion of the floor and another on the south. At sunrise the ridge at the foot of the east wall is very bright. Spurr remarks (*Geology Applied to Selenogy*): 'The crater, like that of Copernicus, is partly obscured by thin ash deposits—around Kepler appears uniform for a distance of 20-30 miles, beyond which it separates into rays extending over 100 miles from the crater.' Moore, 33-inch Meudon refractor, found a cleft on the floor, to the south of the central mountain and from east to west. Y. W. I. Fisher, of Brussels, 2 February 1942, 18h. 20m. to 19h. 15m., saw a whitish glow near the earthlit limb east of Kepler. Faint radial bands extend to the east wall, reported by Haas in 1938, and clearly seen by Moore and Wilkins with the latter's 15¼-inch reflector, 1951.

LETRONNE (see Section XX).

LOHRMANN, −923 −008 [German selenographer, 1796-1840]. A crater 28 miles in diameter, with a rather dark floor on which is a central hill. South-west from the crater, A, a cleft runs to Hevel. West are three other clefts. Another cleft runs from the east wall to a crater on the west wall of Riccioli, while a fine cleft runs from the south wall eastwards towards Riccioli. Goodacre mentions three parallel clefts on the west. The cleft from the crater A to the south-west wall of Hevel has a high bordering bank on the east.

LOWE, −988 −102 [American astronomer]. A large ring, 60 miles in diameter, close to the limb, with a central ridge, a crater, 1, on the west wall and a larger, 2, on the north-east floor. On the east wall are two lofty peaks. West are craters and south-east a ring, 12, while north-east is the crater B. Closely north-west is a large, distorted ring with walls of moderate height.

MÖSTLIN, −649 +085 [German mathematician, 1550-1631]. A small crater, south-east of Kepler and on the Oceanus Procellarum. A little hill adjoins it on the north. East is the slightly smaller crater, F, and west the still smaller crater, G. South are two old rings, R and T.

271

OLBERS, −962 +124 [German astronomer, 1758-1840]. A crater 40 miles in diameter, with walls rising 10,000 feet on the east and with a crater, A, on the west crest. On the outer west slope is a crater-chain. On the interior is a central ridge, highest in the centre; also some craterlets and two mounds. Olbers is the centre of a ray system, but since the chief rays lie eastwards they are not very easy to detect.

REINER, −812 +120 [Italian mathematician, died 1648]. A crater with bright and terraced walls, rising 10,000 feet above the dark floor on which are two hills. Reiner is 20 miles in diameter, and from the north and south walls runs a ridge. Close on the west is the remains of an ancient ring. On the east is another old ring, with a gap in its west rim. Its floor is dark, and the low walls are remarkably bright. Wilkins noted a cleft-like marking south of this ring, 29 March 1923.

The western segment of the 'wall' of the ancient ring west of Reiner, mentioned above, has some altitude, and under a low sun casts appreciable shadow.

RICCIOLI, −961 −055 [Italian Jesuit astronomer, 1598-1671]. A large walled-plain, 100 miles in diameter, with broken and discontinuous walls of no great height, averaging 4,000 feet. Little detail, beyond a few ridges, some craters and hills, has been recorded by most authorities. The interior, however, contains a large amount of fine and most interesting detail first mapped by Wilkins, 8 April 1952, with the great Meudon refractor.

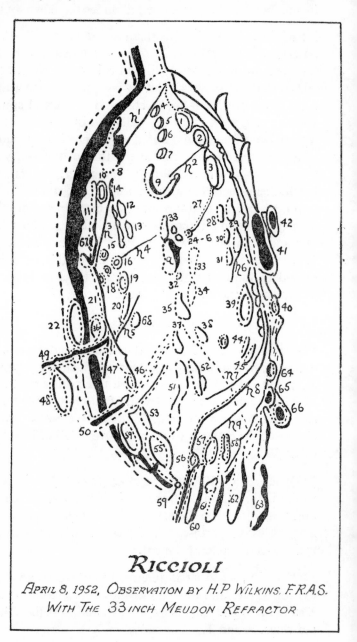

RICCIOLI

April 8, 1952, Observation by H. P. Wilkins. F.R.A.S. With The 33 inch Meudon Refractor

The west wall contains a large crater depression, immediately to the north of which a prominent valley from the Lohrmann region cuts through it. There are two craters in its course, one on the section cutting the wall. Farther north another but more shallow valley cuts the wall, and this was traced, though faintly, to an isolated hill. There is a wide gap in the south wall, partly closed by débris. The east wall is more complex than the west and is terraced, with evidence of landslips at intervals. Following the wall northwards there is a double crater on the crest with a shallow, lagoon-like depression immediately to the west. A few miles farther north is a small crater. On the north-east the wall is broad and contains three craters; it bends westwards and then north again, with spurs and ravines.

Nearly in the centre of the floor, but a little south, is a high and isolated hill. South is a low ridge-like elevation and a partial ring, open to the south. From this ring a cleft runs to the middle crater of three on the south-east of the floor. Four craterlets are spaced from the ruined ring to the gap in the south wall, while on the west is a lofty mountain mass. From this a cleft runs to the south-east wall.

Concentric with the west wall is a discontinuous ridge, with two craters on the north. This ridge crosses the sites of the two valleys already mentioned. East of the central hill are some mounds, from one of which a short cleft runs northwards. West of the hill, and between this and the ridge, are some craterlets, from one of which a delicate cleft runs to the short ridge south of the central elevation. There is also a delicate cleft from the main west ridge towards the central elevation.

On the northern portion of the floor are several mounds and craters, one double. From the shallow, lagoon-like depression on the east a curved cleft issues and turns west, dying out on the floor. East of this and skirting the foot of the inner east slope is another, roughly concentric, cleft which turns north, passes through a small crater and thence through the north wall. To the east of this is a third, but shorter, cleft beginning at a crater. This system of concentric clefts was quite unknown before and was confirmed by Moore with the 33-inch refractor. Several small craters were also noted, the whole being as depicted on the special chart. Nothing under 30 inches aperture will, probably, reveal them.

SAHEKI, −933 −051 [Contemporary Japanese astronomer]. This was formerly known as Grimaldi B, and some information has already been given under the heading Grimaldi. It is the bright crater on the north interior of this vast walled-plain, but is not perfectly regular as the west wall bulges slightly. A low ridge runs north from Saheki, and there are two craters to the north-east.

SUESS, −737 +076 [Austrian geologist, 1831-1914]. A small crater on the Oceanus Procellarum, 4 miles in diameter, with a smaller crater, D, on the west, and another, B, on the north. East is a large, ridge-bordered formation, X, and beyond it the crater, C.

SVEN HEDIN, −970 +050 [Swedish explorer]. A vast ringed-plain, totally omitted by Goodacre. The first critical study was by the late Dr. S. M. Green, and his drawing was published in B.A.A. Memoirs, 6, 3. It is 60 miles in diameter, and there is a crater on the west wall, another on the east crest, two breaks in the west rampart and also gaps in both the north and south borders. There are four principal ridges on the floor running from north to south; the central of these ridges is very rugged, and has at least two craters on its crest, seen by the Authors, 8 April 1952, with the great Meudon refractor. On the east wall are two craters, while on the inner north-east is a large crater with some hills and a ridge on its floor. There is a gap on the south wall of Sven Hedin, from which a cleft runs along the inner slope, passing in its course through two craterlets, bends to the west, and ends at two more craterlets close under the south-east inner slope. A crater breaks the north wall of a large crater on the inner north-east, and there is a craterlet-chain on the outer north-west slope on the large crater. On the floor of this large ring are several ridges, and on the outer west four craterlets and south of a crater on the outer south glacis. Farther south is Ingalls. Moore and Baum give, B.A.A. Memoirs, 36, 3, a sketch of this area including a cleft from the north-west wall of Sven Hedin running north-west and passing through a large, imperfect ring, with another ring on its north. To the east of Sven Hedin are craters, and several partial enclosures abutting on the east wall. Moore has seen an obscure ring on the southern portion of the floor of Sven Hedin and a cleft cutting through the north-west wall. To the north-east lies the crater-ring Baum.

WICHMANN, -611 -131 [German astronomer, 1821-59]. A bright crater, 8 miles in diameter, on the south-west rim of an ancient ring. This old ring has had a portion of its south wall removed by erosive forces, but there is a crater on its interior, and a mound on the north.

To the west are other ancient rings, and north-west some hills, none of any particular height, and some craterlets.

XX

This section is occupied mainly by rugged upland, the only sea surfaces being part of the small but interesting Mare Humorum, and the Mare Orientalis—the latter so close to the limb that it is extremely difficult to examine.

In this section lies Gassendi, one of the grandest and most majestic of all the walled formations, with its complex system of interior clefts. Another cleft system is associated with Mersenius. Also in the section are the double crater Sirsalis-Bertaud; the great ruin known as Darwin; the dark-floored Billy, and many other interesting objects. The lofty Cordillera Mountains appear on the limb.

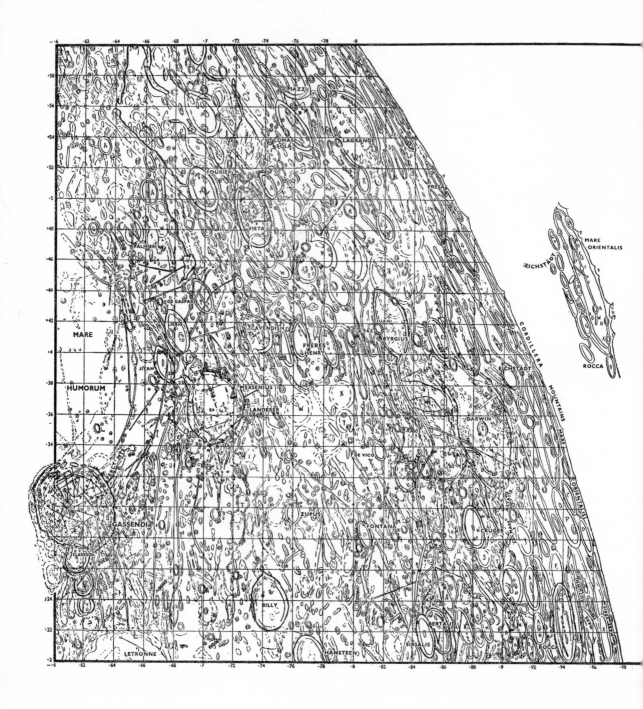

XX

ÆSTATIS, MARE, —900 —253. The 'Summer Sea'. A dark plain extending from the east wall of Crüger to the imperfect object, A, west of Rocca; and thus north-east of Darwin.

AUTUMNI, MARE, —957 —250 to —981 —184. The 'Autumn Sea'. A narrow dark plain to the east of Rocca, and separated from the Mare Veris by a ridge.

BERTAUD, —858 —222 [contemporary French astronomer]. This was formerly known as Sirsalis A, but has been renamed in honour of the distinguished French astronomer of the Meudon Observatory. It is 22 miles in diameter, the walls rising 3,000 feet above the floor, and is overlapped on the west by Sirsalis. East is a cleft, curving on the south; and farther east are some low rings, one with a craterlet on its east wall.

Wilkins, 7 April 1952, with the Meudon 33-inch refractor, found a small crater on the south-west, where Bertaud joins Sirsalis. From this point begins a delicate cleft running south, then passing through four craterlets with their walls in contact. Farther south the cleft passes through a larger, distinct craterlet. South of this craterlet the cleft once more becomes crateriform in nature, with five enlargements, to end up as a true cleft. On the inner north-east slope of Bertaud is a minute craterlet, and above it a long, dark marking, probably a ravine.

BILLY, —744 —239 [French mathematician, 1602-79]. This crater is 31 miles in diameter, appearing somewhat elliptical or even polygonal, according to the libration. The walls rise 3,400 feet above the floor, which is itself depressed 1,000 feet. On the floor are two light spots on the north, two craterlets on the south, and larger but less obvious patches on the east and west; Neison recorded a low hill in the south-west, and Moore, using an 8½-inch reflector, on 9 March 1952, recorded a grey circular patch in the south-east, possibly the remains of an old ring. On the inner south-east slope is a fault or dyke, while on the plain to the south-west of Billy is the bright crater, A. There is a partial ring to the south-east, and another nearer the wall. On the west is a mountain mass, and between it and Billy a hill. On the south-west are two craters, some cones and hills. Billy is distinct under any illumination, due to the dark hue of its floor. There is a shallow valley concentric with the outer west wall.

BYRGIUS, —826 —420 [Swiss clockmaker, 1552-1632]. A crater 40 miles in diameter, with walls rising 7,000 feet. There is a very bright crater, formerly known as A but now called La Paz, on the west crest. La Paz is always visible, and is the centre of a ray system. There is a smaller crater on the south-east wall of Byrgius, and another on the north-west rim. There is a pass in the north wall, through which passes what is probably a prolongation of the great Sirsalis cleft. On the floor are two low rings and a ridge. There are also some hills under the east wall.

To the north-east is the crater D, complete with central mountain, while east is the larger crater C, with a ridge down the centre of its floor. C stands on the south end of Darwin. South is a large but low ring, within which are two prominent craters. North is a great mountain ridge, bordering the Sirsalis cleft and rising to 10,000 feet at some peaks but culminating in a gigantic peak of 13,000 feet. The crater H is deep and easily seen, while west of it is another lofty mountain ridge running to some large rings.

CAVENDISH, −735 −415 [English scientist, 1731-1810]. This object is 32 miles in diameter, with broad and terraced walls rising 7,000 feet on the east but only 4,600 feet on the west. There is a crater on the south-east wall, and a smaller, central-peaked crater to the south. The larger crater has a crater-chain flanking it to the east. From its west wall a longer crater-chain runs to a larger ring on the south. From this larger ring a cleft runs to De Gasparis. On the floor of Cavendish are some low rings, and there is a crater, B, on the west wall. From B a cleft runs to Liebig. Just outside the north-east wall is a crater, C, from which another crater-chain runs north. West of this are several low rings.

CLARKSON, −616 −268 [English selenographer, 1889-1954]. This crater was formerly known as Gassendi A, and is described under that heading.

COMAS SOLÁ, −760 −548 [Spanish astronomer, 1868-1937]. A 35-mile ring to the west of Lagrange, and shown by Schmidt and Goodacre. Schmidt shows two craters on the west wall, one on the floor under the east wall, and a central ridge. Wilkins has found another crater under the west wall, one to the north of Schmidt's crater, a mound on the east and a curved ridge, also a depression on the central ridge.

CORDILLERA MOUNTAINS, −220 to −360. A great mountain range on the east limb due east of Crüger, with peaks of 18,000 feet, one of the highest being E, to the south-east of Rocca.

CRÜGER, −880 −287 [German mathematician, 1580-1639]. This crater is 30 miles in diameter, with low walls, and a dark floor on which can be seen a central hill and two minute pits. West of it is the crater A, with a small central hill and three craterlets on the floor, lying close to the Sirsalis Cleft. On the south is the crater E, while on the south-east the wall of Darwin is prolonged by a lofty mountain ridge.

DARWIN, −888 −368 [English naturalist, 1809-82]. This is a vast mountain-walled depression to the north-east of Byrgius, always foreshortened into an ellipse. It has bright walls, rugged in places, but not lofty. The rather dark floor contains some interesting detail. On the north is a large dome, the highest on the visible surface, discovered by R. Barker; it can be seen even with a 3-inch telescope, though larger apertures are required to make its form evident. This dome is traversed by two clefts, branches of the

278

Sirsalis Cleft. The southern component was discovered by Wilkins in 1924. Barker describes the dome as presenting a cindery aspect, with a lighter patch on the east. Just west of the dome is a curved ridge; Moore has seen indications that this is really part of a very ancient ring.

On the southern part of the floor, which is in general very level, is a hillock in the centre, with a crater on the west. Farther south is a horse-shoe shaped formation, H, open on the north, and probably a ruined ring. At the south end of the floor are a mountain ridge with a crater, some hills, and the craters K and L. The walls are highest on the south-west, and are broken by craters in places; there are three prominent craters on the east crest. In both north and south walls are breaks, and that on the north has a craterlet on the western headland. East are some irregular depressions. The north-west outer slopes are deformed by craters and depressions.

DE GASPARIS, —698 —437 [Italian astronomer, 1819-92]. A ring to the south-west of Cavendish, and south-west of Liebig, with low walls which are cut by two clefts from the east wall of Liebig. A cleft on the south runs to a hill, while a cleft also runs from the north wall, curving east to a long ridge. Another cleft parallel to this is easily seen. On the interior are three clefts, crossed by another, running south-west to north-east. To the south-west is another cleft, which runs from a hill south of De Gasparis to a crater south of Liebig. Yet another cleft runs from the east wall, and joins one connecting De Gasparis with Cavendish. Between these craters is a shallow valley which, on the north, becomes a crater-chain. Two clefts cut through the north wall of De Gasparis, and connect with a wide cleft running from Liebig to the south-west wall of Cavendish. The whole of this region is traversed by clefts.

DE VICO, —817 —337 [Italian astronomer, 1805-48]. A small but deep crater; the walls rise 4,500 feet above the floor, which is smooth. It stands on the west of a plateau which is terminated on the east by the great mountain ridge from the west side of Byrgius. East of De Vico the ridge rises 6,000 feet. Adjoining on the south is the ring J, with low rings on its west, and the obscure formation, Y, open on the north. To the west are some small craters, and there are others on the north.

The crater A, to the north-east, is traversed by the great Sirsalis Cleft, which appears to have cut through the north wall, but seems to pass under the south wall (by a tunnel?). On the floor of A are a craterlet and a hill. East of A is a partial ring, L, curving to the wall of Darwin. South of A is the mountain M, and south of this a short cleft. South-west is the great 13,000 feet peak associated with the Byrgius ridge.

EICHSTÄDT, —904 —385 [German mathematician, 1596-1660]. This crater is 32 miles in diameter, with low walls and a smooth floor. To the east is a large, shallow ring. Eichstädt lies east of Darwin. On the north are two craters and a valley, V; south is the crater D, from which a long ridge runs to the south. North-east is a large walled-plain, B, with a smaller, A, on its south-west. From A another valley runs to the north, to the large ring, P.

FONTANA, −807 −283 [Italian astronomer, 1585-1656]. A bright crater, 30 miles in diameter, with low but bright walls and a central hill. There is a craterlet on the west wall, and a low pass has been seen on the south wall. To the north is a plain, crossed by several clefts, and closely outside the north wall are three low-rimmed craters. To the west of Fontana is a very old ring, open to the north; to the east lie numerous craterlets and the great Sirsalis Cleft, here broad and deep. Barker has found a cleft running from near the north wall of Fontana northwards, with a branch passing to the south of a considerable mountain, crossing the Sirsalis Cleft and eventually ending at the cleft closely west of the crater Crüger A. The main cleft curves to the north-east, and connects with the great cleft to the north-west of Sirsalis (B.A.A. Memoirs, 36, 1).

FOURIER, −699 −506 [French physicist, 1768-1830]. A crater 36 miles in diameter, with terraced walls, and a crater on the south-west just below the crest. On the floor is a central crater, with a smaller to the north; also a ring, open to the south, abutting on the inner north slope. On the west is a ring crossed from north to south by a cleft, and beyond this object is a long cleft running to Palmieri. South of Fourier are two large craters; to the east lie Vieta and some crater-chains. The smaller crater, D, on the south-west, has a central hill. The walls of Fourier rise 9,500 feet at one peak on the west, but only 6,050 feet on the east. Neison mentions a cleft to the south, between the wall and the crater, D, and also shows a cleft within Fourier, running from the inner south-east wall through the west rampart and continued to the mountain mass, De Gasparis Alpha. This latter object has not, however, been confirmed, and its existence is doubtful.

FRESÁ, −854 −500 [Italian astronomer]. A well-formed regular ring-plain close to the limb, north-east of Lagrange. It is one of several rings in this area.

GASSENDI, −611 −301 [French theologian and astronomer, 1592-1655]. This is one of the most beautiful and important of all lunar walled formations, and has been carefully observed. Within its encircling walls will be found all types of lunar formations, and most of them are bright enough to be detected at any stage of illumination.

Gassendi is 55 miles in diameter, and lies on the north border of the Mare Humorum. The floor on the north is 2,000 feet higher than the plain. The walls on the west contain peaks of 6,300 feet and 9,300 feet above the floor, but on the east the wall is still higher, and attains 9,000 feet, to the north of the triangular depression, H. On the south the wall is very low, and wanting in parts, as though this portion had been melted down by the once-liquid material of the Mare. Some isolated hills remain to mark its site. Those portions of the wall which remain on the south-west and south-east are only 500 feet in height, and fine away to mere razor-like pieces of rock. The north-east wall is cut through by several passes, through which clefts pass and run towards Letronne.

The interior of Gassendi, which is lighter than the adjoining Mare Humorum, is full of detail. Nearly in the centre is a fine group of mountains, the highest peak being on the west and rising 4,000 feet, overshadowing the other and lower eastern peaks at sunrise. Neison mentions a craterpit on the summit of the eastern peak. On the south-west are two craterlets, remarkably bright at Full; mounds; ridges; and what appears to be the remains of an inner ring, concentric, or nearly so, with the main rampart. The best-preserved fragment is on the west, a space of 10 miles intervening between it and the main wall. The most remarkable feature within Gassendi, however, is the great system of clefts which can be seen in good instruments. Neison shows 35, and the special chart in this work 38. The more prominent can be seen in instruments of 4-inch aperture upwards, but the more delicate clefts, and associated craterlets, require large apertures. Two of the most prominent clefts run from the chief central mountain to the south, diverging as they proceed. Between these is a much finer cleft, also a craterlet. Some observers have declared this craterlet to be double, but the Authors failed to confirm this with the 33-inch Meudon refractor. The north wall of Gassendi has been deformed, and in part destroyed, by the intrusion of the great ringed-plain, Clarkson, with sharp crests and a central mountain. The actual details of this region are too complex for ready description, and reference should be made to the special chart of this formation.

HANSTEEN, −773 −206 [Norwegian astronomer, 1784-1873]. A crater 32 miles in diameter, with fine, terraced walls rising 3,800 feet above the floor. There is a crater on the south crest, on the farther side of which is a small hill; also two craterlets, connected to the wall by a ridge. On the outer west slope are depressions and a plateau. To the north-west is an old ring; north, a fine curved valley; and on the north-east a low ring, with a crater on its south. East of Hansteen is a cleft, beginning at a crater on the south and passing a hill close to the north-east wall. On the floor of Hansteen are some ridges, a few hills, and a craterlet close to the north wall. On 10 July 1941 Haas found a luminous speck moving over the surface close to Hansteen, with an estimated diameter of 0″·1 and stellar magnitude +8; this may well have been due to a lunar meteor.

HENRY, FRÈRES: Paul Henry, −764 −408, Prosper Henry, −783 −403 [celebrated French opticians and astronomers, makers of the Meudon and Nice objectives: Paul 1848-1905; Prosper 1849-1903]. Two large rings, one east of the other. That on the west (Paul) contains a hill on the north of the floor and a cleft on the south; that on the east (Prosper) three hills near the centre, others north and south, and a landslip on the east. South of Prosper Henry is the crater G, with a craterlet on its inner east wall. West of Paul Henry is a low-rimmed crater, with a crater to the north-west. Abineri has found two narrow, dusky bands within Paul Henry, on the inner west slope; and another within B, a crater to the west.

HUMORUM, MARE, (eastern portion). The 'Sea of Moisture'. The eastern portion of this little plain is more remarkable than the western, since some of the finest of all the systems of clefts are found around its margin. They comprise the intricate systems connected with Liebig, Palmieri and Mersenius. On the plain itself are several small craters, the largest being L, to the south of Gassendi, which great formation is itself traversed by numerous clefts. The clefts do not follow the contour of the Mare as closely as in some other instances, but strike out across the surface, all in a general north-to-south direction.

The longest of the clefts originates at the crater Jiyah, and can be traced to the northern side of Gassendi F, a crater south of the border of Letronne. There are also some obscure rings on the surface of the plain; one of these lies against the south-east wall of Gassendi, and there is another in the far south, due west of Liebig. Great attention to this area has been paid by A. P. Lenham.

JIYAH, −673 −392 [Spanish astronomer, 1070-1105]. This crater was formerly known as Mersenius D, and has been mentioned above. It lies on the eastern shore of the Mare Humorum, and north-west of Liebig. It has a central mountain of no great height, a craterlet on the floor at the south end, and a hill on the north. A cleft crosses the floor from a valley between it and Liebig, and cuts through the walls of two craters on the outer north; thence it runs north to the prominent mountain mass east of Gassendi, and south of the Percy Mountains. There are craterlets on the walls of Jiyah, and on the north is a low but broad ridge, with summit craterlets. To the north-west are two craterlets and the crater E, with a smaller on the north, from which another cleft runs north-west. On the south is a low ring, and still farther south the crater F. From F a coarse crater-chain runs south. A long cleft runs north, passing the west wall of F, while another cleft begins at the north wall and can be traced almost to the south-east wall of Gassendi.

JUÁN (invisible at mean libration), [Spanish geographer, 1713-73]. This is a ring on the farther hemisphere, south of Mare Orientalis and north-east of Fresá and Lagrange G. It has three craters on its west wall, while around are several rings. To the west lie the Cordillera Mountains, and to the east, between Juán and the limb at maximum libration, several ridges.

LAGRANGE, −800 −545 [French mathematician, 1736-1813]. A vast walled-plain over 100 miles in diameter, with a more or less connected wall, terraced on the east and with a crater-row on the outer north-west. On the north-west is the intruding ring, K, and there is a small crater, A, midway along the west wall. On the south wall are two craters, with a peak between them. On the floor are a central meridional ridge, a hilly mass on the south-west, a crater-chain on the south-east, and some craters and a dark spot, X, on the south-west. East of Lagrange are the craters B and C, each of great size; west, beyond some ridges, lies Comas Solá. On the north-east are the craters E, F, G and Fresá. From the west side of K runs a craterlet-chain, while a ridge extends northwards from K towards E, which contains hills and a crater. L. F. Ball has found a wide, shallow valley-cleft running from the crater A towards the north-west.

LANDERER, −731 −360 [Spanish astronomer, 1841-1922]. A small, distinct crater, 10 miles in diameter, closely outside the east wall of Mersenius.

LA PAZ, −816 −416 [contemporary American astronomer]. This used to be known as Byrgius A, and is described under that heading. It is the centre of a minor ray system.

LETRONNE, −662 −182 [French archæologist, 1787-1848]. Obviously a once-complete ring, on the border of the Oceanus Procellarum. The east wall, a fine curve, tapers to a point on the north. The west wall rises 3,000 feet, and has craters on the outer slope. On the floor is the remains of a central peak, seen by Arthur Mee as two shallow craters; west of it is a small crater. On the south lie a hill and some curved ridges. On the north-west is the distinct crater, A; both north and south are smaller craters, and to the west a low ring. Wilkins once saw a delicate cleft near the south wall, with a craterlet at each end.

Goodacre (B.A.A. Memoirs, 32, 2) shows the central peak as one of four; a white spot with a central craterlet to the east of it; and a conspicuous, halo-surrounded crater near the south-west wall. This portion of the wall consists of craters and ridges, and there is a hill on the floor close to the wall at this point. West of the central mountain group is a low ring, with a crater-chain running north from it. There is also a row of three or four craterlets south-east of A. A wide valley runs from the south-east wall, extending south-eastwards. From Gassendi, a delicate cleft runs to the south-east wall of Letronne. On the east rim is a ruined ring. Many longitudinal valleys between low ridges traverse the interior, but can only be seen for a short time each lunation.

LIEBIG, −682 −411 [German chemist, 1803-73]. This interesting formation was formerly called Mersenius A, but is certainly important enough to merit a name of its own. The lofty walls bear a crater on the inner west, one on the north crest; and there are a low ring and a crater-chain on the north-east. From the east wall two clefts pass under the west wall of De Gasparis, cut through its wall and continue beyond. On the south wall of Liebig are two small craters with a larger to the south, from which two clefts run eastwards to a mountain mass. The cleft on the south skirts this mountain, and then turns west to join a long cleft, which, after traversing some craterlets, passes east of a ring which contains three hills and lies on the border of the Mare Humorum. A well-defined cleft runs from the south wall of Liebig P, and there is a shorter cleft on the west, joined by that from Doppelmayer. A crater-chain runs from the north wall of P to a small ring, becoming a true cleft as far as the ring, X; beyond this it ends, some distance to the south-east of Gassendi. Between this ring X and Liebig is Jiyah, cut through by another cleft which can be traced to the mountainous district south-east of Gassendi. This cleft is duplicated for some distance on the west, while from two craters to the north-west of Jiyah a fine cleft originates, passing through a hill in its course. Between this larger cleft and the wall of Mersenius is a cleft, which may be traced as far as the east border of Letronne.

MERSENIUS, −709 −368 [French mathematician, 1588-1648]. A great formation 45 miles in diameter, with fine terraced walls, rising 7,000 feet on the west but still higher on the north, where the wall is broken through by valleys. The south wall is also cut by valleys, and just beyond the south-east crest is the crater H. Here the crest is broad, and has three craters on the outer slope. On the convex interior of Mersenius is a nearly central craterlet, one of a chain from the south wall. From three craterlets on the west wall, a cleft crosses the floor near the central craterlet. Along the inner west is a cleft, passing through a craterlet near the foot of the wall and sending out a branch to the north component of a short craterlet-chain. There is also a short cleft near the south rampart. On the south glacis is a ring with a craterlet on its north rim; to the east is another crater, from which two clefts run eastwards for about 5 miles and then join a craterlet-chain which traverses the floor from north to south. East of this are two more clefts, traceable as far as a crater south of H. A cleft runs from the north wall of Mersenius as far as Letronne. The north wall of Mersenius itself is peculiar, as it is prolonged northwards, and there is a crater-chain developing into a cleft and running as far as the crater F. To the west of this crater-chain and towards the cleft already described is yet another cleft, starting at a hill and ending at a craterlet near a small mountain mass. To the east Wilkins, using a 12½-inch reflector, on 18 November 1934, found a cleft skirting the east wall and running south-east.

ORIENTALIS, MARE, The 'Eastern Sea'. This is a fine plain on the extreme southeast limb of the Moon, first drawn in detail by Wilkins. It lies to the east of Eichstädt and Rocca, and is only visible under favourable conditions of libration. On the interior lie a meridional ridge, with craters at intervals, some hills, and three craters on the east; also one, B, on the south-east wall. The eastern wall bears at least five peaks, some of which are probably rings seen in profile. Between Eichstädt and the Mare is a shallow ring. To the east of this, and on the border of the Mare, Moore found a small double peak and a massive mountain block of moderate altitude (16 December 1948: 6-inch refractor). Moore also records a broad, winding valley along the inner east wall. Three long, straight clefts have been suspected to cross the southern portion of the floor, while on the north a coarse valley cuts through the north-east wall. There is also a cleft beginning just outside the north-east border, and running east for about 40 miles.

PALMIERI, —652 —478 [Italian physicist, 1807-96]. A very peculiar formation on the south-east of the Mare Humorum, with a wide gap in its south-east wall. To the west end of this portion of the wall is a partial ring. The floor of Palmieri is crossed by two clefts, one running in a north-south direction through the north wall and thence to the west of Liebig. The other cleft crosses the first on the floor. There is a third cleft on the east. On the outer south-east slope is a crater, while to the west is the deep crater, G, with a smaller crater between it and the wall. There is also a crater-row close by. On the east is a magnificent mountain arm, which can be traced from Lehmann in the far south (Section XXI) to the mountain, De Gasparis Alpha.

PERCY MOUNTAINS, —640 —325. This name has been given to the remarkable and very prominent mountain spur or ridge which extends from the east wall of Gassendi, just south of the great triangular depression or landslip on the eastern side of this formation. The mountain arm runs south-east for some 50 miles, gradually fining away as it proceeds.

ROCCA, —940 —227 [Italian mathematician, 1607-56]. A great walled-plain, close to the limb and thus difficult to observe. It is 60 miles in diameter, foreshortened into a narrow ellipse with the major axis north and south. The interior is traversed by a strong mountain ridge, and there are two craters on the south-west, as well as other ridges. The two craters, F and G, are easily seen, but there is also a small craterlet, I, on a ridge concentric with the west wall. On the eastern rampart are at least three peaks. West of Rocca is the ring, X, containing a central crater, while south-west are two large craters, A and D. A has a central mountain and D the remains of an ancient ring under the west wall. South of Rocca is the low-walled ring, E, while to the east are the formations F and X, several ridges, and a crater-chain.

SIRSALIS, −849 −218 [Italian astronomer, 1584-1654]. One of a pair of overlapping rings (the other component is Bertaud). Sirsalis is 20 miles in diameter, with lofty walls bearing peaks rising to 10,000 feet. On the floor is a central hill, but otherwise the interior is smooth. From the north wall a craterlet-chain runs northwards; while from a craterlet on the south rim of a low ring to the north-west a cleft runs to the south. This is the great cleft described below. With the 33-inch Meudon refractor, 7 April 1952, Wilkins found an exceedingly delicate craterlet on the south-west rim of Sirsalis, with a mound or peak to the north of it. There is also some object, possibly a landslide, just below the north-east crest.

SIRSALIS CLEFT. This is the longest cleft yet detected on the Moon. It begins at a small crater to the north-west of Sirsalis, as a crater-chain (shown as such by Schmidt), and then runs past the west wall of Sirsalis to a small crater on the south-west. This crater is one of a pair, and the cleft, passing between them, runs south, curving slightly, towards the crater Crüger A. Immediately opposite this crater are two enlargements, probably craters, and Crüger A is connected with the great chasm by two fine clefts. From the north wall of Crüger A a cleft runs north towards Bertaud, and divides into three. One branch, 3, runs to the great cleft; another, 4, to the depression X, north of Crüger. From the point of junction, a fine cleft begins, and runs towards the south-east wall of Bertaud. Where cleft 3 enters the great cleft it is continued on the other (western) side as a cleft, 6, to the mountain ridge from the north wall of Fontana. Passing Crüger A, the great cleft tends slightly west, with occasional enlargements, and thence to the crater De Vico A. It cuts through both walls of this crater, and crosses its floor a little south of the centre. In its course is a distinct craterlet. Another craterlet lies between the cleft and the south wall of De Vico A. Passing De Vico A, the cleft curves first south-east and then south-west, and is here crateriform in character. Proceeding south along the east side of the great mountain arm from Byrgius, it runs to this formation, into the interior of which it passes. In this part of its course it throws out numerous branches, depicted by Dr. S. R. B. Cooke and confirmed by Thornton. One branch runs to Darwin, cuts through the wall and thence across the floor to the large dome on the northern portion of this great object. There are other branches, as mapped. The great cleft is easily seen, but the entire system is rarely observed, requiring a good instrument and favourable conditions. Much of it consists of craterlet-rows. Schmidt was the first to realize this fact, but it was not detected by Goodacre or Elger.

VERIS, MARE, —960 —280 to —968 —220. The 'Spring Sea'. The name given to a small dark plain to the east of Rocca, close to the limb. On the south-west is the Mare Autumni, and on the east are several large rings, including X, which has a crater-chain on its west.

VIETA, —732 —488 [French mathematician, 1540-1603]. A fine crater 50 miles in diameter, with lofty, terraced walls rising 15,000 feet on the west and 10,000 feet on the east, but low on the south. A ring intrudes on the north, Vieta having overlaid this older crater. On the floor is a small central hill, with two craterlets on its north; three craterlets near the north wall; some low hills near the west wall; and a craterlet south of the centre, from which a ridge runs to a ruined ring abutting on the south wall. There is also a low ring under the south-east rim. A distinct cleft runs to the ruined ring on the south-east, and Wilkins has found a cleft crossing the northern portion of the interior. On the south-east are overlapping rings; elsewhere the surroundings contain craters and ridges. To the east are the bright crater, D, and the ruined rings, R, S and T.

Between Vieta and Lehmann is a sort of colossal walled-plain, traversed by ridges dividing it into a number of separate enclosures. The most lofty ridge runs down the centre, and rises in a considerable peak at Fourier Gamma. Between this ridge and the west border is a long cleft, opening into lagoon-like enlargements on the far south. Haas has seen the sunrise shadow in Vieta darker than in neighbouring formations.

ZUPUS, —760 —296 [Italian Jesuit astronomer, 1590-1650]. A crater about 12 miles in diameter, with very low walls, linear on the west, enclosing a dark speckled floor on which are two craterlets near the south rim. Zupus stands on the east wall of a very low-rimmed ancient ring, and its dark hue makes it distinct under high light. Pickering noted changes within Zupus which he ascribed to the growth of vegetation. Webb described it as a valley, and it was shown as a dark spot by Riccioli in his 1651 map.

XXI

A section which consists of a small portion of the south-east limb. The chief formations are the walled plains Bouvard, Inghirami and Piazzi; the latter extends into Section XX. A part of the magnificent walled formation Schickard (described in Section XXII) is also included, and on the limb appear the lofty peaks of the Rook Mountains, some of the highest on the Moon.

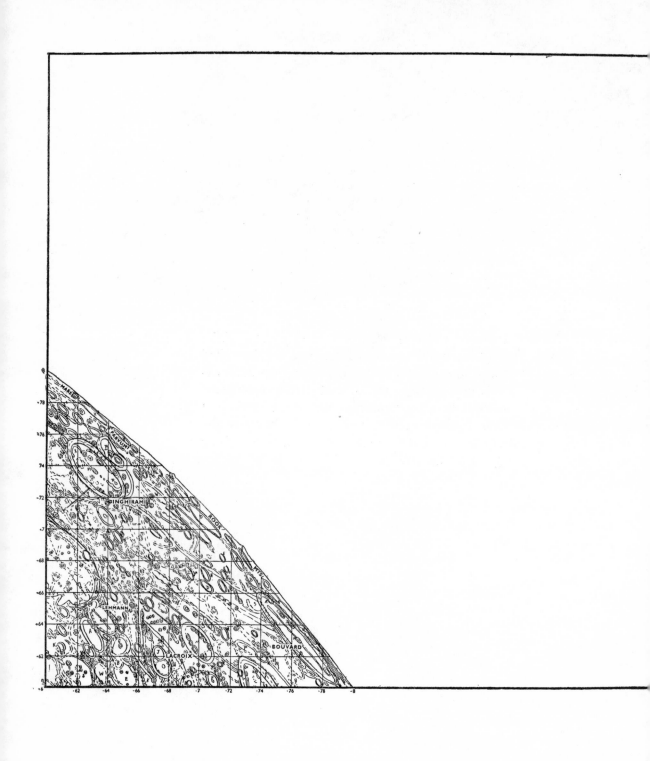

XXI

BOUVARD, —765 —630 [French mathematician, 1767-1843]. A great walled-plain 80 miles in diameter, with peak-surmounted walls rising to 6,000 feet on the east and 10,000 feet on the west. There is considerable terracing. Bouvard is, however, inconveniently close to the limb, which is probably why Schmidt omitted it. On the inner east slopes are three craters, A, C and D; a ridge runs down the slope, and on the inner north-east is another crater. The interior contains a meridional ridge, the highest point of which rises to form a central peak. To the west of Bouvard are some old rings, one of which (S) abuts on the south-west wall. From the north wall a wide valley runs northward, flanked by mountain ridges.

INGHIRAMI, —630 —737 [Italian astronomer, 1779-1851]. A beautifully terraced ringed-plain 60 miles in diameter, with a wall rising 12,500 feet above the depressed interior, on which is a small central mountain, as well as a number of craterlets, some low curved ridges, and, in the north, two dark spots, probably depressions. There is a crater on the inner east slope; a partial ring, X, on the inner south, with a very low-walled ancient formation north of it; and another incomplete object, R, on the inner north-east. On 23 August 1953 Moore, Reid, Baum and Hutchings, using Reid's 9-inch reflector, detected a series of dark, band-like features on the east wall, and these have since been confirmed. Abutting on the outer east is an abnormal compound formation, B, and beyond, closer to the limb, a deep crater, H, in which Moore has recorded a central mountain. From the north wall of Inghirami a strong ridge runs to Bouvard; this is the most marked of a number of parallel ridges in the area. On the outer west is the bright, deep crater, A, which is surrounded by ridges in a manner indicating that it is the central crater of an old ring. To the east and south-east of Inghirami is the dark plain known as the Mare Parvum. On 29 December 1952 Wilkins, with his 15¼-inch reflector, discovered some new clefts running southwards from Inghirami to the region between the limb and Wargentin, one of which showed crater-like enlargements. Probably the western cleft connects with the cleft crossing the north part of Wargentin. These objects are, however, very delicate, and require a large aperture and good conditions.

LACROIX, —677 —613 [French mathematician, 1765-1843]. A somewhat deformed crater 20 miles in diameter, with a low ring, J, on the south-east wall, and a feeble central peak. On both east and west are mountains and craters, and to the north several old rings, R, K, P, N; between R and K is a mountain, M. The walls of these obscure and irregular rings are flanked by rows of delicate craterlet-chains, only visible under very good conditions. From the south wall of Lacroix a ridge runs southwards. Between

T

Lacroix and Bouvard is a low-walled obscure formation with craterlet-rows under its east and west walls, and an interior crossed by two narrow light streaks; this was named 'Lower' on the earlier editions of the 300-inch map, but the name has been transferred to a more appropriate formation. To the north of this object is a crater, F, with a central peak.

LEHMANN, −638 −642 [German astronomer, 1800-63]. A crater 28 miles in diameter, north of Schickard; the interiors of the two formations are connected by passes. On the floor can be seen a ridge and two nearly central craterlets, and a ridge and a craterlet-row on the east wall just below the crest. To the north is a ring, G, with low, broad walls and a central craterlet, while to the north-west are the craters A and B. There is a little peak in the west wall of Lehmann.

PARVUM, MARE, −756 to −792. The 'Little Sea'. A dark area close to the limb, east and south-east of Inghirami.

PIAZZI, −752 −587 [Italian astronomer, 1746-1826]. A formation 80 miles in diameter, partly in this section and partly in Section XX. The walls are irregular in height; in places they attain 6,500 feet, but are full of depressions, resembling a tumbled mountain mass rather than a connected rampart. On the west wall are three craters, of which C is the largest. In contact with C, on the floor, is an imperfect ring open to the north. The floor also includes a crater, A, and some meridional ridges.

ROOK MOUNTAINS, −380 to −480 [English astronomer, 1622-66]. A range of very lofty mountains, far too close to the limb to be well seen. Four or five of their peaks rise to something like 20,000 feet.

XXII

The largest of all the lunar ringed structures, Bailly, over 180 miles in diameter, lies close to the limb, with the giant peaks of the Dörfel Mountains beyond, and often visible in profile on the limb. Other great craters include Schickard, Longomontanus and Scheiner; each of these is full of interesting detail.

Close to Schickard is the remarkable object Wargentin, the floor of which is raised above the surrounding surface and it thus resembles a plateau. On the surface are many fine details, nearly all detected by the Authors with the great 33-inch refractor of the Meudon Observatory.

In this section is Hainzel, the result of the fusion of two rings, and Schiller, a long but narrow formation and one of the finest examples of these abnormal features.

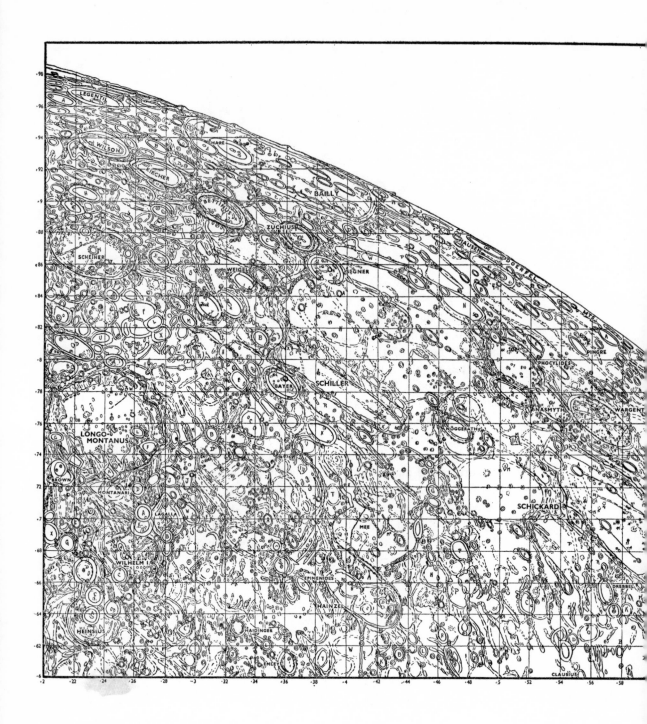

XXII

BAILLY, —360 —920 [French astronomer, 1736-93]. The largest of all the lunar ringed formations, the 'seas' alone excepted. It is 183 miles in diameter and the walls bear peaks rising 14,000 feet on the east and from 10,000 to 13,000 feet on the west. Despite its great size it was missed by the earlier selenographers, and it appears for the first time in the map of Cassini (1680). Mädler gave a good and detailed drawing in *Der Mond*, based upon observations on 14 and 15 November 1835, when libration was very favourable.

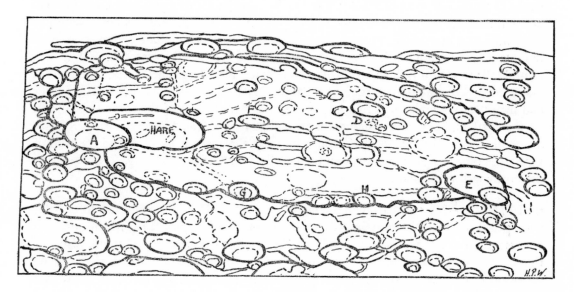

BAILLY
H. P. Wilkins

On the enormous interior is a large crater, B, near the south wall, and this is one of the deepest of secondary formations. Its walls rise 14,000 feet above its depressed floor and on this floor is a central mountain and a ridge on the east. B is now called Hare, after the American selenographer of that name. It abuts on the smaller crater to the west. Hare has charted 140 objects on the floor of Bailly, based upon a photograph taken by him with his 12-inch reflector, 4 October 1950.

The interior of Bailly to the east of Hare is slightly raised above the remainder and is traversed by a cleft from the crater B, west of Hare, to a ridge near the east wall. One of the peaks on the east wall of B contains a summit craterlet. From the north wall of

293

Hare a meridional ridge runs towards the north wall. This ridge rises into little peaks here and there; the peak nearest Hare was shown as a hill by Mädler but is depicted as a crater by Hare. Wilkins has noted several parallel ridges from the ridge on the north-west to the main west wall.

In addition to the above-mentioned details there are numerous craterlets, ridges and hills on the interior; for these reference should be made to the map.

Dr. S. M. Green reported the existence of a fine ring 75 miles in diameter, with a central peak, abutting on the south wall of Bailly. This is the 'Hausen' of Schröter. It has been confirmed recently by T. W. Rackham, H. N. D. Wright, Mrs. G. E. Stone, and Moore. Adjoining it to the west is a ring of similar size but lesser depth. Another large walled-plain lies along the limb.

BAYER, −357 −783 [German astronomer, 1572-1625]. A fine crater with lofty walls; peaks of 8,000 feet exist in places; a crater lies on the south crest, a crater-chain just below the west crest. The inner slopes are terraced. On the interior is a crater south of the centre, and two craterlets. Gaudibert depicted a central mountain to Bayer. A great mountain arm on the north rises 7,000 feet. On the south is the crater A, with a twin central hill; west of it is the crater B. To the west are three large enclosures, that farthest east has a coarse crater-chain running from the south-west wall, curving across the floor and then bending westwards to a large ring on the north rim of the second enclosure. To the north and beyond the mountain arm, already mentioned, is a large ring, K, with a smooth floor. To the west of K, and occupying the space between it and the wall of Bayer, are other rings with craters on their walls. North-east is the ring, R, abutting on the north wall of Schiller.

BETTINUS, −316 −895 [Italian scientist, 1582-1657]. This fine crater has lofty walls with peaks of 13,000 feet, terraced inner slopes, on the western of which are two craters; another lies on the east, while on the interior is a central mountain, also low ridges. On the west is an ancient ring. To the south is a gigantic mountain arm, towering 12,000 feet and there is another peak of 9,000 feet near Rost. On the outer south is a crater-row. Beyond the outer east glacis is the crater, A, with a curved mountain arm on its north extending to the wall of Bailly. Between Bettinus and Kircher is another conspicuous ridge, and some small craters with, to the south, a fine ring with two craterlets on its north wall. To the north-east are other lofty mountain ridges; indeed, this portion of the surface abounds in objects of this type. With the ridges are isolated mountains, craters and some abnormal formations of peculiar shape, generally fragmentary, the destroyed portions being, usually, on the north.

BROWN, −212 −729 [English mathematician, 1866-1938]. A peculiar and interesting formation on the north-west outer slope of the great walled-plain, Longomontanus. It is a crater, the southern portion of which has been destroyed by the intrusion of a ring with two craterlets on its floor. From its north wall run several craterlet-chains. There is also a shallow valley. To the south-east of Brown is a square enclosure on the inner north-west slope of Longomontanus.

CLAUSIUS, —555 —600 [German physicist, 1822-88]. Although this crater is only 8 miles in diameter, it is conspicuous, and has a craterlet on the south crest with another on the northern. There is a small central hill on the interior. To the north-west is a heart-shaped crater, B, a striking object, with a crater on its north-west rim, and another on the inner north-east. To the north-west of B is a smaller crater, C, while on the west of B, beyond two craterlet-chains, is the large ring, F, with three craterlets in a row on its interior. South of Clausius is the crater D, which overlaps another to the south.

DÖRFEL MOUNTAINS, —200 to —430 [German astronomer, 1643-1688]. A great range on the south-east limb, with peaks well over 20,000 feet in altitude; δ east of the north end of Bailly, is of great height, while β and γ attain at least 26,000 feet.

DREBBEL, —570 —655 [Dutch physicist, 1572-1634]. A crater 18 miles in diameter with terraced walls, pierced by a gap on the north, and a crater on the south-east. On the floor is a low central hill. Wilkins found the gap in the north wall occupied by a crater. To the north is the low ring, K, with a central craterlet. A partial ring abuts on the north-east of K. To the west is a remarkable forked ridge, from which a long ridge runs south. On the eastern side of this ridge is the crater, B. This ridge in reality forms the western boundary of a large, low ring on the north-west of Schickard. To the east is a small mountain and the crater, G. North of G is a larger crater. On the north-west is a fine line of old rings, with low walls, which can be traced as far as the deformed ring, D, which slightly overlaps an older ring. In its course this line of ancient rings passes the lofty mountain ridge, Beta. A low-rimmed crater, C, with two craterlets on its floor, lies to the south-west of D. South of C is another mountain, in part an extension of its southern wall. South of this mountain mass are the craters, F and G, and east of them a discontinuous crater-chain.

DRYGALSKI, —180 —983. A large walled-plain on the limb, beyond Legentil and not far from Casatus. It is so badly placed that it is excessively difficult to examine, and our knowledge of it depends almost entirely upon the work of the late Dr. S. M. Green, E. A. Whitaker and the Authors.

Green drew it on 9 September 1938, and recorded a fine, double central peak and a crater on the inner south-east, as well as a crater on the south-west crest. The Authors have confirmed the former. The outer north-east wall is disturbed by another crater, perhaps 15 miles in diameter and of some depth; the whole north wall is fairly lofty, crowned with peaks and craterlets. The total diameter of Drygalski is about 95 miles.

Moore had a good view of the formation on 17 January 1954, with his 12½-inch reflector, and confirmed most of the known details. Drygalski can aptly be described, as Bailly too has been, as a 'field of ruins', though the north and south walls are massive and still of some height. Six craters and three hills were seen on the north wall; the south wall appears to be relatively undisturbed, but the eastern slopes are so gentle that it is difficult to tell just where the true 'wall' begins. Further observations are necessary before we can regard our knowledge of this interesting object as at all complete.

EMLEY, −362 −610 [contemporary English selenographer]. A small crater to the north-west of Hainzel, with a craterlet and a ridge on the floor and craterlets on its east wall. To the south-west is the crater, L, with a smaller crater between them. South is a ridge curving southwards to Epimenides, and forming the east rampart of a large, ancient ring. West are two craters with their walls in contact, while on the east are hills and the low ring, T, also the still larger W and X. North are mountains of only moderate height.

EPIMENIDES, −372 −658 [Cretan poet, *circa* 596 B.C.]. A crater west of Hainzel, with a central peak. To the west is a craterlet-chain on the east rim of an old ring. South of this craterlet-chain is the low-rimmed crater, S, also with a low central hill. Farther south are craterlets and the crater A, with a mountain to its south-west. South of A are two craters.

HAIDINGER, −328 −631 [Austrian geologist and physicist, 1795-1871]. A small ring between Heinsius and Hainzel, with a craterlet on the south crest, another on the floor and a ridge concentric with the east wall. To the north-west is the crater A, with another on the west. Farther west is a triangular formation, C, with a crater, G., on its south wall. North of C are two low rings. On the south are the remains of old rings, hills and craters and, on the far south, a large ring full of detail, chiefly craterlets and hills. The south rim is almost obliterated with little craters, while on the east wall is the crater Epimenides A.

HAINZEL, −410 −656 [German astronomer, *circa* 1570]. A large and most interesting formation, being a mountain-ringed formation of abnormal shape. The diameter from north to south is 60 miles. Its shape is the result of the partial fusion of two nearly equal rings, the walls averaging 9,000 feet (Neison 10,000 feet).

The north component, the south wall of which intrudes upon the floor of the other, contains several craters, including a crater-row along the foot of the inner east wall and several obscure rings on the southern portion. One of these rings, open on the north, has a hill at either extremity. There are also some isolated mounds, while from the west crest a ridge tends north to a craterlet-chain, beyond which it becomes a fine cleft and may be traced to the cleft system of Ramsden. Adjoining the north wall are the remains of old rings.

The southern component includes a curved mountain arm which, except for a slight

296

break, joins the west wall and is, probably, the relic of a once-complete ring. There are also some craters and a crater-chain, just below the east crest. This Neison shows as a cleft.

Hainzel is difficult to find at Full, as only a few points, chiefly crater walls, can then be made out. The surroundings contain many old rings, some mere curved ridges, while on the south-east is a large ring with low walls, but prominent at sunrise, and now named Mee.

HARE, −323 −932 [contemporary American astronomer]. This is the prominent and very deep crater on the southern portion of the interior of Bailly and was formerly known as Bailly B. Its walls rise 14,382 feet above its floor, and there is a smaller ring, A, adjoining it on the south-west. (See under Bailly.) There are five craterlets on the outer east, while Mädler declared that the wall was cut through by two valleys on the south-west, thus putting its floor in communication with that of B. These valleys have not been detected by other observers. Fine work has been done here by Lenham. On 10 October 1954 the Authors, using Wilkins' 15¼-inch reflector, discovered that the north part of the floor of Hare is occupied by an old ring.

HAUSEN, [German astronomer, 1693-1743]. This is the large formation beyond Bailly, described with that formation. This is the true 'Hausen' of Schröter. It is not identical with the 'Hausen' of the I.A.U. Map, nor with Franz' 'Hausen'. Some way away, along the limb from Bailly, are the other features referred to; A is a deep object, actually one component of a large old ring, and between this and the limb is the deep crater called 'Hausen' in the I.A.U. Map.

The confusion over the nomenclature in this region is unfortunate, and underlines the need for standardization. It is of course true that the whole area is extremely difficult to chart, since all the formations are so badly foreshortened, and there is scope here for the skilful observer equipped with a moderate telescope.

HEINSIUS, −234 −635 [German astronomer, 1709-69]. A very peculiar formation 45 miles in diameter. There are two large intruding rings on the south-east (B and C). The crater B has a central hill; C has a break in its south wall and a small double crater on the outer south.

On the floor of Heinsius is a crater, A, with a central mountain. This crater makes a triangle with B and C on the walls. There is a crater on the crest of the south-west wall and another on the north-west. On the western portion of the floor are three craters. North of A is a very shallow depression. In the north-west wall is a cleft, shown by Schmidt. The inner slopes are finely terraced, and there are some landslips at the inner foot. From A a craterlet-chain runs to the west wall. The walls are prolonged on the south-west, beyond B to the fine, large crater, D, which has two hills on its floor; one, nearly central, has a pit on its summit. North-west are a low enclosure, K, crater-chains and craters. On the north-east is a series of old rings, and a shallow valley runs east from the east wall. This valley is flanked on both sides by old rings.

KIRCHER, —277 —917 [German mathematician, 1601-80]. A grand crater with massive walls rising at peaks 18,000 feet above the depressed floor on the south, where there is a craterlet. On the floor is a ridge. The west wall ends where the east wall of Wilson begins, the narrow gap being occupied by many craterlets. From the terraced inner slope on the east a short ridge projects on to the floor. Lohrmann drew a central peak in Kircher.

On the north is a crater with a gap in its west wall and a craterlet on either side. To the south-east is an elongated depression with a crater-chain on its outer south, while the surface south of Kircher swarms with craters of moderate dimensions but of surprising depth.

LAGALLA, —281 —700 [Italian philosopher, 1571-1624]. A peculiar and pear-shaped formation to the south-east of Wilhelm I, with broad, terraced walls, broken on the north by the crater B, to the north of which is another crater. The narrow south end of the floor is occupied by a crater, while on the other part of the floor is a central craterlet in the middle of an old ring. A cleft crosses the floor just south of the central craterlet and runs to a crater, 5, on the north-east wall. On the outer west are two great craters, slightly encroaching on the wall of Lagalla; these are A and K. A encroaches upon K, and K itself encroaches upon the wall of Wilhelm I. To the south-east is the crater, P, the large, low ring, W, and a crater-row beyond the latter.

LEGENTIL, —233 —965 [French astronomer, 1725-92]. A large crater very close to the limb, and thus only well seen under favourable libration. The walls are lofty and there are some craters on the floor. Moore has also recorded a ridge on the inner east. On the west is a deep crater, and there is another on the north. South-west lies the great ruined formation, Drygalski. Legentil lies south of Bailly.

LONGOMONTANUS, —248 —761 [Danish mathematician, 1562-1647]. A grand ring, one of the largest of all the lunar walled-plains, 90 miles in diameter, with very complex walls, abounding in ridges and rocky spurs, with a crater-chain on the east and on the inner south-west slope. On the south are old and partial rings, also some on the north, with numerous craters.

On the dusky interior is a group of hills near the centre, consisting of three principal and several lesser masses. To the south are craterpits, and there is a small ring touching the inner western slope. On the crest at this point is a crater. A mass of craters lies on the north-eastern portion of the interior, also some low hills and mounds. All around are many craters. To the west of the centre is an isolated cratercone, with a very minute hillock just to the east of it. Wilkins found a delicate cleft, 24 December 1944, a little to the west of the central mountain group.

The large enclosure, K, on the inner north, has two craterlets on its west rim and a fine craterlet-chain farther west, from which it runs down the broad slope and on to the floor on the western side of an intrusive mass, evidently the remains of an old ring.

The inner south-west slope is distinguished by dykes of rock which stand out very prominently at times, while the relic of an old ring lies on the inner south.

To the north are the craters B and C, with numerous ridges and smaller craters. A similar confused mass of ridges and craters lies on the east; on the south the craters increase in size and numbers up to the wall of Scheiner.

MEE, —420 —687 [Scottish-Welsh astronomer, 1860-1926]. A large mountain walled enclosure to the south-east of Hainzel, with low walls, prominent at sunrise and sunset. On the eastern side of the interior is a crater, and south of it a mountain nearly in the centre of the formation. This might be regarded as a central peak.

A low ring, from the south of which two craterlet-chains run to the wall, lies on the south-east. A distinct cleft traverses the floor bending around the central hill. From this central hill, which is of peculiar shape, two craterlet-chains run south across the floor and there is also a long mountain ridge, while on the inner east is a well-defined ring, S, to the south of which is a peculiar object with a small floor, but enclosed on the west by a very broad, low wall. The south wall is broad, with a crater on the west and distinct mountain masses to the east of it, followed by a gap. On the east are the craters S and T, with a crater-chain between them. North of these craters are the partial rings, N, P and L, extending to the east wall of Hainzel.

On the south-west is a great curved mountain ridge, divided by a valley and narrow on the south but widening on the north.

MONTANARI, —246 —717 [Italian astronomer, 1633-87]. A small ring north of Longomontanus, with a craterlet on the floor and a peculiar pointed enclosure on the west. To the east is the crater D, which is surrounded by craterlets. On the south, beyond a crater-row, are the depressions K and R, on the inner north wall of Longomontanus.

NASMYTH, —533 —773 [Scottish engineer and selenographer, 1809-90]. A depression between Phocylides and Wargentin. The walls have a pass into Phocylides. On the floor are at least sixteen craterlets; one, 3, is nearly central; while, on the outer north, is the crater B, with a curved ridge connecting it with the crater Phocylides C, farther south. North-west of this ridge is a small mountain, M.

NÖGGERATH, —472 —756 [German geologist, 1788-1877]. A crater to the east of Schiller, with a smooth floor and four craterlets on the walls, which are terraced. South-west is the crater G, and many craterlets. On the south is the low ring, H, the only part of the wall of any height being on the north-west. North-east are the craters J, F and E, the latter with very low walls.

PHOCYLIDES, —509 —797 [Dutch astronomer, 1618-51]. A great crater, 60 miles in diameter, with terraced walls rising 9,000 feet above the interior. There are some depressions on the western crest, which is higher than the eastern, two craters on the inner south-east and smaller on the lower slopes. On the south crest is the crater F, with a central hill. South of F is a low ring, E, to the east of which are three craters. On the south are large rings, F and H, the latter with craters on its north wall. On the interior of Phocylides are craterlets, and some craterlet-chains near the foot of the walls. On the north is the ring, B, with a bright floor on which are five small craters and a low ring. To the east is the crater K, while on the outer west is a short ridge with a craterlet-chain flanking it on the west.

On the south-west are two large rings, seen by Wilkins, 10 March 1953, and overlapping each other. They have also been seen by Moore, but not, so far, by anyone else. The ring to the east has finely terraced walls, a crater at both the north and the south end and a small crater on the inner south-east.

Haas finds the sunrise shadow within Phocylides is darker than that within Schickard. D. W. G. Arthur has found several crater-chains on the slopes of this fine formation.

PINGRÉ, −551 −809 [French astronomer, 1711-1796]. A crater 12 miles in diameter, with a smooth floor. This is not the Pingré of Mädler, which is the crater to the south-east known now as A. South are several craters and large overlapping rings, lying west of Hausen.

RENART, [Spanish astronomer, 1878-1946]. This lies partly within this section and partly within Section VII. It is a large ring south of Wurzelbauer, with a crater, A, on its north wall, a crater, F, on the east and craterlets and hills on its floor.

ROST, −306 −833 [German astronomer, 1688-1727]. A crater 30 miles in diameter, with lofty walls; here and there peaks attain 7,200 feet on the west, and there is a crater on the north crest. On the interior is a nearly central crater. The east wall is low in places, and here is a low-rimmed ring, with a giant central hill. On the south is an ancient ring, and, west, two deep craters.

SCHEINER, −230 −870. [German Jesuit astronomer, 1575-1650]. A great crater, 70 miles in diameter, with walls magnificently terraced on the inner slopes and of great height. Some of the wall peaks attain 18,000 feet above the depressed floor. There are craters on the inner south and east slopes. To the west of the crater, on the south slope, is a smaller crater, and east of it a partial ring, from which a narrow edge runs across the floor. This was described by Webb as a partition. On the interior are a nearly central crater, five craters to the north of it, another at the foot of the inner north slope, several hills and a craterlet. To the south-west is an old ring, the site of its former wall being now marked by hills.

SCHICKARD, −590 −700 [German mathematician, 1592-1635]. A large walled-plain, 134 miles in diameter, but with low walls averaging only 4,500 feet, the highest peaks rising 9,500 feet on the west and 8,380 feet on the south.

The shaded interior has a triangular dark patch on the north-west, with remarkably sharp boundaries; there is another on the north and a third near the east wall. On the south wall is a crater, E, with a smaller crater on its east. On the edge of the large dark area is the crater A, which is connected by a cleft to a smaller crater on the north. The

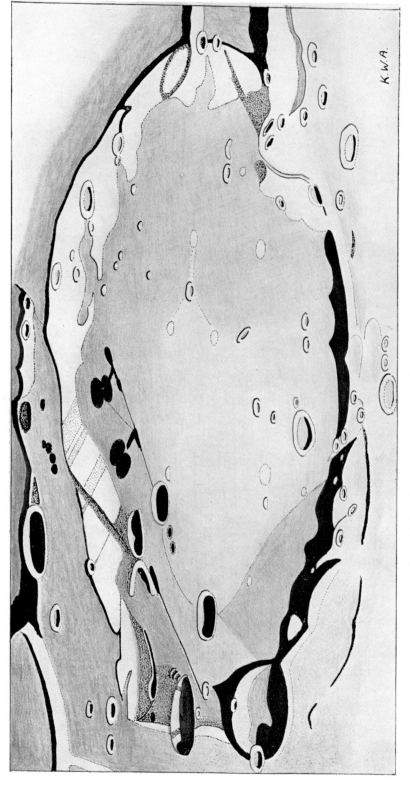

K.W.A.

9. Schickard. Drawing by K. W. Abineri, 8½-inch reflector

10a, 10b, 10c. Region of Schickard, Schiller and Bailly under Three Different Conditions of illumination. Photographs by Lyle T. Johnson, 1954

connecting cleft runs roughly concentric with the east wall. The cleft continues north and ends in a craterlet-chain. From some craters at the foot of the inner east wall a short cleft runs to three small craters farther north. Near the west wall is a crater from which a cleft runs into the dark area on the northern portion of the floor. In this dark area are some craterlets. Close under the east wall Elger found a cleft.

At the northern end of the floor Wilkins has seen twelve craterlets, a small landslip and four craters on the inner slope. Here, too, is a projecting ridge. On the outer west slope is a large, shallow depression. Emley and Burrell found the dark areas to be variable in tint. So easily seen are these dark areas that they are shown, although imperfectly and named, on the map of Langrenus.

Elger gave a good sketch of the northern portion of the interior in the *English Mechanic*, 28 November 1884, and the area is well shown in the Paris Atlas, Plates LXI and LXIV.

Wilkins noted an abnormal appearance of the floor, 31 August 1944, with an 8½-inch 'With' mirror. On that occasion very few craters were to be seen, but a large number of light spots which strongly contrasted with the dark areas.

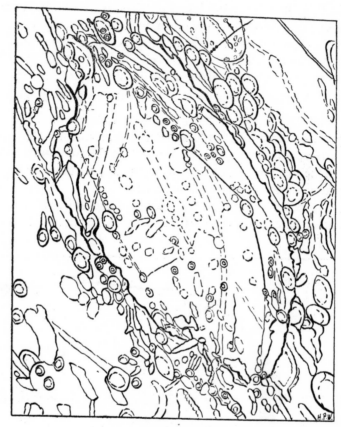

SCHICKARD
H. P. Wilkins

Moore twice saw a similar appearance in 1939.

The large dark area on the north has a long but narrow brighter streak in the centre, and on this streak are four craterlets. A drawing of Schickard by Dr. S. R. B. Cooke appears in the B.A.A. Memoirs, 36, 3.

SCHILLER, −396 −783 [German astronomer, *circa* 1627]. An elliptical formation, 112 miles in length and 60 miles in width towards the south, but tapering towards both ends. It is obviously the result of the fusion of two rings. On the inner south-east are large masses with small craters near the crest. On the interior and south of the centre is a faintly marked ring with a craterlet on its south rim. East of the centre of the floor and near the east slope are two little hills. There is also a shallow ring on the north-east crest. A ridge, broken half-way, lies on the floor at the northern end. This ridge has a craterlet on its west and two smaller craterlets on its east. To the west of Schiller is an ancient ring.

SEGNER, —386 —856 [German physicist, 1704-77]. A crater 45 miles in diameter, the walls being broken on the north, while on the floor is a crater. A strong mountain arm from the west wall runs to Schiller. Another ridge runs from the north-east wall and curves on the north, thus enclosing a space, resembling an old ring. Within this area are some craters and low rings, the walls of many of these rings being marked by craterlets, a most interesting spectacle. To the north are many low, ancient rings.

WARGENTIN, —565 —761 [Swedish astronomer, 1717-83]. A most interesting and peculiar formation, 55 miles in diameter, with a floor elevated 1,400 feet above the outer surface, with traces of a former wall on the south-west where a segment rises 500 feet. On the western rim, or what remains of it, are three little peaks, but the edge is sharp in places, especially on the eastern side.

Goodacre found the floor concave and uniform in hue, but Wilkins has seen two darker patches on the north, and R. Barker thinks these are variable in tint.

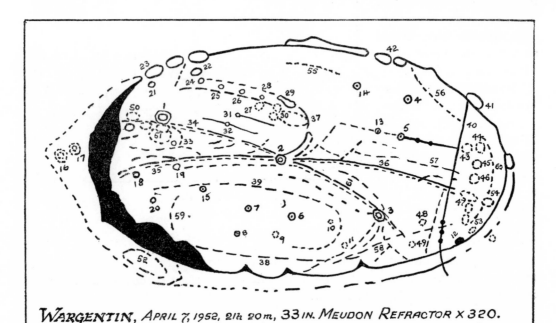

WARGENTIN, APRIL 7, 1952, 21h 20m, 33 IN. MEUDON REFRACTOR x 320.

Observations by H.P. Wilkins F.R.A.S. & P.A. Moore F.R.A.S.

The Authors of this work found, 7 April 1952, with the great 33-inch Meudon refractor, the following features:

There are three peaks on the west wall, but the east wall is only represented by isolated fragments, cut through, on the south, by two valleys. To the east of these valleys are three isolated masses, considered by Moore as depressions, i.e. craters, but considered doubtful by Wilkins. In any case, the interior depressions, if they exist, are shallow.

The most prominent ridge, 35, extends from the south wall to a small crater, 2, nearly in the centre of the plateau-like interior. Here the ridge divides into three: one branch, 61, tending to the north-west with a distinct crater, 3; another branch, 36, running almost due north, while the third ridge, 37, curves eastwards to a rocky mass, 29. This last branch is continued by the ridge 28. Other and shorter ridges were also detected as shown on the special chart, which was first published in the B.A.A. Journal.

On the south-east portion of the interior is a whitish crater, 1, noted by several previous observers and very distinct. North of this crater are two clefts, 31 and 32, each connected with minute pits. Moore suspected a third cleft in this region.

The northern portion is traversed by a straight cleft, 40, discovered by F. H. Thornton, 18-inch reflector. This is not an easy object even with the 33-inch refractor. Wilkins discovered a short branch, 5, which ends on the south at a craterlet and passes through two pits. Between the long cleft and the northern rim are several objects, either hills or craterlets, and an obvious pit, 12, at that time filled with shadow. Of the remaining features many are low hills or mounds, but numbers 6 and 7, also 8, 4, 13, 14, 15, 16, 17, and probably 18, are undoubted craterlets.

The object marked 38, running concentrically with the west rim, is either a slightly marked ridge or a delicate cleft. The mass of detail recorded by the Authors and shown on the chart shows how a formation, comparatively smooth in small apertures, is seen in a great telescope to be, in reality, covered with minute detail.

WEIGEL, −333 −848 [German mathematician, 1625-99]. This crater is 20 miles in diameter, and has steep walls and a smooth floor. There is a crater on the north rim. West are lower rings, many overlapping.

WILHELM I, −257 −683 [German astronomer and prince, 1532-92]. A great ring 60 miles in diameter, with walls rising 11,000 feet on the east and craters on the south crest. There are also three craters on the south-east with a low ring beyond them and a larger crater, B, on the east. On the floor is a low ring on the south, a ruined ring west of the centre, four craterlets on the south, two craters and a low ring on the north-west. To the east are craterlets and hills, while on the north-east is a low ring, west of which are four craters. To the south-west and on the outer slope are three craters and a valley; this valley is, in part, a crater-chain and tends south-west. On the east, beyond a crater-chain, are three craters, with fragments of others on their east walls and glacis.

WILSON, −238 −936 [Scottish astronomer, 1714-86]. A grand crater, 40 miles in diameter, with lofty walls. On the floor is a low central ridge and a crater on the inner west slope. On the outer north-west is a peculiar depression, K, with interior craterlets. On the north-east is the crater Kircher, and on the south, beyond some craters, Legentil.

To the south-west are the craters A, Z and C, with a crater, F, on the west. North is a large ring, K, with many craterlets on its floor. Of these L is the largest, but the craterlet M, on the north crest, is still larger. North of M is the crater H, with a smooth floor and a craterlet-row on its outer south slope.

ZUCCHIUS, −369 −876 [Italian Jesuit mathematician and optician, 1586-1670]. A great crater, 50 miles in diameter, with broad, terraced walls rising 10,000 feet in places. On the inner west slope is a crater, while on the floor is a compound central mountain and a crater-chain on the west. It is the centre of a minor ray system. On the west wall is the peak, Beta, and west the ring, C. To the south-east are several craters, of which A, B and D are the most prominent. D has two craterlets on its inner east, while A overlaps B. Farther south-east is the wall of Bailly and the wall peak, Epsilon. Haas has found the sunset shadow in Zucchius darker than those in the neighbouring formations.

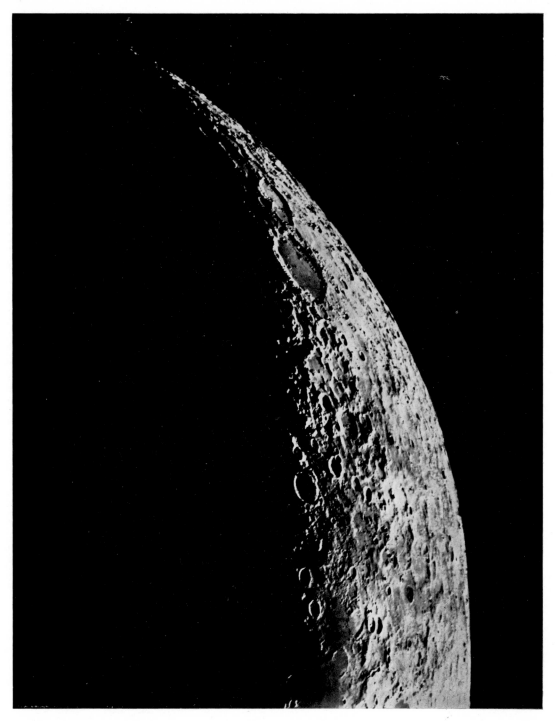

11. The South-East Limb Region near Lunar Sunset. Photograph taken at Mount Wilson Observatory

12. Clavius. 200-inch photograph, Mount Wilson and Palomar Observatories

XXIII

This includes the southern region on either side of the prime meridian and is crowded with formations of all sorts. Of these Clavius, Maurolycus, Stöfler and Maginus are examples of the gigantic enclosures. Moretus, Casatus and Curtius represent the smaller formations, while Tycho stands as the centre of a great ray system.

The portion bordering the southern limb, including the actual pole, is illustrated by a drawing and recent photographs by E. A. Whitaker, of the Royal Observatory, Greenwich, inserted by the kind permission of the Astronomer Royal, Sir Harold Spencer Jones. Mr. Whitaker is also responsible for the description of the formations Cabæus, Malapert, Newton, and the South Pole.

There are no 'seas' in this region and few clefts, but numerous craterlet or crater-pit chains exist. Examples of these will be found radiating from Tycho.

The map has been revised and details found on the recent photograph taken with the Mount Palomar 200-inch telescope have been inserted. It is the most detailed and crowded of all the sections; much of the finer detail will require large instruments for its detection.

U

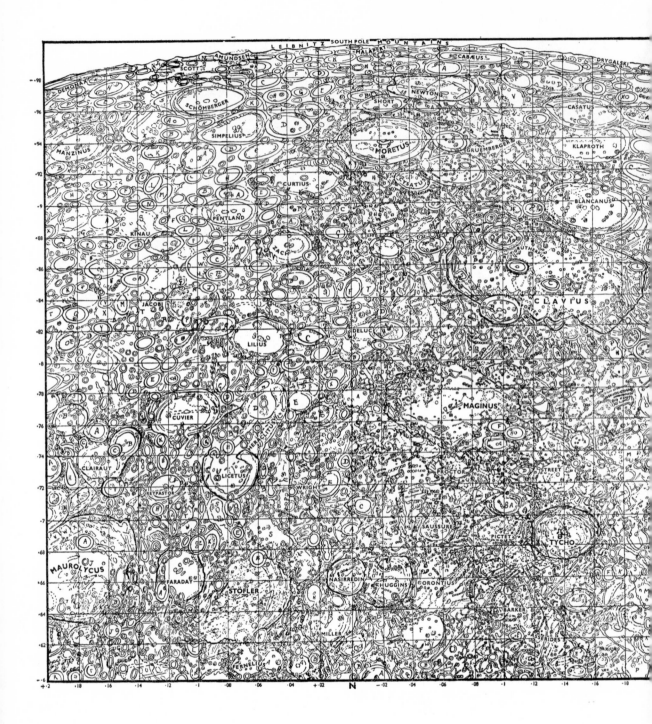

XXIII

AMUNDSEN, +090 −989 [Norwegian Polar explorer, 1872-1928]. An interesting formation very close to the limb; it adjoins Scott, and is only visible under favourable conditions of libration. Our knowledge of it is due entirely to the work of Arthur and Abineri (J.B.A.A., 61, 49) and the Authors.

Two rings divide Amundsen from the southern wall of Scott; the two formations are about equal in size (each 66 miles in diameter, according to Arthur), but Amundsen is the shallower. The walls are broken in the south by a large craterlet, A, 18 miles in diameter. The outer glacis of the east wall is very gentle, and is disturbed by several depressions and low ridges.

The interior of Amundsen contains several features of note. Moore has detected a long ridge of moderate altitude crossing the floor in an east-west direction; this has been confirmed by Abineri. Several more hills and ridges have been charted, and doubtless more remain to be discovered.

Using $8\frac{1}{2}$- and $12\frac{1}{2}$-inch reflectors, Moore has charted four considerable craters between Amundsen and the limb, all so badly placed that they can only be seen under conditions of maximum libration. The largest of the four, some distance south-west of A, appears to be some 20 miles in diameter.

BARKER, −096 −642 [contemporary English selenographer]. This crater disturbs the east wall of Orontius, and is described with that formation.

BLANCANUS, −163 −894 [Italian astronomer, 1566-1624]. A fine walled-plain, 57 miles in diameter, on the south-east of Clavius, with walls of slight elevation above the outer surface, but falling in a broad, rugged and disturbed slope to the interior on which is a central group of three peaks, the most westerly being brighter and more regular than the rest. Between these peaks and the very broad inner south slope are three prominent craters, hills and craterlets. At the foot of this slope are shallow depressions; along the inner east and north slopes are apparently landslips, while, on the crest of these slopes, are well-formed craters. The south-east wall is also disturbed by craters; here, where the foot-hills project on to the floor, a crater-valley runs down the slope to the floor. Between the central mountain group and the western slope is a shallow crater; another lies between the elevations and the east wall; there are also some craterpits on the northern portion of the interior, which is more smooth than the southern. The inner slopes are remarkably bright, while the walls rise 12,000 feet above the light-grey floor.

CABÆUS, −050 −996 [Italian philosopher, 1586-1650]. A grand, deep walled-plain 60 miles in diameter, surrounded by extremely rugged and lofty mountains, but too near

307

the limb to be examined in detail. The inner slopes of the south wall are deeply terraced, and appear to contain a few crateriform enlargements. The east wall rises to a fine peak, and the north wall to an even loftier peak, of the order of 20,000 feet above the general surroundings, and presumably much more than this above the interior. This peak plunges the greater portion of the interior into shadow, and also effectively obscures most of the floor even at most favourable libration. From this peak a prominent mountain range runs in a curve almost as far as Newton A. Closely east of this range commences a wide, deep crater-valley, which expands until it almost reaches the deep crater, Newton E. This valley is shown by Schmidt, who numbers it 334 in his list.

Beyond Cabæus and near the mean libration limb there is a very steep and prominent mountain, which can be clearly seen on the photograph facing page 320, even though much of its base is in shadow. To the north-east of Cabæus lie two considerable ringplains, A and B, each about 35 miles in diameter, and still farther east lies Drygalski.

CASATUS, −152 −953 [Italian mathematician, 1617-1707]. A majestic ring-plain 70 miles in diameter, with walls rising on the west to 18,000 feet, and on the east in a grand peak to the great height of 22,000 feet above the floor. Along the crest of the west wall is a crater-chain; the wall here appears as a mighty line of white cliffs. At the foot of the inner south-east wall is a row of mountain masses, like huge boulders. On the inner south slope is a large crater, and on the northern portion of the floor is another, C, of considerable depth; in addition there are some craterlets and hills. Wilkins has counted at least eleven craterlets. East is a crater, E, with another on its floor at the south. Beyond Casatus, on the south, two high mountains can sometimes be seen, together with mountain ridges and lesser peaks.

Goodacre queried the existence of the high peaks on the walls, but recent micrometrical measures confirm the earlier estimates.

CLAIRAUT, +166 −737 [French mathematical genius, 1713-65]. A walled depression, much deformed by the intrusion of two large rings, A and B, on the south. On the north wall of B is another smaller crater, C. There are also other craters on the walls, two on the north-west being the largest. On the interior is a nearly central crater, D, which overlaps an older ring. Between this crater and B are some craterlets. The walls of the craters A and B are broken by craters. Clairaut is 30 miles in diameter. It is evidently the result of the fusion of several rings due to the focus of eruption. Another example of a similar type is Heinsius, while numerous less-prominent specimens can be found.

CLAVIUS, −140 −850 [German Jesuit mathematician, 1537-1612]. This magnificent object, familiar to every observer, is a huge walled depression about 145 miles in diameter. The west wall, between the large craters Rutherford and Porter, is the only part of the enclosure which is materially above the outer surface. The broken, terraced walls on north, east and south exhibit on the inner slopes a range of mighty cliffs, disturbed by depressions and rise 12,000 feet above the floor, with peaks soaring 5,000 feet higher. The inner north-east slope exhibits vast landslips, and there is another on the interior

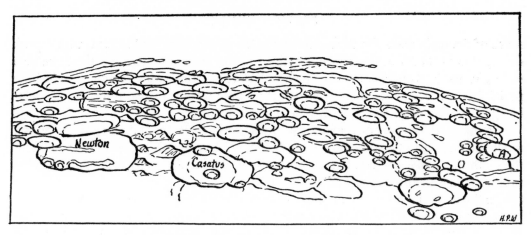

THE LIMB REGION BEYOND NEWTON AND CASATUS

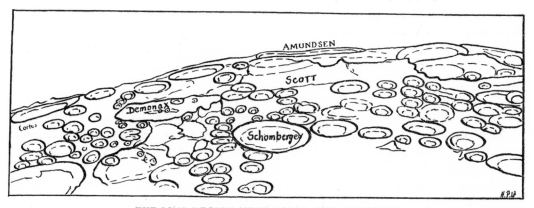

THE LIMB REGION NEAR SCOTT AND AMUNDSEN

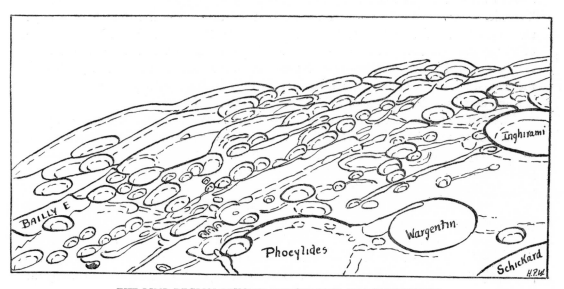

THE LIMB REGION BEYOND PHOCYLIDES AND WARGENTIN

All by H. P. Wilkins   15¼-inch reflector

north of the main mass. On the south wall is the large crater, Rutherfurd, with a peak on the interior north of the centre. South of it is a distinct crater, and there are also some pits and hills on its floor. The north wall of Rutherfurd, which contains some little peaks, has a broad outer slope from which radiate several ridges, three in particular being very prominent. Rutherfurd is 25 miles in diameter.

On the north rampart of Clavius is a similar ring, Porter, containing a triple central mountain and part of a curved ridge on the floor. There are also some craterpits under the south wall and elsewhere. East of Porter is a large and decidedly rectangular depression which has deformed the wall at this point.

On the floor of Clavius are five large craters, diminishing in size eastwards, arranged in a curve concave to the south. In addition, there are numerous craterpits and craterlets, especially on the southern portion of the interior. A number of low hills and little peaks are also to be found, chiefly near the walls and south-east of the centre, near the crater E. One of these hills forms the relic of a central peak, and bears a minute pit on its western flank. West of the crater D, which is the largest and the most westerly of the great floor craters, is a curve of minute craterpits, noted by Krieger and shown on one of the Mt. Wilson photographs. They are not unduly difficult in a good telescope, but are not easy objects.

The late Mr. Arthur Mee, in a sketch, 6 May 1892, showed twenty pits on the southern portion of the floor, and it is certain that these are only a few of what can be detected under favourable conditions. The inner southern cliffs are very rugged with two large craters on the crest; at its west end this portion of the rampart is disturbed by large irregular depressions filling the space between Rutherfurd and the ring Blancanus.

So large is Clavius that, when on the terminator, it appears as a great bay filled with black shadow which perceptibly blunts the south cusp to the naked eye. Gradually the crest of the entire wall becomes visible, followed by fine rings of light, the walls of the large floor craters. As R. Barker remarks, 'like looking down the funnels of a large steamer, a wonderful sight with a power of 600.' When the floor is revealed, the shadow of a high peak on the west wall is cast in striking steeple-like outline. The larger floor craters retain shadow when the rest of the floor is fully illuminated. For this reason, the central hill of the crater, D, can be seen for only a comparatively short time. There is some detail on the interior of D in addition to this hill.

The surface to the east of Clavius is rugged; on the west is a chaotic mass of rugged highlands, with small craters, often in pairs; the surroundings on the north-east contain several very irregular enclosures. On the north-west there is a strong indication of parallelism, and the hilly ranges running from north-east to south-west are crossed by others radiating from the rampart.

On the floor to the north of the crater E is a low-rimmed object, probably a ruined ring. There are also indications of others elsewhere on the vast interior. Strange to say, no clefts have as yet been detected within Clavius and none are shown on the recent photograph taken with the Mt. Palomar 200-inch telescope. Clavius is really a gigantic pit deeply sunk below the level of the outer surface, and from the summit of the great peak on the west wall to the floor of the interior crater D, the best measurements indicate a distance of no less than 24,000 feet. At one stage of sunrise, and again at sunset, the convexity of the interior is exhibited by the central portion alone being illuminated. When the east wall is on the morning terminator, the many irregular depressions associated with its outer glacis are seen to the best advantage.

CURTIUS, +032 −921 [German astronomer, 1600-71]. This great mountain-walled depression, 50 miles in diameter, is situated a little to the west of the central meridian. It has a very massive border, rising to a great height on the south-west and also on the east, where the rampart is crowned by a bright, rounded dome. Gigantic terraces descend to the interior, on which are a central crater, some craterlets, hills and a ruined ring on the floor close to the inner north slope. Whitaker found a cleft on the floor to the east of the central crater. On the south and west crests are craters, that on the west being the larger; beyond it is a portion of an ancient ring now overlapped by Curtius. A chain of large and deep craters runs north from this ruined ring as far as Zach. On the south-west portion of the floor are three hillocks, or more probably cratercones, best seen under evening illumination when this part of the interior alone remains free from shadow.

CUVIER, +103 −770 [French palæontologist, 1769-1832]. A regular ringed-plain, 50 miles in diameter, with highly terraced walls rising 12,000 feet on the west and slightly more on the east above the interior on which is a low central hill, small craters on the eastern part and also on the western, while there are some craterlets on the lower inner slopes. These craterlets appear as bright spots near Full Moon. South of Cuvier is a plain circled by craters, and sprinkled with numerous irregularities. This is probably a ruined ring, as suggested by Goodacre. Under high illumination, indications of another and still larger ancient ring may be traced on the south-west of Cuvier.

CYSATUS, −043 −914 [Swiss astronomer, 1588-1657]. A ring-plain 28 miles in diameter to the west of Gruemberger, with a peak on the south wall and a crater, D, on the north. Below is a crater-chain. The inner slopes are broad and finely terraced, especially on the south. On the rather small floor is a low central mountain, difficult to detect. Between Cysatus and Moretus is a high ridge, and on the west of this an irregular depression. Wilkins has noted three prominent craterlets on the floor of Cysatus.

DELUC, −028 −819 [Swiss geologist, 1727-1817]. A ringed-plain about 28 miles in diameter to the south-west of Maginus, with which it is connected by some irregular depressions. On the south crest is a deep crater, with a much larger one abutting on its south-west. A large crater, H, has deformed the wall on the north-west, and there is also a craterlet on the east. To the south of this craterlet is a peak. The inner west slope is broad, and there is a row of foot-hills along the south wall. On the interior are two craters and several minor objects. To the west of Deluc is a large irregular depression, bounded, on the south, by a mountain ridge; and many rings and elevations on its surface. East is a circular ridge-bordered area, which has been encroached upon by Deluc. Within this feature are some craterlet-chains.

EINSTEIN, +047 −949 [Albert Einstein, great scientist, 1879-1955]. Formerly Simpelius D, diameter 28 miles, with lofty walls retaining shadow long after sunrise. On the floor are some craterlets.

FARADAY, +113 −673 [Great English scientist, 1791-1867]. An irregular ringed enclosure which has intruded to a considerable extent on the south-west portion of Stöfler. On the north-west wall is a crater, A, above which rises the rampart of Stöfler; another crater, C, with a central peak, occupies the crest of the south-east wall. This crater overlaps another and still larger ring, which has terraced walls and some craterlets on the crests. To the east of the crater, C, are smaller craters, and, on the south, beyond the wall, is a group of irregular enclosures. The west wall of Faraday is disturbed by craters on the inner slopes; there is also a small but prominent crater on the crest. The crest of the east wall is thin and sharp. On the floor is a central peak.

The inner west slopes contain two craters; near the south-west inner slope is a distinct crater with a hill to the east of it, and under the south-east slope is a low ring. There are also some craterlets scattered over the surface. Along the outer slope of the west wall is a chain of craters; of these the largest are on the south.

FERNELIUS, +068 −617 [French scientist, 1497-1558]. A walled-plain 40 miles in diameter. It lies closely north-east of Stöfler, and is dwarfed by that great and important object. The floor is fairly level, though it does contain a number of small craterlets. To the east of Fernelius is an imperfect formation, A, 17 miles in diameter; this lacks part of its western wall, so that the interior is joined to that of Fernelius.

GRUEMBERGER, −076 −920 [Austrian mathematician, 1561-1636]. A large walled-plain 58 miles in diameter, closely north-east of Moretus; its outer north-west glacis is common with that of Cysatus, so that it is a member of the imposing group of formations of which Moretus is the chief. Gruemberger is roughly pear-shaped, tapering to the west, where the wall is interrupted by a shallow crater; on the floor, rather south-east of the centre, is a conspicuous crater, A, and there are many other small craterlets dotted over the floor. To the south of Gruemberger, and east of Moretus, is a fine crater, A, 19 miles in diameter.

HERACLITUS, +064 −755 [Greek philosopher, circa 540-480 B.C.]. This adjoins Licetus, and is described with that formation.

HUGGINS, −024 −660 [English spectroscopist, 1824-1910]. A walled-plain 42 miles in diameter. It lies between Nasireddin and Orontius. Its western wall has been destroyed by the intrusion of Nasireddin, and even the remaining walls are of no great altitude; they slope gently on to a floor which contains much detail, including what appears to be the remains of an old central peak.

JACOBI, +104 —836 [German mathematician, 1804-51]. A formation 41 miles in diameter. The walls are of some altitude, rising in places to nearly 10,000 feet; they are broken in the south-east by a crater, J, and in the north by an incomplete crater, P. The floor contains a considerable amount of detail, including a very prominent central crater. The environs of Jacobi are extremely complex. To the north there are indications of an old ring, 60 or 70 miles across, that may once have existed in the space enclosed by Jacobi, Cuvier and Lilius.

KINAU, +128 —872 [Bohemian selenographer, *circa* 1850]. A formation 26 miles in diameter, some distance south-west of Jacobi. It has lofty walls, broken by crest craterlets in the south, south-west, west and north; and a central mountain, as well as a craterlet, on the eastern part of its floor. Despite its size and depth, Kinau is not easy to identify, as it is surrounded by other formations of comparable dimensions; and neither it nor its neighbours seem to present any features of special interest.

KLAPROTH, —158 —934 [German chemist, 1743-1817]. A mountain-walled plain, 60 miles in diameter, on the north of Casatus. It is more shallow than Casatus, and there is no real south wall as the rugged rampart of Casatus intrudes. The inner slope here is very rugged, with many spurs jutting on to the floor. From the north wall two strong promontories encroach on the interior, on which is a crater on the south-east, many pits and also craterlets with some very low ridges. There is also an elongated hill near the centre of the floor, with a ridge running west from it and dividing into two arms which reach the south wall. Most of the craterlets are difficult to detect. Outside the north wall is a crater, A, with a peak on its south-west wall. North of A is another crater.

LEIBNITZ MOUNTAINS, —002 to +220 [German mathematician, 1646-1716]. The most imposing and massive of all lunar mountain ranges, situated a little beyond the limb in mean libration but occasionally brought into striking profile by libration. This mighty range is then seen to stretch over an arc of more than 30 degrees, and the peaks often prolong the cusp in the crescent phase. Some of the peaks then shine like stars on the edge of the darkened portion. Arthur Mee and Goodacre recorded some of the peaks as being very brilliant and as showing prismatic colours, the Moon being young. In January 1888 Mee noted the summits of several as apparently snow-covered. Some portions of the range appear to be the profiles of great rings.

The majoriy of the peaks range from 16,000 feet to 17,000 feet. Schröter measured some rising from 26,000 feet to 30,000 feet. These measures were confirmed, in part, by Mädler, Neison and others. Neison found, as the result of careful measurement, a height of 33,000 feet for one peak (ϵ on his map). Several other peaks attained heights of from 27,000 feet to 29,000 feet. These measures are relative to the base, and not to a common level as on the earth.

The most striking view, libration being favourable, is probably obtained with a young Moon between the third and fourth days of the lunation. The unilluminated portion is then rendered visible by earthshine and easily seen with low telescopic power. On 12 May 1940, with a 9½-inch telescope, Wilkins noted one peak overlapping a large, low ring.

LICETUS, +080 −730 [Italian philosopher, 1577-1657]. A very peculiar ringed-plain, 46 miles in diameter, the south wall having been destroyed; and this places the interior into communication with a wide, irregular enclosure, now known as Heraclitus. Heraclitus has high walls and a central ridge, partly projecting into Licetus, with craters on either side. The walls of Licetus are lofty, with a broad inner west slope, at the foot of which is a crater. On the north slope is a crater and, beyond, the ring, K. There are crater-chains on the outer east and west slopes.

On the floor of Licetus is a low central hill, with three peaks and a crater on the west, and another abutting on the inner east slope. There are also hills and craterlets. On the south-east end of Heraclitus is another ring, C, deep and with a central hill and a crater west of it. On its south wall is a crater and a narrow pass. This ring is much depressed below Heraclitus, and on the east is a group of irregular enclosures. Neison records two clefts near the east wall of Licetus; one of these Goodacre declared to be a narrow ridge; the other appears to be a ravine running along the inner east slope. On the south-west inner slope is the remains of a ring, within which is a crater. The north wall of the ring is reduced to a fine edge, overlooked by Goodacre.

LILIUS, +063 −814 [Italian physician, died 1576]. A fine ringed-plain 32 miles in diameter, with steep and finely terraced walls, especially on the inner slopes. These are disturbed by a crater on the east and by the ring, A, on the west. This has disturbed a crater on its west wall and has some small craters on its floor. On the interior of Lilius is a fine, steep central mountain with two lower hills, one to the west and the other to the east. There are also several craterlets on the floor; one close to the inner north slope is easily seen, and another is under the south-west wall. The south wall is higher than the western, as may be well seen near sunset.

MAGINUS, −085 −770 [Italian astronomer, 1555-1617]. A great mountain-walled depression, 110 miles in diameter, with more or less ruinous walls and broad inner slopes, disturbed by numerous craters, especially on the east and the north. Many projections run on to the floor, forming little bays, several being the relics of once-prominent rings. The lower reaches of the slopes are very gentle; the outer glacis is equally gentle and little elevated above the surface, especially on the south and the north-east.

The crest rises 14,000 feet above the interior on the west. Of the numerous ring-plains that have broken the symmetry of Maginus, the largest is G, on the south-east, 30 miles in diameter with broad west slopes, a triangle of craters on the north-east, a crater on the south and craters and craterlets on the floor. East of G are other craters. On the north-east is a group of large craters, some with central peaks. The most southerly of these craters is N, which lies quite out on the floor, on the north edge of which is a ruined ring with fragmentary walls. On the western side of the floor are many craters; the largest, A, has a crater-row running north-east. A little to the west of the centre of Maginus is a group of hills, the highest attaining 2,000 feet. South-west of this is another mountain group, and farther south a large ruined ring lies against the inner slope. Another low ring is B, near the west wall, with hills on its interior; others are found on the east. With powerful telescopes the floor of Maginus is seen to be sprinkled over with numerous craterpits, hillocks, swellings and craterlets. Neison gives a fine chart in his work, Goodacre another. Being enveloped in the rays from Tycho, Maginus is difficult to detect at Full. The ring Maginus I is now called Proctor.

MALAPERT, +018 −995 [Belgian astronomer, 1581-1630]. Although described by Neison as the southernmost ring-plain on the Moon, this formation has the appearance of an irregular enclosure of about 35 miles diameter, bounded on the east by Malapert Alpha, and on the west by Leibnitz Beta, both very lofty mountains. The north and the south walls are much lower, allowing a portion of the floor to be viewed when libration and illumination are suitable. To the north are two deep, valley-like formations, and farther to the north lie C and K, two ring-plains each of 20 miles diameter. To the west of these there is an almost straight row of craters, running in a southerly direction, from Schömberger K almost as far as Malapert E. The whole surface hereabouts is extremely broken and rugged, and only the more prominent features are shown in the diagram, on page 320. On the northern slopes of Leibnitz Beta is E, a rather irregular depression, but which becomes quite prominent after First Quarter and makes a convenient landmark for visual observations. Leibnitz Beta is an extremely massive mountain, extending from Malapert to Scott, a distance of about 40 miles, with an average height of 15,000 feet above the surroundings.

MANZINUS, +171 −926 [Italian philosopher, 1599-1677]. A large walled-plain with wide and terraced walls, exhibiting evidences of landslips on the south and disturbed on both south and north by several craters. From the east wall a mountain arm tends north-east; this ridge is lofty and is said to rise from 10,000 feet to 14,000 feet. On the interior lie a nearly central crater, some others and a low hill, Beta. On the inner south-east are the craters G, L and M, while outside, on the north, is a crater, B.

MAUROLYCUS, +180 −663 [Sicilian abbot, 1494-1575]. Another great formation with lofty walls, and which has encroached on an older object on the south; the border here being broken by a crater, A. What remains of this ancient ring is very rugged. Another ruined ring may be traced on the north-east and contains some craters. This ring has itself been encroached upon by another, which abuts on the wall of Faraday. Other imperfect rings exist on the west, and also on the floor itself, the largest of these rings being defined by the mountain group north of the centre, curved ridges and a chain of three craters, M. On the inner north slope are two horse-shoe-shaped formations; farther west are two craters, R. South of this is another ruined ring. The inner west slope of the partial ring on the south contains some little bays, probably

315

ruined rings. In addition to the massive central mountain group there are several craters, the largest, C, lying between the mountains and the crater A. The outer west slope contains a valley and a short cleft traverses the floor of the ancient ring outside the north-east wall.

MILLER, +010 —633 [English chemist, 1817-70]. A ringed-plain about 30 miles in diameter, the south wall of which has been destroyed by the intrusion of Nasireddin and a crater, H, which has a central peak. Other rings, C and A, together with the smaller ring, B, occupy the outer slope of the north wall. The inner slopes are broad and terraced, with a crater-chain on the north; on the crest above is a trough-like depression. Another lies to its east. On the summit of the west wall is a peak, conspicuous at sunset and overhanging a low ring occupying the valley between it and Stöfler. On the interior of Miller is a large multiple central mountain, a low ring on the south, a crater on the east and craterlets.

MORETUS, —036 —941 [Belgian mathematician, 1602-67]. A glorious ringed-plain, 75 miles in diameter, with beautifully terraced walls, falling in a broad slope to the floor and with rows of foot-hills. The outer south-west wall is very broad, and rises to 9,000 feet with a crater-row below the crest and a distinct outer terrace. A lofty peak lies on the north-west from which a terrace sweeps south along the inner slope. The north crest contains some peaks, and is lowest midway. The wall on the east rises 9,000 feet and is finely terraced; of these terraces, one, running into the crest at its east point, is especially noteworthy.

On the somewhat dark floor is a magnificent central mountain, rising 7,000 feet, according to Mädler—the highest central mountain on the entire Moon. It has steep slopes and a shallow depression near the summit. At the base, to the north, are three craterpits, well shown on a Mt. Wilson photograph. Several peaks form a rough circle near the south slope; these isolated rocks are also well shown on a Mt. Wilson photograph. Other, lower hills, may be detected under a low sun. The outer south-east wall is very broad, with spurs enclosing a row of shallow rings, of which A and C are the most prominent. Gaudibert saw a craterpit on the summit of the central peak of Moretus.

NASIREDDIN, +003 —660 [Persian astronomer, 1201-74]. A fine crater, 30 miles in diameter, with regular, terraced walls, broken on the south by a crater. On the floor is a nearly central crater with two bright hills on the east and south, all three close together. A ridge crosses the floor from north-west to south-east. On its south flank is a minute craterlet. The rest of the interior is very uneven, and a fine, dark line, either a fault or a cleft, traverses the eastern portion. There are also several pits. South of Nasireddin are three confluent craters, while the formation itself intrudes upon Huggins.

NEWTON, —061 —973 [Sir Isaac Newton, 1643-1727]. This great formation is usually considered as the deepest of the lunar depressions, a peak on the west attaining 24,000 feet, according to Mädler. Neither Schmidt nor Goodacre show any detail on the interior but Neison refers to a few craters and mountain ridges.

The abnormal shape strongly suggests that the formation is the result of the coalescence of two or more rings. Wilkins was the first to publish a chart showing any detail on the interior of this fine, deep but unsymmetrical mountain-walled object. The diameter is about 70 miles. Neison states that the greatest extension measures 143 miles, obviously erroneous unless the separate formations to the south-west are included.

The interior appears to descend in stages, rather in the manner of Boussingault but less regularly. This appearance is particularly noticeable near Last Quarter, when the shadow cast by the east wall descends in three curves. The deepest portion is asymmetrically placed to the north and is never quite free of shadow when seen under strong southerly libration, even at relative co-longitude 90 degrees. Mädler's claim that neither Sun nor Earth are ever visible from some parts of the interior seems valid, and is confirmed by A. N. Neate (Journal, B.A.A., 62). The visible portion of the interior contains a number of small formations, depressions and curved ridges. The latter appear to separate the portions of different depth, while a double peak situated on the south-east edge of the deepest part completes the more prominent features.

The wall, except for small sections at the north-east and south-west, and where it abuts on the ring A, on the north, is very lofty, the highest portion being that on the west and north, and keeps the entire interior in shadow even when the terminator is beyond Casatus. Neate found that this portion rises 15,000 feet above the outer surface and 30,000 feet above the deepest portion of the floor, but this result requires further confirmation. He also found that the inner north slope lies at an angle of 45 degrees The west wall is continued in a southerly direction to a point west of B, where the fine rings, A and B, 40 miles and 25 miles respectively, lie on the south.

ORONTIUS, −057 −650 [French mathematician, 1494-1555]. An irregular, once nearly circular, depression, its symmetry having been destroyed by the intrusion of Huggins. It is also imperfect on the south-west, where a wide valley runs round the west of Saussure. On the northern portion of the floor is a roughly circular depression with a smooth floor, ringed around by craters. On the inner south-east are many spurs resembling partial rings. On the east the crest has been broken by a fine ring-plain, Barker, containing craters and craterlets. A smaller but deep crater adjoins it on the north-west. Outside the south wall of Orontius are irregular depressions with separating walls of very thin character. On the interior are an immense number of craterlets and pits, including some craterpit-chains radiating from Tycho. Of these, three are easily traced; the most northerly ends at a low hill.

PENTLAND, +085 −904 [Irish geologist, 1797-1873]. Another fine ring to the north-west of Curtius, 45 miles in diameter. The finely terraced walls rise to a thin crest, 10,000 feet above the interior, on which is a double central mountain. A crater lies on the inner west slope. South is a large ring, A, with a pass into Pentland. Farther south is H, while on the west is a remarkable series of rings.

PICTET, −100 −690 [Swiss astronomer, 1752-1825]. A ring 40 miles in diameter, immediately to the west of Tycho. Its broken east wall rises in two terraces to the crest of Tycho. The west wall is regular: on the north is a small deep crater. West of this is a pass into a large ring, C, the interior of which contains a low ring on the south-east, with a crater on its north-west rim. There are also three craterlets and rows of pits, all tending towards Tycho. This ring, C, is intruded upon by Barker. On the south wall of Pictet is a large crater, A, with a twin central peak and breaks in both its north and south walls. The floor of Pictet is covered with rocky masses, craterlets and many pits; the southern portion is especially rough.

PORTER, —098 —830 [American artist and explorer, associated with the Mt. Palomar 200-inch telescope]. (See Clavius)

PROCTOR, —067 —724. A ring on the outer north of Maginus and named after Mary Proctor, daughter of R. A. Proctor, 1862-   . There are some craters near the inner walls, and pits and craterlets scattered over the interior.

REYPASTOR, +122 —718 [Spanish astronomer]. A crater 18 miles in diameter, with regular walls and a central peak, between Faraday and Cuvier. Closely north is a smaller, well-formed crater, H.

RUTHERFURD, —101 —874 [American selenographer 1816-1892]. This crater used to be known as Clavius A, and is described with Clavius.

SASSERIDES, —130 —633 [Danish astronomer, 1562-1612]. A very irregular depression, 60 miles in diameter, to the north-north-west of Tycho. Its north wall has been altogether destroyed by four craters, of which the inner has a large central peak. Of the two on the east, one overlaps the other. On the east wall is a deep crater, and farther south the boundary is very rugged; there is also a low deformed ring. A curved crater-row occupies the west crest; on the floor are numerous craterlets, pits and shallow depressions as well as ridges. Between the ridges are craterpit-rows all radiating from Tycho.

SAUSSURE, —058 —687 [Swiss philosopher, 1740-99]. A walled depression, 30 miles in diameter, to the south of Orontius, with terraced walls rising 8,000 feet on the east, where there is a craterlet on the crest. On the south the wall is lower, and broken by depressions. On the north and north-west are craters. The outer west slope descends into a wide valley, enclosed by a curved mountain ridge whose 7,000-feet summit is broken by craters, concentric with the west wall. The valley is closed on the north by the rim of Orontius; here low and crater broken. On the interior of Saussure is a double craterlet, slightly west of the centre, and several other craterlets and hills. Between Saussure and Pictet is a remarkable mountain ridge like a watershed, the flanks of which are pitted with craterlets. One chain stretches from the east wall of Saussure over the north end of the ridge to the west wall of Pictet A.

SCHÖMBERGER, +097 —973 [German mathematician, 1597-1645]. A large ring with lofty and terraced walls with craters on the outer slopes and some low hills on the interior. South is the formation Scott, with Amundsen on the south. There is a crater close to the central part of Schömberger.

SCOTT, +080 −990 [English Polar explorer]. This object lies south of Schömberger, but is rather larger; Arthur gives the diameter as 66 miles. It was first mapped in detail by Arthur and Abineri (J.B.A.A., 61, 46), and additional studies have been made by the Authors. Scott lies close to the limb, but is visible under conditions of mean libration, and is well shown on Plate VI of the Paris Atlas.

Scott has fairly well-defined walls, higher generally than those of its southern neighbour, Amundsen. The shape approaches that of a parallelogram, the north-west 'corner' being marked by a high peak; the south wall adjoins that of Amundsen, and forms a boundary between the two formations. It is broken here by a prominent craterlet, B, 10 miles in diameter. The north-east wall is also broken by a craterlet, E, extending south-eastwards from which is a crater-chain. This chain was first detected in its entirety by Moore, but previously Arthur had shown two of its component craterlets, and Abineri three.

There is considerable detail inside Scott. On the north-west floor lies a deep crater, Q, first recorded by Abineri; it can be a prominent object, but its walls, though high above its own interior, are of negligible height above the surrounding floor of Scott, and in the early stages of the lunation it is masked by the shadow of the high wall-peak previously mentioned. Other craterlets and ridges lie on the central and eastern parts of the floor of Scott.

The environs of Scott are interesting. Between the wall-crater E and the deep, conspicuous formation Schömberger A are three craterlets, one of which is of some size; and east of E is a curiously shaped formation, lettered 57 on Abineri's chart, which at times appears almost square.

SHORT, −034 −964 [Scottish optician, 1710-68]. This ring is 35 miles in diameter and lies immediately south of Moretus. The south-east wall is common with that of Newton, and hence very lofty. The other portion is much lower. There is a small bright central crater with a small hill on its southern edge. On the eastern slopes are several depressions. To the south-west is B, a ring about 20 miles in diameter, on the prime meridian. South of B are three small craters in a line. On the outer north-west is a crater-row, and farther west the craters Simpelius C and D.

SIMPELIUS, +077 −956 [Scottish mathematician, 1596-1654]. This irregular formation has lofty walls rising to 12,500 feet above the interior on which are several craters and also depressions along the inner south slope. The inner slopes are terraced and there is either a peak or a crater half-way up the inner west slope. Two large rings encroach on the north-east, and there is a fine ring on the north-west with a central mountain. South of this elevation is a crater. There are craters on the inner south slopes of this ring, also a partial ring under the south-east rim.

SOUTH POLE. This is situated beyond Malapert Alpha, which lies on the prime meridian, but its exact location cannot be determined with much accuracy because of the very mountainous nature of the region. However, measures made by Whitaker indicate that it is situated on the northern slopes of the uppermost mountain range, directly above the eastern interior of Malapert, as seen in the photograph opposite. The whole region appears to consist of long mountain ranges, doubtless ring-plains seen in profile. There is a ring-plain beyond Schömberger M, with a well-marked crater on

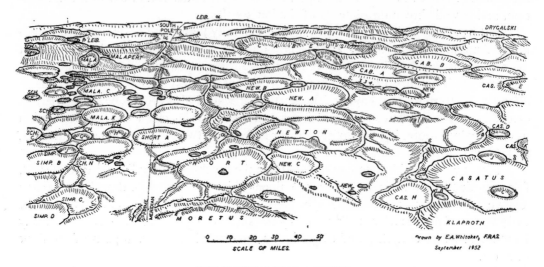

THE SOUTH POLAR REGION
E. A. Whitaker

the crest of its eastern wall. There are indications of another ring directly behind Malapert, and a third between this and the east wall of Amundsen. Apart from these, and a few bright craters, the region appears to be just mountain ranges, as already mentioned. Observation of the region beyond Leibnitz Beta, Malapert and Cabæus is, of course, a matter of considerable difficulty. It only becomes visible at all under strong southerly libration; the angle of illumination is always low, which, combined with the mountainous nature of the district, means that large areas are lost in shadow; this combined with the foreshortening make the district a challenge to the most assiduous selenographer.

STÖFLER, +075 −655 [German astronomer, 1452-1534]. A large mountain-walled depression, disturbed on the west by the intrusion of Faraday. The remaining walls are very rugged and most symmetrical on the east, where the crest is thin and sharp. The inner slope here is broad with evidences of landslips. On the south wall is a deep crater, F, the interior of which is level. Under a high sun the floor is very level, and crossed by rays from Tycho; and is noteworthy for some dark spots, similar to those within Alphonsus and Grimaldi. The largest is of triangular shape, the base lying along the inner east slope. A row of minute objects, probably craterpits, traverses this from north

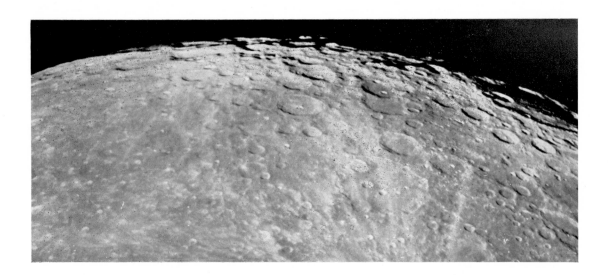

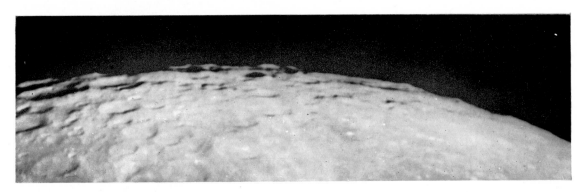

13a, 13b, 13c. The South Polar Region under Three Different Conditions of Illumination.
Photographs by E. A. Whitaker, Greenwich Observatory

14a. Region of Janssen and the Rheita Valley.
Photograph by E. A. Whitaker, Greenwich
Observatory

14b. The Limb Region near Mare Australe. Photograph by
E. A. Whitaker, Greenwich Observatory

to south. South-west is a smaller patch with a pit on its north edge. A long dark streak runs north-west along the south slope of a large landswell, dotted with craterlets which also exist on the south. Three are very bright, and there are also some very shallow bowl-like depressions. A chain of these occupies the north-west, but is only visible in large instruments. Beyond, the west slope rises to Faraday, against the east wall of which is a large irregular depression with some smaller ones on the north and south. On the south-east outer slope are two large, almost square, depressions, with rows of confluent craters on their east borders. J. Cooke has measured the east wall, and finds peaks ranging from 8,000 feet to 12,000 feet in altitude. About sixty craterlets are shown on the map on the floor or walls.

STREET, —131 —724 [English astronomer, *circa* 1661]. This is 35 miles in diameter and is shallow, lying south of Tycho. The east wall has been disturbed by two craters. On the north-east is a shallow depression. The north wall consists of a mass of depressions, while on the north-west is a deep crater. Another crater lies on the south-west, and from this the surface slopes gently down to the floor, on which are two small craters east of the centre, large shallow depressions, craterpits and ridges, all rather delicate objects.

TYCHO, —142 —684 [Danish astronomer, 1546-1601]. At Full, this is the most prominent of all lunar formations, as it is the focus of the most extensive system of bright rays. The walls, which rise over 12,000 feet above the floor, contain peaks rising 5,000 feet higher, and are formed of a number of linear segments, the whole approximately circular. The west crest is elevated to some extent above the outer surface, and is broken by a small crater on the north-west. On the south-east is a large elliptical depression, and the inner slopes here are very broad and deeply terraced. The lower slope is more steep than is usual in the lunar rings. The east wall, as it continues towards the north, does not quite join the northern segment; here a gentle slope leads into the interior. The extreme diameter is 56 miles, measured from crest to crest.

On the interior is a prominent central mountain, rising 5,000 feet. On its north-west flank is a smaller and lesser elevation, on the summit of which is a craterlet. From the east end of the central mass a rocky spur runs north and, curving, encloses a shallow ring. There are also several pits, and numerous rounded hills, including rows of minute asperities, with a general east-to-west direction, all requiring considerable optical power for their detection. There is also a cleft-like object on the inner north-east slope, shown by Gaudibert. In addition to the two chief mountains near the centre is a third, not easily seen. Dr. W. H. Steavenson found, 6 March 1933, some pits and a short cleft to the south-west of the principal central elevation, with the aid of a $20\frac{1}{2}$-inch reflector. This cleft was confirmed by Wilkins on 5 June 1949, with a 12-inch telescope. There are many minute pits on the interior.

South-east of Tycho, Schröter drew and described a ring which he named Robert Smith. It is an easy object, being the depression Street H.

From the north wall multitudes of pits in chains radiate in all directions, over the slopes and across the floors of Orontius, Pictet and Sasserides. The magnificent system of bright rays associated with Tycho is described in the Introduction; they completely conceal many large formations such as Maginus. Mädler said that 'the Full moon knows no Maginus'.

WRIGHT, +012 −719 [American astronomer, died 1952]. A crater 18 miles in diameter, east of Licetus. There are three craterlets on the floor. Closely south-east is a smaller but equally well-formed ring, D.

ZACH, +045 −872 [Hungarian astronomer, 1754-1832]. A great mountain-walled plain, with high walls rising over 13,000 feet, and finely terraced on the inner slopes, which are broken by a crater on the south-west. There are also adjoining craters on the north-west and east. From the last-mentioned crater a strong mountain arm runs north-east to Deluc, containing several lofty peaks. The north and south-west crests of Zach are crowned by many little peaks. On the interior is a nearly central crater, with a curved ridge on its east. There are also two hills near the inner north slope, and several smaller irregularities. Two large rings connect Zach with Curtius; these have a low rim where they join and are very deep. East of Zach is a crater, R, with craterlets on its north and south crests. From this crater R, Barker found a delicate cleft running eastwards. With the exception of a large irregular depression, a level plain extends east to Clavius. This plain is covered with innumerable, though minute, hillocks, craterlets, pits and low ridges. Between the east wall of Zach and the crater mentioned above is a valley depression, from which a crater-row runs up the outer south-east slope. Between Zach and Lilius are many rings and craterlets; one of the craters lies within a low ring midway between the two formations. Zach in its general appearance bears some resemblance to the terrestial crater-lakes of Coatepeque and Ilopango in Salvador, or to Haleakala in E. Mauri, and may have been formed by similar forces; it is evidently of volcanic origin.

XXIV

The largest formation is Janssen, a vast mountain-ringed plain on the interior of which are craterlets, hills and some fine examples of clefts. On the south, and close to the limb, is Demonax, almost entirely explored within the last few years. Near it is Boussingault, the best example of a great ring, within which is another within which, in its turn, is yet a third ring.

We have a fine specimen of a double ring in Steinheil and Watt, while the greatest valley on the lunar surface, that associated with Rheita, lies within this section.

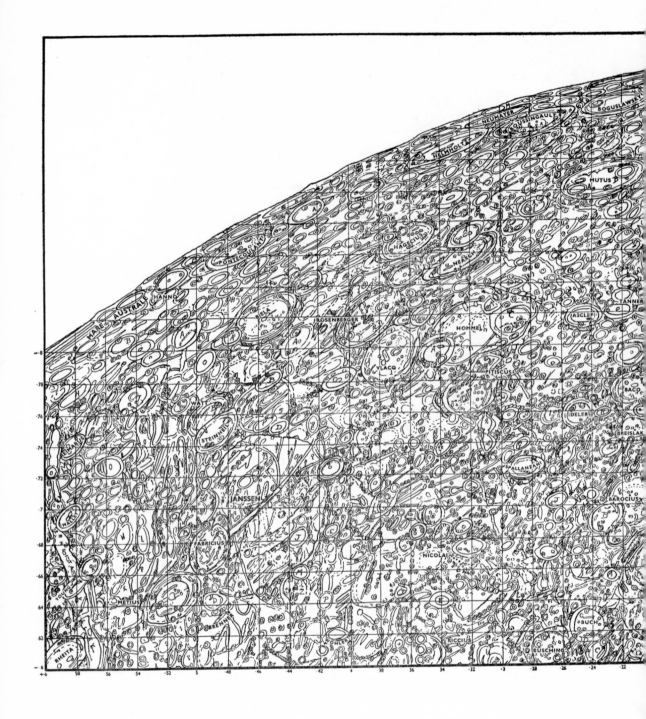

XXIV

ASCLEPI, +248 −814 [Italian astronomer, 1706-76]. This crater lies between Hommel and Tannerus, and bears a crater on its south crest. The walls are terraced, and there are two craters on the north wall and a craterlet on the floor. To the north-east are three large craters, G, D and A. These are at the east end of a rough crater-chain ending, on the west, at the east wall of Hommel. To the south-west is a pair of craters, and south a short crater-valley, also numerous craterlets and hills.

AUSTRALE, MARE, +560 −820. 'The Southern Sea.' A dark plain on the south-west limb of the Moon, extending for about 400 miles from north to south, and 200 miles from east to west and divided by a light-streak, according to Neison. On the south-east are narrow valleys; here Franz shows twelve crater-valleys. The northern portion has three large rings on its east border, a high peak on the west and craters on the slope. On the surface are ridges, craters and ruined rings. A fine ring abuts on the west wall with three hills and a crater on its floor; another crater lies on the south but is smaller. This smaller ring has a central mountain. There are also some fragmentary rings on the northern portion; many of these have only their south and west walls still remaining. In the centre is an obscure ring, on the floor of which are two craterlets with the remains of another on the south. There is also a ruined ring west of Oken, with a mountain arm between them. Altogether there are at least twenty-four craterlets, five obscure rings and numerous hills and ridges on the northern portion of the Mare. The west wall contains five peaks which are probably rings seen in profile.

The southern portion is smooth as far as Hanno. There is a large ring west of Brisbane B, with two craterlets near the west wall. There are several rings, mainly shallow, and ridges close to the west border. Further observations are required before the details of this plain are properly mapped. It extends on to the averted part of the Moon, and is shown in the photographs taken from the Russian vehicle Lunik III in 1959.

BACO, +205 −777 [English friar and scientist, 1214-94]. A crater 40 miles in diameter, with lofty walls, bearing peaks of 14,000 feet in places. On the interior is a low central mountain, a crater on the west and others on the north-west and the south. On the south crest are craters, while to the north-east are large rings. To the south is the crater, A, with steep interior slopes and a cleft on the outer west glacis; it also has a craterlet on the south-west rim. Outside the east wall of A is a ridge concentric with the wall. On the outer west of Baco is a triangular depression containing a crater, a craterlet and a hill. This crater is surrounded by craterlets and hills.

BAROCIUS, +203 −705 [Venetian mathematician, *circa* 1570]. A great crater 50 miles in diameter, with finely terraced walls, rising 12,000 feet on the east but broken by the crater B on the north-west. B has a central mountain. There are craterlets and a shallow ring on the north.

On the interior of Barocius are a nearly central crater, an ancient ring on the east, with others on this portion; on the west is a triangle of cones. There is a deep ravine on the inner south-west with a crater-chain beyond the crest. Abutting on the south is a small ring with a central craterlet, the first member of a craterlet-chain running south-east to the wall of Breislak.

West are several deep craters, J being the leader of a fine group. Between J and Barocius is a bright little crater, with a smaller on its west rim. North-west are other craters and a valley, V, with many craterlets and hills. On the outer north-east is a magnificent crater-chain, while on the inner north-east a small, partial ring may be traced, its south wall having been completely destroyed and the gap partly occupied by a crater.

BIELA, +448 −818 [Austrian astronomer and soldier, 1782-1856]. This crater is 46 miles in diameter, and has terraced walls, 9,000 feet in altitude on the south but broken by a crater on the north. This crater has a central peak. Farther south is a large ring. On the depressed floor of Biela is a central mountain, also some low ridges and a crater on the east, and two rings on the inner north-west. The crater A intrudes on the north-west, with the larger crater, F, farther off. On the inner south slope is a depression with a crater at each end. South is the ring, B, with terraced walls, a central hill and two craters on its floor. The outer east glacis of the crater B is very broad, and just beyond is a craterlet-chain. In the far west is the large and deep crater, A, with a chain of hills on the east portion of its floor. West of A are the three overlapping craters, B, g and H.

BOGUSLAWSKY, +203 −956 [German astronomer, 1789-1851]. A great formation, 60 miles in diameter, near the limb. The walls are terraced and crowded at intervals with peaks, ranging from 8,000 feet to 11,400 feet on the north. On the floor is a large crater with hills on the east. Neison remarks that the environs appear to be some of the wildest on the Moon. West are three craters, and these are followed by Demonax. North is Boussingault, and north-east a chaotic mass of craters, ridges, pits and hills all jumbled together. Of these the largest is the great ring, F, to the south-west of Mutus. The north wall of F has been altogether destroyed by the intrusion of three craters, and there are two others on the south wall. On the floor of F are five craterlets and a ridge.

The inner north-west slope of Boguslawsky is very broad, and contains the large crater already mentioned.

BOUSSINGAULT, +273 −942 [French chemist, 1802-87]. A most interesting object, being an arrangement of three almost concentric rings. The outer one is 70 miles in diameter and has terraced walls, with craters on the east and west crests. Abutting on the east are three overlapping rings, diminishing in size to the north. On the north-west is a large ring with terraced walls and a crater on the inner north-west slope. The floor contains a central craterlet-chain.

Boussingault may be divided into three parts. The outer ring encloses an inner which is not quite concentric, but displaced towards the west; and within it is a still smaller ring. The second ring, and also the third, have little peaks on their walls, and also some craters and craterlets, finely seen by Wilkins, 5 October 1952, with Dr. W. H. Steavenson's 30-inch reflector. The inner ring has a row of pits on its floor, from north to south, also hills. There is a deep crater on the north wall of this ring, with a central mountain on its floor. On the west wall of Boussingault are four craterlets.

Just under the south crest and on the main inner slope is a splendid, though delicate, craterlet-chain ending, on the west, at the little crater, N. On the inner north-west slope is a shorter craterlet-chain.

BREISLAK, +208 −744 [Italian geologist, 1748-1826]. A ring to the north of Baco, from which it is separated by a small crater. The walls are broad, with a crater, F, on the south-west and the crater B on the north. From B a valley runs north. Adjoining on the north-west is the crater G, with a central hill and two hills on the east portion of its floor. It also has three craters on the south wall and one on the north. On the floor of Breislak are two craterlets, four hills and a ridge on the east. A craterlet-chain runs north-west to a crater on the south wall of Barocius.

BRENNER, +482 −640 [Austrian selenographer, 1855-1928]. This is really an enclosed surface near Metius. On the west boundary are some low rings, of which A and V are the deepest. On the south is the crater B. On the interior of Brenner are numerous ridges and several small craters.

BUCH, +236 −631 [German geologist, 1774-1853]. A crater 30 miles in diameter, with narrow walls and a crater-row on the outer south. To the west are old rings and a crater-chain, increasing in size as it proceeds, runs to the north, along the east wall of Büsching. A low ring, C, abuts on the north-east.

On the floor of Buch are some low-rimmed pits on the south, and a larger on the north. On the outer south is a low ring, the wall of which is highest on the north-east. The ring, C, has a gap in its north wall, and a craterlet-chain on the east. A few miles to the east of this craterlet-chain is a long formation, evidently the result of the fusion of three craters, and a striking object under favourable conditions.

BÜSCHING, +272 −617 [German geographer, 1724-93]. A crater 36 miles in diameter, with terraced walls rising 4,000 feet and broken by three craters on the north. A valley runs south-west from the wall. On the floor is a central ring, also craterlets, ridges and a bright crater on the inner west. On the western portion is an old ring. There is a fine craterlet-chain on the outer west slope, while beyond it is a peculiar double and distorted formation on the east rim of a large ring. There is also a crater-chain on the east wall running to the floor of Buch. The surrounding region literally swarms with craterlets.

CORTÉS, +170 −983 [Spanish explorer]. This is a ring with a central peak, but only visible in extreme libration owing to its position on the farther hemisphere. It lies west of Demonax. West of it is a mountain marking the farthest we can see at that point.

About 1½ diameters west, and along the limb from Cortés, Moore has found a similar formation, so far on the averted hemisphere that it cannot be seen at all except under extreme libration, and even then imperfectly.

DEMONAX, +178 −979 [Greek philosopher, *circa* 200 B.C.]. This great crater, the centre of which has been found by D. W. G. Arthur to be in +1780 −9790, is a prominent formation south of Bogulawsky, shown by Schmidt but not shown by Goodacre. A chart appears in B.A.A. Memoirs, 36, 3. This was compiled from observations by Abineri, Arthur and Moore.

The walls can be traced on all sides except, possibly, on the south-east. The diameter is 75 miles. On the inner south slope are craters. A, 10 miles in diameter, is bright; on its northern flank is a smaller crater. On the inner south-west are double formations, with a crater between them. On the east crest is a crater, J, and there are large craters to the south. On the outer north-east is a large, deformed ring, E, with a double crater on its west wall. Farther west is a crater-chain. To the north-west is a large crater and there are others on the slope. On the limb at mean libration, in −964, is a large ring, 40 miles in diameter. Arthur has also noted a high peak on the limb to the north.

On the interior of Demonax are two craterlets near the centre, with a ridge to the west. Wilkins continues the ridge to the east, and has also found two markings, one a shallow crater-chain, crossing the floor from north to south. There is a curved object on the northern part of the floor, running east to west, probably a crater-chain; and also a chain of small, disconnected craterlets running along the south glacis. East of these latter is a branched ridge.

DOVE, +353 −730 [German physicist, 1803-79]. A ring 11 miles in diameter to the north of Pitiscus, with a ridge on the west part of its floor. Dove is the most prominent of a series of enclosures extending south-east to north-west, at the north-west end being the ring H, full of craters. Abutting on the south is the lower ring, B, and east of Dove and B are two elongated craters.

To the south-west is a sort of bright plain, dotted over with rings with, in general, low walls, many craterlets and hills. This plain extends to Vlacq. The whole forms a confused and wild region.

FABRICIUS, +490 −680 [Dutch astronomer, 1564-1617]. A crater 55 miles in diameter, with terraced walls, low on the north but rising 9,700 feet on the south-west, where there are two crest craters. There is a lower portion on the south and from this a cleft runs south. On the east are craters on the outer slope, also a craterlet on the north-east crest. To the south-west is a large ring full of craters.

On the interior is a central mountain, to the north of which is a shallow depression, and there is a high ridge on the east. On the western portion is another ridge and a craterlet. D. W. G. Arthur found a crater on the central ridge, 30 November 1947.

On the north-west wall is a peak, Delta, of 7,500 feet, but on the east the wall is lower, although the peak Beta rises 8,400 feet. Towards the north the altitude declines. To the west is the crater, B, with two craterlets and chains running from the north wall of B to Metius. A long cleft, 9, runs north outside the east wall and thus on the floor of Janssen. The surface between B and Mallet is occupied by a remarkable valley, in part crateriform, and the large, low rings, L and W.

HAGECIUS, +372 −861 [Czech physician-astronomer, 1525-1600]. A peculiar object 48 miles in diameter, with terraced walls broken by craters on the north and west, and with a small crater on the floor near the east wall, together with a few craterlets. On the north is a large, old ring, and beyond this the rings bordering Nearch and Rosenberger.

The west wall has been almost obliterated by the intrusion of five craters. Of these B is the most prominent, and has a central hill. It overlaps an older ring on the east. There follow two craters with their walls in contact, the end one having overlapped a small ring. Immediately to the west of B is a remarkable pear-shaped crater, with a central hill and flanked by craterlets. On its north are two double craters and a little valley extending south-west to the ring Helmholtz A. The peak Beta, on the north wall of Hagecius, is about 8,000 feet in height, and must present a striking appearance from the low and partly destroyed ring to the north. On the outer slope of this ring is the bright crater D. South is a deep crater, E, with a central hill and a fine, depressed ring on its east.

HANNO, +517 −845 [Carthaginian navigator, *circa* 500 B.C.]. This crater is 40 miles in diameter, and has a dark floor on which is a hill and a crater. North is a crater-chain. Hanno lies at the extreme southern end of the Mare Australe, from which it is separated by a strong mountain ridge and three craters abutting on the west wall. North-east, beyond several rings, is the crater Biela A. There are three craterlets on the outer west slope of Hanno, and north of these craters is a mountain ridge rising into a very considerable peak, at times visible in profile on the limb.

HELMHOLTZ, +332 −925 [German surgeon, 1821-94]. A crater 60 miles in diameter, with high walls and craters on the inner west and east. Near the centre of the floor are two mountains, and there are other hills and a crater on the eastern portion. West is a mountain, and the large craters, W and B, close to the limb. On the east is the crater D, and south the great ring Boussingault, while on the south-west is Neumayer. On 15 August 1954 Moore (12½-inch reflector) noted some curious ray-like features, crossing both Helmholtz and Neumayer, and evidently coming from the averted hemisphere.

HILL, +377 −707 [contemporary English selenographer]. This was formerly known as Lockyer H, and is described under that heading.

HOMMEL, +320 −820 [German mathematician, 1518-62]. A vast depression 75 miles in diameter, with a crater, A, on the north. This contains a central hill and two craters on the inner north. On the east is another crater, with craters inside, and west of it is a low ring.

The inner west slope is dotted with numerous craterlets, and the surroundings are a confused mass of craters. On the inner north slope is a jagged crater-chain running from the high portion of the wall, near C, to the floor. C is only of moderate depth, and its interior stands higher than that of Hommel. The more or less level portion of the floor, the only part not intruded upon, contains a low ring on the east, some hillocks and ridges. On the west wall of C, and thus on the inner south slope of Hommel, is a depression, K, between the crest and which are several craters, while beyond is the very similar formation, P, with a central craterlet.

The inner west slope is very broad and full of depressions, and on the north-west is a deep though small crater. Much débris appears to have been deposited on the surface to the east of C and may be traced as far as Asclepi.

IDELER, +248 −757 [German chronologist, 1766-1846]. A ring to the west of Baco and Breislak, with a crater, R, on its east wall and a smaller, A, on the south-east. The walls are terraced, and on the floor are three craters and a faint central peak. There are craters on the north-east wall, while it overlaps an older ring, I, on the west. South is the crater B, with craters between it and I, while north is a pear-shaped formation, L, and craterlet-chains.

JANSSEN, +460 −705 [French astronomer, 1824-1907]. A colossal enclosure, over 100 miles across, with walls high on the south, but low on the north and with great rings on the rim. The very uneven surface contains a line of craters on the west, two low rings on the north-east, a low central mound and many others. Under the east wall is a depression, J, with a mountain arm to the north. A wide valley from Fabricius crosses the floor in a curve to the south-west, in part a crater-chain. East of the central elevations the cleft divides with a branch to the south-east. There are other clefts on the south and south-east, but their exact positions and extent are still somewhat doubtful.

D. W. G. Arthur found a terrace with a steep fault on the inner south-west. On the south a peculiar mass projects on to the floor, probably a landslip.

Harold Hill, to whom we owe a fine drawing, finds the central mountain to be complex in character and that the great valley-cleft has rugged banks, also that the curved south branch does not join the main cleft. On the other hand, Wilkins has apparently seen the valley continuous from end to end. Dr. S. R. B. Cooke, in B.A.A. Journal, 56, 8, shows several cross clefts, three craterlets north of the central mountain, but not seen by Hill. There are three very minute craterlets south-east of the crater H.

D. W. G. Arthur has seen enlargements along the great valley-cleft; these have been confirmed by Wilkins with the 30-inch reflector belonging to Dr. Steavenson. Indeed, the whole of the coarser portion is a crater-chain. Arthur also saw interior landslips, and confirmed Hill that the curved southern branch does not join the main cleft.

Wilkins, however, has seen a fine connecting fissure with the 30-inch. Arthur also found that the central peak is the east wall of a poorly-defined double depression, from which a deep crater-cleft runs towards Fabricius. He also draws a shallow, elongated depression from the crater H to Fabricius, and confirmed one of the three craterlets drawn by Hill.

The southern portion of Janssen is more smooth than the northern. Schmidt shows one of Hill's craterlets, and Wilkins all three. The cleft, 5, was seen, in part, by Arthur. The southern portion of the interior contains some very delicate clefts.

LOCKYER, +413 −722 [English astrophysicist, 1836-1920]. A crater 30 miles in diameter, with bright lofty walls and a floor on which is a central hill, also a craterlet on the inner west, and a crater on the west crest. To the east are old rings and a crater, G, with a central hill, also a low ring H, containing two large craters. To the west is the interior of Janssen. H is now called Hill.

MALLET, +574 −710 [Irish engineer, 1810-81]. A crater at the south end of the great Rheita Valley, with several hills on its floor. On the south-west is a ring, open on the south, into what is really a continuation of the Rheita Valley, to another crater and thence beyond as a valley, flanked on the east by Reimarus. The south and east walls of Mallet are flanked by a crater-chain.

METIUS, +527 −650 [Dutch astronomer, 1571-1635]. A crater 50 miles in diameter, with terraced walls rising in one great peak to the height of 13,000 feet. On the west crest is a crater, and there are others on the north and the east. On the outer east slope is a bright crater, A, with broad walls and craters on the south. On the floor of Metius lie a central mountain with a summit crater, some hills on the east and a large crater on the inner north-west, craters on the north-east and a ridge on the southern portion. To the west are rings, including an old ring near the Rheita Valley.

MUTUS, +225 −899 [Spanish astronomer and navigator, died 1650]. This great crater is 50 miles in diameter, and has lofty terraced walls, abounding in peaks, rising 14,000 feet on the west, where there is a crater. The wall is somewhat lower on the east, and here is a crater on the slope. On the floor lie a crater south of the centre, two craters on the north and some curved ridges on the west, evidently the remains of old rings.

NEARCH, +331 −852 [friend of Alexander the Great, *circa* 325 B.C.]. A crater 38 miles in diameter, with six craters on the floor and a cleft near the east crest. To the west are many large rings and east a crater-chain. On the south is the great intruding ring, A, with terraced walls and a central hill, with lower elevations on the floor. The outer west wall of A is flanked by a fine crater-chain. Abutting on the north of A, and thus on the north-west wall of Nearch, is another ring with a central ridge, and north of this is the great crater, D, with terraced walls and a central mountain. To the west lies Hagecius, and north-east Hommel.

NEUMAYER, +306 −947 [German scientist, 1826-1909]. A very deep ring 50 miles in diameter to the west of Boussingault and close to the limb. The floor is smooth except for two hills on the north-west. West are the crater M and ridges, and on the far west, in the farther hemisphere, a large ring, A, with mountain ridges on its north. (See the special charts.)

NICOLAI, +323 −674 [German astronomer, 1793-1846]. A small crater with walls rising about 6,000 feet above the floor, which is smooth except for three minute craterlets on the north. To the south-west are some old, low-rimmed craters, curving north to a large, ancient ring. Some of these old rings contain low central hills and one a central craterlet. North is a relatively smooth surface with the crater E on its border. East of E is a sort of bay, with a fine crater-chain running south-east. Between this and Nicolai are some craters arranged in a row.

PITISCUS, +327 −769 [German mathematician, 1561-1613]. A crater 52 miles in diameter, with walls rising 10,000 feet on the west, where they are narrow. There is a fine crater on the inner south-east slope and others on the south-west. On the floor is a crater to the north of the centre, a smaller crater to the south, some hills and low rings. On the north are two large confluent craters, while on the west are ancient rings. On the east is a large depression full of craterpits, and well seen under evening illumination. On the south-east the wall of Fabricius adjoins. Due south are some most remarkable, deformed formations, L and P among them, while there is also a magnificent crater-valley traced as far as the crater Janssen. On the north-east is the plain of Brenner and, far west, the great Rheita Valley.

PONTÉCOULANT, +472 −856 [French mathematician, 1795-1874]. A grand ring, 60 miles in diameter, and overlapping an older ring, 40 miles in diameter, on the north. On the floor, which is dark, are some hills and craters. One of these is nearly central, and from it a fine cleft runs across the floor to the north wall. On the south are two craters with their walls in contact, and east the crater G, with a central ridge and overlapping a smaller crater on the north. West are some craters and a long ridge close to the limb. On the southern part of the interior of Pontécoulant is the relic of an ancient ring.

REIMARUS, +587 −737 [Danish mathematician, died 1600]. A crater on the extreme south of the extension of the Rheita Valley, with three hills on its floor. East is the crater, A, its north wall having been occupied by craters, and east of this is the ring, J, with a central crater, a crater on the north-west rim and others on the west wall. North are the craters B and C, and on the north-east the crater K, with a central hill and three ridges on the western portion of its floor.

RHEITA, +590 −605 [Bohemian friar and optician, 1597-1660]. A great crater 42 miles in diameter, with high walls rising 14,000 feet on the north-east and with remarkably sharp crests. On the south-west crest are four craters, and there are several craterlets on the inner south-west. There are also craterlets on the inner east slope, which is terraced.

On the interior is a central mountain with a lower hill on the west, a small landslide on the north and a low ring on the inner north. On the southern portion are some hills and ridges. To the north-west is a large but low ring. West are craters and ridges, while on the east is the great valley. Dr. Karl Müller found a double crater on the inner north slope.

RHEITA VALLEY, +576 −594 to +595 −682. A great valley, one of the finest on the Moon, to the east of Rheita. It is 115 miles in length and 15 miles broad at the widest part, and is encroached upon on the north by Rheita. The north end is rounded, and is doubtless the fragment of an ancient ring. On the floor, south of Rheita, are two hills, a craterlet on the south and a cross ridge. Farther south a low ring lies across the valley, with a crater containing a hill and two craterlets on the east border at this point. This is the crater K. The valley now expands slightly, with large rings on the west, and reaches D with a triple central hill. This is the crater now called Mallet. G. P. Kuiper has maintained that the Valley was produced by a meteoric impact, but close examination of the structure of the Valley shows that this explanation is quite untenable.

RICCIUS, +355 −602 [Italian missionary, 1552-1610]. A crater 50 miles in diameter, measured from east to west, with a crater on its south wall and several craters on the floor. To the east is a crater-row, and south some confluent rings.

ROSENBERGER, +387 −818 [German mathematician, 1800-90]. A crater 50 miles in diameter, with a dark floor on which is a central hill. On the eastern portion are two craters, three craters on the west, a low ring on the south, ridges and craterpits. The walls are low and the inner slopes are very rugged; on the south a crater slightly intrudes. This crater is D, and has a central hill. West and south are old rings. The inner west slope contains many craters. On the north it adjoins Vlacq.

SPALLANZANI, +285 −721 [Italian scientist, 1729-99]. A fine crater, to the south-west of Barocius, with broad walls and some hills on the floor. South is the crater G, and east the pear-shaped crater L. All around is a confused mixture of craters and ridges.

STEINHEIL, +480 −750 [German physicist, 1801-70]. One of a double ring, that on the west being Watt. Steinheil contains ridges and craterlets, a ring on the inner east, and the walls are terraced. They rise 11,000 feet above the floor. West, beyond a crater-chain, is a fine long valley, with another farther to the west. South are ancient rings and craterlet-chains from the south wall. There is also a cleft in the disturbed region to the south.

TANNERUS, +207 −832 [German mathematician, 1572-1632]. A crater 20 miles in diameter, with two craters on the south wall and a smooth floor. West is a large ring, D.

VLACQ, +372 −802 [Dutch mathematician, *circa* 1660]. A grand ring, 56 miles in diameter, to the east of Rosenberger, with lofty walls, rising in peaks 10,000 feet on the east but 8,000 feet on the west. On this portion of the wall are some craters. On the floor lie a central hill, five craterlets on the north, and a curved ridge, while a craterlet-chain runs north from the south wall. Under the east wall are two low rings. To the south-east is a large crater, from which a crater-chain runs along the crest and then down the inner east and south slopes.

WATT, +484 −762 [Scottish engineer, 1736-1819]. The western component of a double ring, the other being Steinheil. On the interior are ridges and craterlets under the south wall. Wilkins found, 20 May 1950, some dusky bands on the broad inner north slope. There are faint indications of terraces on the inner west slope, and some tiny pits seen with Dr. Steavenson's 30-inch reflector.

WÖHLER, +410 −619 [German chemist, 1800-82]. A small, somewhat elliptical crater, to the west of Riccius, with rows of craters on the east and a low ring abutting on the south. To the west of this ring is a larger one. On the north-west is a deep little crater. The floor is quite smooth.

YOUNG, +586 −668 [British physicist, 1773-1829]. A crater on the west side of the Rheita Valley, with three craterlets on its interior and a crater on the outer west. North are two craterlets, and a low ring. These cut across the valley at this point from the crater K on its eastern side. The crater K has a central hill, and two lower hills and a craterlet on its floor.

XXV

A section on the south-west limb, small in area but nevertheless containing some interesting objects. Part of Furnerius is included, but this great walled plain has already been described in Section X. Close to the limb is the dark Mare Australe; this has received little attention in the past, and our information about its details depends almost entirely upon observations made by K. W. Abineri, E. A. Whitaker, and the Authors.

XXV

AUSTRALE, MARE, +560 −820. The 'Southern Sea'. This little-known object cannot be classed as a true 'sea', as it consists of mere patches of Mare material, light grey in colour and nowhere a smooth sheet. This material appears also to overlay the floors of Oken, Pratdesabá and other neighbouring ring-plains. The east-to-west length is, in all, about 200 miles, and there are narrow winding valleys to the south-east; Franz recorded twelve crater-clefts in the area. On the west, too unfavourably placed to be shown on the mean libration chart, is the fine ring Pratdesabá; and the crater Oken can be recognized under most conditions of illumination.

On the northern portion of the Mare, Wilkins has recorded the following details: three large, low-walled rings, a high peak to the west, and numerous ridges, craterlets and incomplete rings. Near the centre of the ill-defined Mare, an obscure ring containing two craters, with another smaller formation of the same type south of it. West of Oken is the deep crater Ibañéz, breaking a larger ring-plain with low walls, and closely north of this another, similar in size. Southwards the Mare extends as far as Hanno, and Wilkins has recorded a large, comparatively smooth ring west of Brisbane. The western 'border' is made up of ridges and shallow rings, nowhere well defined. The whole region can only be well observed just before the Sun sets over it. Much of our knowledge of it is due to the fine work of Abineri. The Mare extends on to the averted portion of the Moon, as was shown by the Lunik III photographs of 1959.

BRISBANE, +608 −766 [Scottish astronomer (Governor of New South Wales), 1770-1860]. A crater 30 miles in diameter, south of Vega, with a central ridge and two craters on the inner west. On the eastern outer slope are the craters F and G, with a smaller one between them. To the north, between Brisbane and Peirescius, is a large central-peaked crater, A; south-west the large ring, B, with four craterlets on its floor, and west of B a ring, H, with a smooth floor. On the south, between B and H, is a craterlet-chain. West of H, and near the limb, is the ring G, overlapped on the west by two craters.

FRAÜNHOFER, +662 −634 [German optician, 1787-1826]. A crater 30 miles in diameter and 5,000 feet deep, with craters on the south and west crests. The walls are terraced, and broken in the north-east by a crater, G, and a smaller one north-west of it. To the north-east of Fraünhofer is a large, low-walled ring. There is a crater-row running northwards, parallel to the east wall of Furnerius, as far as the peak Furnerius Delta. The floor of Fraünhofer contains several craterlets (one nearly central) and some low, curved ridges.

IBAÑÉZ +371 −679 [Spanish mathematician, 1825-91]. A crater to the west of Oken, very close to the limb and thus difficult to examine, though it is about 37 miles in diameter and very deep, with bright walls, slightly distorted on the east, according to Moore (8½-inch reflector). Ibañéz lies on the northern part of the floor of a much larger formation, with low walls and a darkish floor; to the south, between this and Pratdesabá, is a crater, and north of the Ibañéz group a second group remarkably similar to it—also consisting of a large, low-walled formation broken by a smaller, more regular one, though here the intruding crater is not so deep or conspicuous as Ibañéz. Northwards, along the limb in the direction of Wilhelm Humboldt, are several other ring-plains of considerable size, all very difficult to map on account of their unfavourable situation.

MARINUS, +751 −633 [Geographer of Tyre, *circa* A.D. 200]. A crater 30 miles in diameter, with a central hill, north-east of the main area of Mare Australe. There is a crater on the west, and on the outer south four craters, each with minute crater-rows under their east walls. To the north are many ring-plains, and some crater-chains. Marinus overlaps an old ring, B, abutting on the east wall; and another crater abuts on the south. East of B is a peculiar elongated depression, G, probably a crater-valley. North-west is the large crater, D, and east of it three rings, two of which have craterlets on their east walls, followed by the ancient ring, W, and the deep craters Furnerius H and K. Marinus is not an easy formation to identify.

OKEN, +701 −691 [German naturalist, 1779-1851]. A crater 50 miles in diameter, with walls that rise to 6,000 feet on the east—where they show a linear tendency—but are lower on the west, and broken by a crater. There is a crater on the inner east slope, and several ridges on the floor, which is in general dark in hue. East is the large crater, A, also with a dark floor, and with a very feeble central hill, as well as two wall-craterlets. North-west of Oken is the large ancient ring, K, with some craters on its floor and the remnant of a central hill; south, the crater D, in which Wilkins has recorded a central hill. From the south wall a long ridge runs southwards in the direction of Peirescius D.

PEIRESCIUS, +636 −725 [French scientist, 1580-1637]. A large ring south-west of Vega, with two craterlets and some low ridges on its floor, and a feeble central peak. Between Peirescius and Brisbane is a considerable crater, A, with a central mountain.

PRATDESABÁ, +631 −772 [Spanish scientist, 1870-   ]. A magnificent ring in the Mare Australe area, fully 80 miles in diameter, but so placed that it is extremely difficult to examine, and cannot be shown adequately on the mean libration chart. It is well shown on a fine photograph taken by E. A. Whitaker on 1 December 1952. The walls are regular, terraced on the west and to a lesser extent on the east. Moore, observing on 15 September 1951, with an 8½-inch reflector, and on 31 December 1952, with a 12½-inch reflector, has recorded the following features: a long central ridge, which does not, however, seem to rise to a pronounced peak; two craters and a depression on the inner

338

south; a depression, probably an old ring, at the foot of the inner south-west slope; and two peaks and a craterlet on the north wall, which is somewhat distorted. There is also a hill on the inner south-west. The north-east wall is broken by a large crater of considerable depth, and outside on the south-east are a number of dark-floored rings with low or non-existent walls, really parts of the so-called Mare Australe. Outside the south wall are two parallel curved ridges, which seem to be distorted and highly fore-shortened rings; in the eastern one there is a hill, which could be taken to represent an old central mountain. North of Pratdesabá, in the direction of the Ibañéz group, the surface is extremely rough and rugged. No map other than the 300-inch shows this area at all adequately, and many more observations will be needed before our knowledge of it can be considered complete.

VEGA, +630 —710 [German mathematician, 1756-1802]. A crater 50 miles in diameter, with walls that are regular on the east but broken on the west by several overlapping rings. The floor is smooth apart from a craterlet under the south-east wall, one on the north-east and several hillocks. The south wall has been broken by a large ring, B, in which Wilkins has recorded a central hill. North, between Vega and Fraünhofer, is a large ring full of low mounds; to the south are some well-formed rings and many craterlets. To the south-west lies Peirescius.

APPENDICES

Appendix I

LUNAR PHOTOGRAPHY

by E. A. WHITAKER, F.R.A.S.

The subject of lunar photography is one which is not normally dealt with at any length in text-books, and information about it can only be obtained by reference to the publications of the various observatories which have undertaken it (in which it is usually very sketchily dealt with) or to scattered articles in various journals. The purpose of this section, therefore, is to try to combine and condense some of this information, together with the writer's own experiences and ideas, into a few pages.

To anyone who has examined a selection of lunar photographs, and has also made visual lunar observations with telescopes of various apertures, it is at once obvious that the finer detail is lost in the photographs. Before we consider the various reasons for this, it would be well to examine the character of a lunar image formed in a telescope, and also some of the properties of photographic emulsions.

IMAGE CHARACTERISTICS

Let us assume that the image-forming element (i.e. mirror or objective) is optically perfect, and is free from coma, astigmatism, chromatic and spherical aberrations; and also let us assume that the atmosphere is at rest and optically homogeneous. Neglecting the effects of atmospheric dispersion, the image of a point source (e.g. a star) produced by this telescope will, of course, consist of the Airy disk (i.e. the spurious or diffraction disk) surrounded by concentric coloured circles, diminishing in intensity with increasing radius (Fig. 1). We can imagine the visible lunar disk as being composed of an almost infinite number of point sources of various brightnesses; each source will produce an Airy disk in the focal plane, and the resultant lunar image will consist of an equally immense number of overlapping disks. The light which goes into the rings surrounding each disk (about one-eighth the total light) will blend to produce a small loss of contrast, and possibly introduce a very small amount of spurious detail.

Since each disk is not uniformly bright over its area, but considerably brighter at the centre than near the edge, it is found that the smallest 'element' of detail visible in the image is smaller than the Airy disk; experiments made by the writer indicate that

340

it is rather less than half the disk diameter, or, more accurately, about three-eighths of the diameter of the first dark ring. This is only very slightly less than the well-known Dawes Limit.

We should be careful at this point not to confuse smallest image detail with the smallest detail on the lunar surface which will be just visible in the image. This latter quantity will depend very largely on the intrinsic contrast of the detail; further experiments made by the writer show that a line of shade (e.g. a cleft) about one-twentieth the angular diameter of the Airy disk is just visible (the eye is very sensitive to the detection of lines), and a partially shadow-filled craterlet about nine-tenths the angular diameter of the Airy disk is just visible as such. In the case of the line of shade, it is

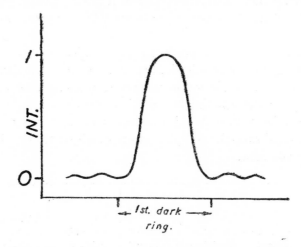

1. DIAGRAM SHOWING LIGHT DISTRIBUTION IN STAR IMAGE

worth noting that the diffraction effects may cause it to appear up to about eight times its true width in the limiting conditions just mentioned.

Since the angular diameter of the Airy disk is inversely proportional to the diameter of the objective (or mirror, of course), it is obvious that the larger the objective the finer the detail present in the image (see Appendix).

It may be mentioned here that the central obstruction (i.e. secondary mirror) perforce used in all except Herschelian reflectors, causes a slight modification of the structure and light distribution of the Airy disk and surrounding rings, which results in very slightly less image detail.

PHOTOGRAPHIC EMULSION CHARACTERISTICS

If an infinitely small 'dot' of light falls on to a photographic emulsion, the resultant photographic image will have finite size, the actual diameter depending upon the type of emulsion, the exposure given, and the processing conditions. This is due to light being scattered from the silver halide grains directly under the 'dot', thereby exposing adjacent grains. The usual way of expressing the minimum image diameter is indirectly, by what is known as the resolving power of the emulsion; this quantity is determined by estimating the maximum number of dots (or, more practically, straight lines) per millimetre, that can just be seen to be separated, using optimum exposure and processing conditions. The resolving power falls off for both weakly and strongly exposed images.

Since the linear diameter of the Airy disk is directly proportional to the focal ratio of the telescope (i.e. focal length divided by objective diameter; equivalent focal length should be used for compound optical systems), and is readily determinable from optical theory, we should now be able to construct a table showing the minimum focal ratio that can be used with various emulsions of known resolving power, in order that the very smallest elements of detail present in the image will be resolved and recorded by the emulsion.

Experiments made by the writer indicate that the practical results are in quite close agreement with those obtained theoretically, but that they are modified slightly in the case of the faster emulsions by the lower contrast characteristic of these emulsions. The following table gives the approximate resolving power of several typical blue-sensitive emulsions, together with some other relevant data, and also the experimentally determined minimum focal ratio for complete image detail recording. Reference to the final column will be made later.

Emulsion Type	Relative Speed	Relative Graininess	Emulsion Contrast	Resolving Power (approx.)	Minimum Focal Ratio (approx.)	Exposure Time for Full Moon at this Focal Ratio (approx.)
Ilford Zenith	Fast	Coarse	Low	40 lines/mm.	f/70	1 sec.
Ilford Special Rapid	Medium	Medium	Medium	60 „	f/45	1 „
Ilford Process	Fairly slow	Fairly fine	Fairly high	90 „	f/25	$1\frac{1}{2}$ „
Kodak B. 10	Slow	Fine	High	120 „	f/18	$2\frac{1}{2}$ „
Kodak B. 4	Slow	Fine	High	140 „	f/16	3 „

Having considered the ability of emulsions to record image detail, we must now inquire into their ability to record a range of brightness. To do this properly would entail lengthy explanations of characteristic curves, emulsion gamma and other allied subjects which are beyond the scope of this article, and are fully treated in any good textbook of photography (e.g. *The Theory of the Photographic Process*, by C. E. K. Mees); it is intended, therefore, to treat the subject as simply as possible.

The brightness range of the lunar surface is surprisingly large; at Full Moon, when there are practically no shadows and almost the entire visible surface is equally illuminated, this range probably does not exceed a factor of about 50 to 1, as it is then due entirely to the difference of reflectivity of the various portions of the surface. At other phases, however, and particularly near the quarters, the factor is much greater than this, since near the terminator the surface is obliquely, and therefore relatively poorly, illuminated. Rough estimates indicate that under these conditions the brightness range exceeds 1,000 to 1.

The emulsion, therefore, must not only be able to record a brightness range in excess of 1,000 to 1, but must also be able to discriminate between small changes in brightness at both ends of this scale, as well as maintain its resolving power. No emulsions are capable of doing this, and a single negative which has received a uniform exposure cannot give a true representation of the lunar surface. This difficulty may be

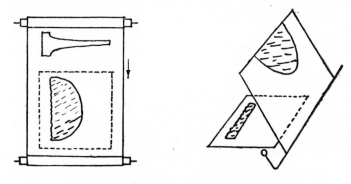

2. DIAGRAMS SHOWING ROLLER BLIND SHUTTER AND
PIVOTED FLAP SHUTTER

overcome to a large extent by giving the poorly illuminated portions near the terminator a longer exposure time. At the gibbous and crescent phases, this is a matter of considerable difficulty, and a revolving focal plane shutter, with slit of appropriate size and shape, would have to be employed. At the quarter phases, however, the necessary gradation of exposure can be effected more simply by the use of the roller-blind type of focal plane shutter. This type was used to secure the well-known 100-inch Mt. Wilson photographs; the slit in the blind was of such a shape and size that the exposure away from the terminator was one-quarter of a second, and increased logarithmically to two seconds at the terminator. The lunar image must, of course, be carefully oriented and positioned so that the slit traverses the image correctly. The ordinary pivoted flap type of shutter fitted to many photographic telescopes may also be utilized to give graded exposures (Fig. 2).

Before passing on to the process of securing positive prints from the negatives, a few brief notes on the relative merits of the various emulsions may be of use. Fast emulsions produce a contrast which is less than the image contrast, for this reason the latitude of exposure time seems considerable, and the graded exposure appears to be superfluous, as apparently nicely exposed negatives embracing the whole brightness range can be obtained with a uniform exposure. We shall see in the next paragraph that non-graded exposures necessarily introduce grading into the printing process. Slow emulsions, on the other hand, produce a contrast which is greater than the image contrast, which means that the range of correct exposure time is very limited, and graded exposures are essential. Strictly speaking, these emulsions are not intended for continuous tone photography, but with a little care they may be used quite successfully. Fortunately, the photographic image contrast increases with increasing development time, and by over-exposing the emulsion slightly (grading is less necessary under these conditions, but still desirable), and subsequently carefully developing with diluted developer, it is possible to watch the contrast slowly increasing, and to arrest it at any desired level. The exposure times quoted are for such exposures, but correct exposure should be found by trial and error, as sky transparency, mirror reflectivity, lens transparency, etc., all exert a considerable influence on exposure time. Another method of reducing the plate contrast is by slightly under-exposing, and developing fully; this will produce an apparently very 'thin' negative, but which will produce quite good positives with the correct paper.

When we come to make positive prints or enlargements, we straight away encounter more difficulties. Since the brightness range of even the most suitable papers (e.g. white-based glossy papers, subsequently glazed) is well under 100 to 1, it will be seen that even the brightness range of the negative cannot be fully reproduced if something approaching the original image contrast is to be maintained. This last feature is very desirable, both from an æsthetic standpoint, and for the ready visibility of detail. As with the negative, however, an apparently greater brightness range can be recorded by exposure grading, which in the case of printing and enlarging is known as 'dodging'. This entails shading the sensitive paper by some means, such as perforated screens, or the hands, in order to give a longer exposure to the parts corresponding to the dense portions of the negative. This process requires a certain amount of practice before good results can be obtained. It need hardly be mentioned that the correct grade of paper should be used to suit the negative contrast; negatives of low contrast will require a contrasty paper, and vice versa.

Positive transparencies on glass or film can, of course, include a much greater brightness range than ordinary prints, but are more costly, and much less easy to handle and to view.

CAUSES OF LOSS OF DETAIL

Having dealt with image and emulsion characteristics, we must now consider the various possible causes of loss of detail, other than the photographic ones already discussed, and the methods employed to minimize these. It will be convenient to consider them, together with some other matters, under the following headings:

(a) Atmospheric seeing.
(b) Image focus and registration.

(c) Chromatic aberration.

(d) Coma, astigmatism and spherical aberration.

(e) Focal ratio, plate size, economy.

(a) The greatest bane of any astronomical photography is poor 'seeing', which is caused by the turbulent mixing, in our atmosphere, of various currents of air of differing refractive index. The seeing varies both in quality and quantity, depending, for any given locality, upon (1) the prevailing meteorological conditions, (2) the altitude of the observed object, and to a certain extent (3) the aperture of the telescope.

The quality of seeing can roughly be placed between two extremes; at one extreme, a star image, although well defined, wanders erratically about a mean position. This type is not detrimental to visual observations, since the eye can follow the wandering. At the other extreme, the image as a whole remains almost stationary, but is structureless and expanded, and 'boils'. This type, of course, seriously affects visual observation.

The quantity, or degree, of seeing can vary over wide limits. At very best, expansion plus wandering may be less than one second of arc, with occasional moments of almost perfect seeing; unfortunately, such conditions are rare in most localities. At worst, however, an image may expand and wander over an area 30 or 40 seconds of arc in diameter. Usually, the seeing is continually varying in quality and degree over a limited range.

The effects of seeing on the photographic image will be obvious; with the wandering type, each element of detail in the optical image will wander over an irregular area whilst the exposure is being made, the size of this area depending upon the degree of seeing, and speed of wandering compared with exposure time. With the expanded type, the optical image will contain little detail, and again the photographic image will be blurred. In order to alleviate the effects of seeing as far as possible, it is clear that we must choose nights when the seeing is good, and preferably tending towards the wandering type. Since the seeing is normally best at the zenith, and always very poor near the horizon, we should make our exposures when the Moon is high in the sky.

The effects of the wandering type of seeing can be minimized by choosing a focal-length-emulsion type combination that will give a correctly exposed image in a length of time which is short compared with the speed of wandering. Normally this will be quite a small fraction of a second, and reference to the table shows that the requisite speed can only be obtained at the expense of losing image detail, because of the inadequate resolving power of the emulsion when using a smaller focal ratio. However, short exposures have one or two other advantages which will be mentioned later.

The effects of the expanded type cannot be minimized, except, perhaps, to a certain extent by the use of a smaller aperture. This will partly convert the expanded to the wandering type, which can be dealt with as above. Since the seeing quality usually continually varies, the better method is probably to await moments when the expansion subsides before making exposures.

It will be seen, therefore, that for any given seeing conditions, there must be an optimum focal-ratio-emulsion type combination which will render maximum detail, at the point where the emulsion resolution equals the image resolution as determined by the size of the atmospheric tremor disk in the consequent exposure time. It would be extremely difficult to estimate this optimum combination by a visual examination of the seeing, as it would differ with telescope aperture. As a very rough guide, however, for very small telescopes, the tabulated combination should be very approximately adhered to for average seeing conditions, since the tremor disk is not much greater than the smallest image detail. Larger telescopes (e.g. 4-inch to 12-inch) may depart rather more from this combination, whilst the large professional telescopes could depart even further. As an example, it would be quite useless to use a fast emulsion at the prime focus of a 9-inch f/8 reflector, since the photographic image would contain no more detail than could be seen visually with an aperture of about 8/70 the mirror aperture, which is one inch.

(b) It is essential that the emulsion is accurately located in the focal plane, of course, and for this reason plates are preferable to films, although, for small lunar images, films are sufficiently rigid. The usual method of focusing by means of a ground-glass screen is not really satisfactory, particularly with small focal ratios, when the image detail is considerably smaller than the texture of the ground surface, and with photographic refractors, in which the blue focus is swamped (visually) by the out-of-focus yellow-green light. The best method is by exposing a focus plate on a star-field, varying the focus and telescope setting slightly between exposures. After development, the focus is reset to the setting which gave the smallest star images.

Relative motion between image and emulsion during exposure must, of course, be avoided, and short exposures minimize the risk of this. For the amateur without an equatorial mounting or clock-driven cœlostat, this immediately sets a limit to exposure time, as he will be obliged to use his instrument rigidly fixed to the ground. Under these conditions, the lunar image will move at approximately the diurnal rate with respect to the emulsion, which is about 16 miles of lunar surface per second. Exposures must therefore not exceed, say, one-eighth of a second in order to avoid serious blurring, and reference to the table shows that this will entail serious loss of detail because of inadequate emulsion resolution.

A clock-driven equatorial, or a fixed telescope with cœlostat, will overcome this difficulty, although another motion, that of the Moon with respect to the stars, now makes itself apparent. This amounts to about half a mile of lunar surface per second, and hence guiding in both R.A. and declination is required (either by direct guiding or by appropriate motion of the plate-holder with respect to the telescope), for more than the shortest exposures.

Another cause of relative motion between image and emulsion frequently encountered is due to instability of the telescope mounting. Wind, accidental knocks, passing traffic, and even the operation of the exposing shutter can cause this relative motion, and the only remedies, apart from strengthening the mounting, are screening from wind, care in operation, and short exposure times.

(c) Chromatic aberration is the inability of an optical system to bring light of all colours to a single focus, and is present to a lesser or greater degree wherever refracting elements form part of the optical train. Before considering this further, we should inquire briefly into the colour sensitivity of photographic emulsions. Ordinary blue-sensitive emulsions are, as their name implies, sensitive only to blue, violet and ultra-violet light; orthochromatic emulsions are sensitive to green and yellow-green light in addition to the blue, and panchromatic emulsions are sensitive to orange and near-red light as well as blue and green, although the green sensitivity is considerably less than with orthochromatic emulsions. There are, of course, other emulsions sensitive to near-infra-red light, etc., but their use is beyond the scope of this article.

Since mirrors are intrinsically achromatic, any telescope employing only mirrors to produce a lunar image will not suffer from chromatic aberration. Any type of emulsion, therefore, may be used with such a telescope; if the mirrors are silvered, it is usually advantageous to employ ortho or pan emulsions, since silver rapidly tarnishes and becomes a poor reflector of blue light. Aluminized mirrors retain their blue reflectivity, and hence the use of these emulsions is not so noticeably advantageous.

So-called achromatic object-glasses are not truly achromatic, and may be divided into three classes, which are dealt with very briefly below:

1. Photovisual object-glasses. These are the most nearly achromatic of the types, and, as their name implies, may be used either visually or photographically with any emulsion type. They are, however, expensive.

2. Photographic object-glasses. These are specially designed to bring the blue and violet rays to one focus; green, yellow and red rays are progressively more out of focus, and hence only blue-sensitive emulsions may be used.

3. Visual object-glasses. These are specially designed to bring the yellow-green rays, to which the eye is most sensitive, to a focus, but the blue and violet foci are spread out along the optical axis. A sharp image cannot be obtained, therefore, with blue-sensitive emulsions. The best method is to employ an orthochromatic emulsion in conjunction with an appropriately mounted yellow-green filter, which will screen off the out-of-focus blue light. Exposure times will, however, be noticeably increased.

As we have already seen, small focal ratio telescopes cannot produce detailed photographs because no emulsions are capable of resolving all the image detail. The only method of overcoming this difficulty, apart from using a secondary mirror (e.g. Cassegrain), is to employ some type of enlarging lens. A Barlow lens specially achromatized for blue light would probably be best, although no doubt a low-power achromatic eyepiece would serve equally well. Ordinary Huygenian and Ramsden eyepieces cannot be expected to yield the very best results, as they are not sufficiently achromatic. The method of estimating the equivalent focal ratio when using secondary enlargement is given in the Appendix.

(d) If the lunar image is centred on the optical axis, the limb is necessarily $\frac{1}{4}$ degree off axis. With mirrors or object-glasses of fairly large focal ratio, the image defects listed here are quite small, and may be neglected. With small focal ratios, however, one or more of the defects may appear at ¼ degree off axis, and cause blurring of the limb regions, even though the central portions may be quite sharp. Auxiliary lenses incorporated for image enlargement may also introduce these defects.

(e) Having dealt with the various causes of loss of detail, this section is devoted to one or two other considerations. Since the diameter of the lunar image is directly proportional to the focal length, it will clearly be more economical to use, for a given objective or mirror, a smaller focal ratio and fine-grain emulsion than a larger focal ratio and fast emulsion. As an illustration, supposing that we have a 4-inch f/16 refractor; the lunar image at its prime focus will be roughly 0·6 inches in diameter, and 1-inch squares of B.4 emulsion would be quite adequate in size and resolving power. By introducing an auxiliary lens, we could make the equivalent focal ratio f/64; the lunar image would now be 2½ inches in diameter, and 3-inch squares of fast emulsion would be required. By using the fine-grain emulsion, therefore, the expense is cut to about one-ninth of that using fast emulsions. Putting it the other way round: for the price of one coarse-grained negative we could obtain nine fine-grained ones, which could include focus plates and trial exposures. The chances of catching a few moments of good seeing are greater the larger the number of negatives secured, of course.

A relatively simple method of securing lunar photographs which can, with a little patience, yield surprisingly good results, and which requires only a reflecting telescope (not necessarily equatorially mounted) and a camera (a cheap box camera may be used, but a more expensive model is preferable) is as follows:

The telescope is provided with a low or medium power eye-piece, and adjusted until the image of the Moon is at infinity. This requires a little care, as some observers focus telescopes to a condition in which the Moon's image is relatively close. The camera, previously loaded with a fast panchromatic emulsion, is also set for infinity.

The required portion of the lunar surface is now brought to the centre of the field of view, the camera held squarely and centrally in front of the eyepiece, and a snapshot taken.

The exact eyepiece position, as well as the correct exposure time, should be determined by experiment. The success of the method depends largely upon the fact that fast panchromatic emulsions are much faster than any blue-sensitive emulsions, with the result that short exposures (fractions of a second) can be employed, thereby greatly reducing seeing and relative motion troubles. The main drawback is the rapid falling-off of crispness towards the edge of the photographs, for reasons already dealt with.

APPENDIX

1. *Angular diameter of the Airy disk, etc.*

$$\text{Angular diameter of 1st dark ring} \quad \frac{=10 \cdot 9}{D} \text{ seconds of arc}$$

(D = objective diameter in inches,
mean wavelength = 5,500 A.).

348

Angular diameter of Airy disk $\quad = 0.8 \times$ 1st dark ring, approx.

$$= \frac{8.7}{D} \text{ seconds of arc.}$$

Angular diameter of smallest element of detail

$$= \tfrac{3}{8} \times \text{ 1st dark ring, approx.}$$

$$= \frac{4.1}{D} \text{ seconds of arc.}$$

2. *Linear diameter of Airy disk, etc.*

Linear diameter of 1st dark ring $= 1.34 \times \dfrac{F}{D}$ microns

(D = objective diameter in inches

F = effective focal length

mean wavelength = 5,500 A.

$1 \text{ micron} = \dfrac{1}{1000} \text{ millimetre}).$

Linear diameter of Airy disk $= 0.8 \times$ 1st dark ring, approx.

$$= 1.07 \times \frac{F}{D} \text{ microns.}$$

Linear diameter of smallest element of detail

$$= \tfrac{3}{8} \times \text{ 1st dark ring, approx.}$$

$$= 0.5 \times \frac{F}{D} \text{ microns}$$

3. *Smallest detail visible with various apertures,* assuming perfect optics and excellent seeing.

Aperture	Smallest Craterlet	Smallest Cleft	Apparent Size of Smallest Cleft
1 inch	9 miles	$\frac{1}{2}$ mile	4 miles
2 ,,	$4\frac{1}{2}$,,	$\frac{1}{4}$,,	2 ,,
3 ,,	3 ,,	$\frac{1}{6}$,,	$1\frac{1}{3}$,,
4 ,,	$2\frac{1}{4}$,,	220 yds.	1 ,,
6 ,,	$1\frac{1}{2}$,,	150 ,,	$\frac{2}{3}$,,
8 ,,	1·1 ,,	110 ,,	$\frac{1}{2}$,,
10 ,,	0·9 ,,	90 ,,	0·4 ,,
12 ,,	$\frac{3}{4}$,,	70 ,,	$\frac{1}{3}$,,
15 ,,	0·6 ,,	60 ,,	$\frac{1}{4}$,,
36 ,,	$\frac{1}{4}$,,	25 ,,	200 yds.
200 ,,	80 yds.	5 ,,	36 ,,

4. *Size of image and focal length*

Lunar image diameter $= 1/110 \times$ focal length, approx.

5. *To find equivalent focal ratio from image and objective diameters*

Equivalent focal ratio $= \dfrac{\text{Image diameter} \times 110}{\text{objective diameter}}$ approx. (provided that the optical beam is not interrupted by diaphragms, etc.).

6. *Relation between exposure time and focal ratio*

Exposure time is proportional to (focal ratio)^2, e.g. f/20 requires four times the exposure for f/10.

Appendix II

LUNAR MAPS

The following comprehensive list of Lunar Maps is due to Señor A. Paluzíe-Borrell, with some additions by the Authors. The diameters are given in inches, except where otherwise stated.

Date	Diameter	Author	Date	Diameter	Author
1610	7 cm.	Galileo	1789		Russell
1612		Lagalla	1797	Globe, 12	Russell
1614		Scheiner	1824	37·5	Lohrmann (unfinished)
1619	49 mm.	Malapert	1830	5	Lalande
1634	21 cm.	Mellan	1837	37½	Beer and Mädler
1640		Gassendi	1838	15·3	Lohrmann
1640		Fontana	1850	Globe	Madame Witte
1644		Argoli	1851	3	Mitchell
1645	13¾	Van Langren	1853	6	Delaunay
1645	18·4 cm.	De Rheita	1859	12	Webb
1646	9·4	Fontana	1859	3·9	Ward
1647	11·4	Hevelius	1860	15·6	Lecouturier and Chapuis
1649		De Divinis	1860		Anmerck
1651	11	Grimaldi	1863	3	Hind
1651	11	Riccioli	1865	7⅜	Dubois
1656	16 cm.	Borel	1869	4·8	Dunkin
1660	12	Kircher	1873	12	Proctor
1662	38 cm.	Montanari	1874	12	Nasmyth
1665	12	Kircher	1876	24	Neison
1667		Hooke	1876	Engravings	Winlock
1671	11	D'Orléans	1877	6$\frac{11}{16}$	Guillemin
1680	20·8	Cassini	1878	73¾	Schmidt
1686	15·7	De la Hire	1880	8	Flammarion
1692	21¼	Cassini	1880	8·5	*Encyclopædia Hesperia*
1694	11	Eimmart	1881	2·9	*Wonders of the Heavens*
1700		Doppelmayer	1881	24 sq.	Harrison
1725	6	Keill	1885	4·9	Proctor
1745		Coetlogon	1887	25	Gaudibert
1745		Catalan	1888	4	Serviss
1749	11·5	Gian-Priamo	1889	13	Fenet
1752		De Ulloa	1890	38	Iturralde
1752	6·25	Figueras y de Grau	1890	8⅜	Fenet (later redrawn to
1764		Lalande			25·5 inches)
1769	5·5	Dicquemare	1890	Globe: 4	
1775	7⅞	Mayer		and 6	Gaudibert

Date	Diameter	Author	Date	Diameter	Author
1891	11·3	T. K. Mellor	1927		Anděl
1891	24	C. P. Powell	1927	$7\frac{14}{16}$	Comas Sola
1892	6·5	Proctor	1928	7	Ascarza
1893	3·3	Mee	1930	200	Wilkins
1895	18	Elger	1930	Relief	Pettit (Mt. Wilson)
1897	5	Mee	1930	6·8	Debes
1897	Globe	Lade	1930		Spurig
1898	10·9	Peck	1931	30	Goodacre
1898	17	König	1931		Pettit
1899	11	Novellas	1931		Spurig
1902		Stuyvært (unfinished)	1933	$4\frac{4}{5}$	Sacco
1902	57·5	Anmerck	1934		Pattee
1902	11·4	Thomas	1934	61·5 cm.	Lamèch
1903	3·25	Flammarion	1935	1 metre	I.A.U. Map
1905	10	R. S. Ball	1936	$33\frac{3}{4}$	Fauth
1905	$2\frac{3}{4}$	Cassell's Pop. Ed.	1936	$7\frac{3}{16}$	Baird
1906	$3\frac{1}{2}$	Dolmage	1937	67, 85 mm.	Humbert (Van Langren:
1907	6	Sacco			Riccioli)
1908	$12\frac{1}{4}$	Porthouse	1938	$5\frac{1}{2}$	Patston
1909	3	Rudaux	1938	110 mm.	Couderc
1909	3·7	Olcott	1940	72 (Relief:	
1910	77	Goodacre		Chicago)	Grünfeld
1910	6·5	Prinz	1943	95 mm.	Rousseau
1910	6	Norton's Star Atlas	1943	$10\frac{3}{16}$	Fresá
1911	Globe	Gaudibert	1944	10	Krause
1912	$7\frac{3}{32}$	Moreux	1946	300	Wilkins
1912	19	Mateo Puras	1947	10·25	Sturain
1913	3·75	Giner	1947	4	Gouroy
1916		Renart	1948	7·5	Rudaux
1919	32	Eizmendi	1948	83 mm.	Bernhard
1919	19	Casillas	1948	83 mm.	Ramon Muller
1920	$8\frac{5}{8}$	Comas Solá	1948	24·5	Ilestre
1920	$4\frac{1}{4}$	Jackson (*Encyclopædia*)	1948	2·75	Whipple
1921	6	Ambrósius	1948	3	Puig. S.I.
1921	110 mm.	Anderer	1949		Maupomé (unfinished)
1923	8·25	Rudaux	1950	6	Calvet
1924	60	Wilkins	1951	24	Astronicá Aster
1924	30	Goodacre (*Splendour*	1959		Miyamoto and Matsui
		of the Heavens)			(photographic)
1925	$3\frac{3}{5}$	Rudaux	1960		Kuiper
1927	18	Lamèch			(photographic)

NEW NAMES IN THE 300 in. LUNAR MAP

No.	Section	Name on Map	Previous Name	ξ	η	Author
1	I	Lyot	Ptolemæus A	−014	−148	Wilkins
2	II	Barcroft	Dollond B	+236	−136	Wilkins
3	III	Giner	Posidonius P	+385	+553	Paluzíe

No.	Section	Name on Map	Previous Name	ξ	η	Author
4	III	Fisher	Vitruvius B	+528	+280	Wilkins
5	IV	Gant	Archimedes A	−098	+470	Wilkins
6	V	De Bergerac	Carlini D	−231	+544	Wilkins
7	V	Mount Dyson	Pytheas Beta	−382	+335	Wilkins
8	V	Porthouse	Carlini B	−307	+505	Wilkins
9	V	Mount Whipple	La Hire Alpha	−403	+474	Wilkins
10	V	Virgil	Bessarion E	−584	+265	Wilkins
11	V	Krosigk	Tobias Mayer G	−435	+298	MacDonald
12	VI	Eddington	Reinhold B	−367	+075	Wilkins-Cameron
14	VII	Hauet	Wurzelbauer D	−243	−592	Paluzíe
15	VII	Lenham	Kies A	−340	−474	Wilkins-Moore
16	VII	Novellas	Agatharchides P	−449	−345	Paluzíe
17	VII	Renart	Unnamed	−212	−602	Paluzíe
18	VIII	Garcia-Gomez	Alpetragius B	−115	−261	Paluzíe
19	VIII	Dublier	Alphonsus D	−014	−260	Paluzíe
20	IX	Romaña	Fracastorius D	+478	−372	Paluzíe
21	IX	Benitez	Pontanus C	+231	−499	Paluzíe
22	IX	Millás	Parrot C	+022	−318	Paluzíe
23	IX	Sisebuto	Azophi A	−410	+190	Paluzíe
24	X	Antoniadi	Hekatæus B	+915	−331	Wilkins
25	X	Santacruz	Abel (Franz)	+816	−570	Paluzíe
26	X	Steavenson	Reichenbach A	+664	−474	Wilkins
27	X	Whitaker	Unnamed	+910	−480	Wilkins-Moore
28	X	Orús	Petavius B	+790	−340	Paluzíe
29	X	Raurich	Hekatæus D	+945	−320	Paluzíe
30	X	Smith	Vendelinus C	+873	−252	Wilkins
31	XI	Fébrer	Schubert B	+987	+022	Paluzíe
32	XI	Watts	Kästner B	+988	−114	Wilkins-Hoag
33	XI	Vernet	Goclenius G	+644	−103	Paluzíe
34	XI	Aller	Langrenus K	+841	−102	Paluzíe
35	XII	Liddiard	Unnamed	+810	+584	Wilkins
36	XII	Recorde	Alhazen E	+925	+308	Wilkins-Mee
37	XII	Cooke	Eimmart C	+810	+382	Wilkins
38	XII	Lower	Hansen B	+953	+247	Wilkins-Mee
39	XII	O'Neill	Unnamed	+730	+260	Wilkins
40	XIII	Paluzíe	Unnamed	+770	+638	Wilkins
41	XIII	Russell	Within Paluzíe	+758	+645	Wilkins
42	XIII	Polit	Hallowes H	+692	+720	Paluzíe
43	XIII	Hallowes	Unnamed	+690	+720	Wilkins
44	XIV	Abineri	Strabo A	+430	+891	Wilkins-Moore
45	XIV	Ball, L. F.	Endymion B	+466	+859	Wilkins
46	XIV	O'Kell	Atlas E	+445	+750	MacDonald
47	XIV	Trewman	Unnamed	+320	+920	Wilkins
48	XIV	Williams	Unnamed	+445	+470	Wilkins
49	XV	Nansen	Unnamed	+087	+980	Moore
50	XV	Shackleton	Gioja A	+014	+996	Moore
51	XV	Peary	Unnamed	+030	+999	Moore

No.	Section	Name on Map	Previous Name	ξ	η	Author
52	XV	Väisälä	Unnamed	−040	+960	Paluzíe
53	XV	Bartlett	Mädler's Square	−115	+878	Moore
54	XV	Haas	Pico E	−131	+681	Wilkins
55	XV	Reese	Pico B	−182	+724	Wilkins
56	XV	Sacco	Scoresby A	+075	+985	Paluzíe
57	XV	The Washbowl	Cassini A (part)	+063	+649	Wilkins
58	XV	Rhodes	Unnamed	−101	+990	Paluzíe
59	XVI	Arthur	Anaximander G	−324	+941	Moore
60	XVI	Aymat	Sharp B	−485	+731	Paluzíe
61	XVII	Najerá	Unnamed	−660	+760	Paluzíe
62	XVIII	Caramuel	Unnamed	−905	+420	Paluzíe
63	XVIII	Armenter	Unnamed	−897	+425	Paluzíe
64	XVIII	Barange	Marius A	−702	+218	Paluzíe
65	XVIII	MacDonald	Aristarchus F	−674	+369	Wilkins
66	XIX	Harris	Riccioli E	−973	−125	Wilkins
67	XIX	Buss	Unnamed	−992	−019	Wilkins
68	XIX	Lowe	Riccioli A	−987	−102	Wilkins
69	XIX	Green	Unnamed	−102	−1·00	Wilkins
70	XIX	Bolton	Unnamed	−103	−0·88	Wilkins
71	XIX	Baum	Sven Hedin E	−980	+090	Wilkins
72	XIX	Burrell	Melloni (Schmidt)	−805	−130	Wilkins
73	XIX	Saheki	Grimaldi B	−933	−051	Moore
74	XIX	Ingalls	Riccioli C	−956	+009	Wilkins
75	XX	Juan	Unnamed	−440	−300	Paluzíe
76	XX	Comas Solá	Unnamed	−760	−550	Wilkins
77	XX	Fresá	Lagrange B	−750	−522	Paluzíe
78	XX	Landerer	Mersenius B	−731	−360	Paluzíe
79	XX	Jiyah	Mersenius D	−673	−392	Paluzíe
80	XX	Bertaud	Sirsalis A	−858	−222	Wilkins
81	XX	La Paz	Byrgius A	−816	−416	Wilkins
82	XX	Clarkson	Gassendi A	−616	−268	Wilkins
83	XXII	Hare	Bailly B	−323	−932	Wilkins
84	XXII	Emley	Capuanus E	−361	−609	Wilkins
85	XXIII	Amundsen	Unnamed	+090	−989	Arthur
86	XXIII	Scott	Unnamed	+080	−990	Arthur
87	XXIII	Barker	Sasserides A	−149	−636	Wilkins
88	XXIII	Porter	Clavius B	−098	−830	Wilkins-Adams
89	XXIII	Wright	Licetus F	+012	−719	Wilkins-Nicholson
90	XXIII	Reypastor	Faraday G	+122	−718	Paluzíe
91	XXIV	Hill	Lockyer H	+377	−707	Wilkins
92	XXV	Ibañéz	Marinus K	+731	−679	Paluzíe
93	Libratory	Cortés	Demonax A	+170	−983	Paluzíe
94	Stereo.	Esquivel	Unnamed	+220	+953	Paluzíe
95	Stereo.	Pratdesaba	Brisbane G	+631	−772	Paluzíe
96	Stereo.	Thornton	Unnamed	−328	+937	Wilkins-Moore
97	Stereo.	Mare Incognito	Unnamed	+870	+530	Wilkins
98	Stereo.	Rodés	Unnamed	−906	+400	Paluzíe
99	I	Alter	Albategnius G	+033	−164	Wilkins

Appendix III

THE MEASUREMENT OF LUNAR ALTITUDES

Many people would welcome some fairly simple and straightforward method of finding the heights of mountains and peaks, either from photographs or when actually observing with a telescope. It is true that the heights of many mountains have been determined, but thousands of peaks are still unmeasured, and it adds greatly to the interest if, noting some peak or crater-wall, its height can be ascertained, at least approximately.

The height of a mountain can be found by several methods; however, only two of these will be considered here. One is the tangent method, in which the distance of a peak from the terminator is noted when the first solar ray touches its summit. This was the first method used, but suffers from the disadvantages that the exact position of the terminator can rarely be determined with any approach to accuracy, especially in the more mountainous regions, and the moment when the summit is first noted is always some time after the moment when an observer on the peak itself would see the first glimmer of the Sun's disk on the horizon.

The second and generally used method consists, not in noting when the peak first makes its appearance beyond the terminator, but in measuring the length of the shadow cast at a particular moment. If photographs are employed, the date and time of exposure must be known. The length of the shadow depends upon two factors: (1) the height of the peak, (2) the height or altitude of the Sun above the horizon as it would be seen by an observer on the peak. Obviously, the higher the Sun, the shorter will be the shadow. Knowing both the length of the shadow and the solar altitude, the height of the peak can be determined.

However, before this can be done certain information must be obtained. The distance of the Moon is constantly varying, and with it the Moon's apparent diameter. The value in miles, feet or other units, of a second and fractions of a second of arc, measured on the lunar disk, also varies. In addition to this, the distance of the peak from the apparent centre of the disk, or from the limb, is also continually varying owing to libration, and this affects the apparent length of the shadow. Except at the apparent centre of the disk, all objects, including shadows, are more or less foreshortened, this effect increasing as the limb is approached. Allowance must also be made for the position of the observer, or the photographic telescope if a photograph is used; in other words, for the Moon's parallax, which varies according to the Moon's altitude.

Some of the information required can be obtained from such works as the *Nautical Almanac*, but here again computations have to be undertaken. The position of the Moon, its semi-diameter, distance and so forth, as set out in the Tables, are *geocentric*; that is, they are as an observer at the centre of the Earth would measure them. Since the Moon is not observed, or photographed, from the centre of the Earth, but from its surface, corrections must be introduced. The object of this paper is to present a simplified method, with as few computations as possible, by means of which the heights may be found with a considerable degree of accuracy.

The first thing to do is to measure the apparent length of the shadow cast by the peak whose height it is desired to ascertain. If we measure a photograph an accurate and finely-divided rule should be used: if measured at the telescope a filar micrometer must be employed. The value of one revolution of the screw, in seconds of arc, will either be supplied by the makers or found by trial on stellar objects. The value varies with the focal length of the telescope on which the micrometer is mounted. For a photograph the scale—the diameter of the Moon in inches or centimetres—must be found. In this way we can say that the apparent length of the shadow is so many seconds of arc. This is the projected length, and indicated by L.

We next want to know the position of the peak P. If this is shown on one of the modern maps, especially that of Wilkins, the rectangular co-ordinates can be obtained without difficulty; these particulars may also be obtained from the list of measures upon which the maps depend. If obtained in rectangular co-ordinates, ξ and η they may be expressed in selenographical longitude and latitude, or vice versa, by the formulæ:

$$\xi = \sin U . \cos V, \eta = \sin V$$

The longitude is denoted by U, and its latitude by V.

Now at any moment the Sun is vertically over some point of the lunar surface; this is known as the sub-solar point and is denoted by S. Together with its co-ordinates, it may be obtained from the *Nautical Almanac*, and its value at the time of observation obtained by interpolation. The co-ordinates of the apparent centre of the disk depend upon the libration. This point is denoted by O, and its longitude and latitude by Y and Z respectively.

Putting the longitude of the sub-solar point, S, as W, and its latitude as X, the distance SO is given by $\cos SO = \sin X \sin Z + \cos X \cos Z \sin (90° - W + Y)$.

And the distance between the apparent centre of the disk and the peak = PO may be found from:

$$\cos PO = \sin Z \sin V + \cos Z \cos V \cos (U - Y).$$

The Sun's altitude at the peak P, which is denoted by A, is given by the formula:

$$\sin A = \sin X \sin V + \cos X \cos V \sin (90° - W + U).$$

The true length of the shadow = B; the apparent length being L, is given by:

$$B = \frac{L}{\sin OS}$$

and the height of the peak , = H, may be determined by:

$$H = B \sin A - \tfrac{1}{2}B^2 \cos {}^2A - \tfrac{1}{8}B^4 \cos {}^4A, \text{ or } H = \frac{\cos (P - M) - 1}{\cos P},$$

where M = angle at the Moon's centre between peak P and the end of the shadow.

The value of a second of arc, measured on the Moon's surface at the epoch of observation, depends upon its semi-diameter, which, in its turn, is dependent upon the Moon's distance from the observer. The geocentric distance, in terms of the Moon's radius or in miles, may be found from the *Almanac*, so all we need to do is to correct for parallax. The distance between observer and peak P is the geocentric distance minus the Moon's radius, in terms of that of the Earth, and equal to ·2725, cos PO minus sin-Moon's altitude at the time of observation. This latter quantity may be either estimated or roughly measured.

Taking the other quantities from the *Almanac*, including the libration, and neglecting some small terms, the height of the peak may be determined with a fair approximation to accuracy.

If the peak whose altitude is required is situated near an already measured peak, we can determine the height of the first with some approach to accuracy, from:

$$H = H' \frac{BD}{AC}$$

where H′ = altitude of already measured peak,
A = length of shadow of known peak,
B = length of shadow of unknown peak,
C = distance from terminator of known peak,
D = distance from terminator of unknown peak.

This method was extensively used by both Mädler and Schmidt, and can, with care, give altitudes within a few hundred feet of the true altitude as found by the rigorous computations.

Appendix IV

LEGENDS, MYTHS, SUPERSTITIONS AND TRADITIONS

Among the many varied and often erroneous ideas regarding the Moon, the following may prove interesting.

There is a widespread idea that the Moon affects the weather. The uprightness, or otherwise, of the Moon, especially the crescent, is considered as a sign of the coming weather. If the Moon is 'on her back' it is a sign of bad weather, as the shape and the position suggests that it can hold water; if upright, or nearly so, it is a sign of good weather. Of course, the precise inclination of the line of the cusps depends upon the season and the Moon's altitude and has no connection whatever with the weather. Neither does the Moon affect the weather in any way. This should be obvious to the most casual, since the Moon is visible over one-half of the Earth's surface at the same time, and all countries do not have the same weather.

If the earthshine is very clearly seen it may be a sign of approaching bad weather; a lunar halo is another weather sign. The Moon doubtless does raise a tide in the atmosphere, and there is an old saying that 'the Moon eats up the clouds', which chiefly means that when Full we can often see dimly through the thinner clouds, merely on account of the brilliancy of the Full Moon. The Moon is supposed to affect the growth of plants; in France the April Moon is known as the 'rust Moon' because, if the sky is clear, plants are frequently affected by frost. Clouds stop the radiation, and since a clear cloudless sky is necessary for the 'rusting', the Moon, if above the horizon, receives the blame. Then again wood cut during the increasing Moon is supposed to keep better than that cut during the decrease; if wood is cut during the wane it floats, but that cut during the wax sinks. Trees pruned at the Old Moon grow less actively than when pruning takes place at New Moon. There is a worst day for this, it is the last Wednesday of the lunar month. Sap in plants rises best at the New Moon, root plants should be sown between First Quarter and Full. Plants sown for their leaves should be sown during the wane. Some plants, such as beetroot, show concentric rings when they are cut, the rings being equal in number to the number of lunations since the plants first appeared.

The ancients solemnly stated that the 'selenotrope' was a tree which turns towards the Moon as the heliotrope does towards the Sun, while the palm-tree sends forth a bough at every rising of the Moon (Cornelius Agrippa). Among the ancient Egyptians the onion was not eaten on account of its antipathy to the Moon. It was often stated that there was more rain between First Quarter and Full and least between Last Quarter and New. Arago asserted this as true for Paris.

Not only plants but animals were affected by the Moon. The ancients supposed that the Moon affected the functions of women, the activities of nocturnal animals, such as cats, panthers, etc., and in some parts of Wales fishes are affected by the Moon, but indirectly. Fish in inland ponds or lakes 'bite' better when the tide is high at the nearest ocean port than at low tide there. Since the Moon is the principal agent is raising the tides . . .

A particularly absurd idea is the often-heard expression: 'moonlight causes blindness'. The idea appears to be that it is harmful if the moonlight shines on a sleeping person: he will have dreams at least; indeed, 'lunacy' means affected by the Moon, as the word itself suggests. If the Moon can blind a person who merely looks at our satellite with the naked eye, how much more so ought it to blind those people, like the Authors, who spend a good part of their lives peering at the Moon through great telescopes!

Skin diseases often begin during the wane and reach their maximum at New to clear at the Full. It has even been suggested that this may be due to some electrical influence! Those who support this notion have advanced the 'fact' that epileptics often become well at Full! Some people allegedly, find breathing more difficult at both New and Full.

In ancient times the Moon was worshipped as Diana, Artemis, Ashtaroth, Phœbe, Lucina, Prosperina and Hecate, while the ancient Arcadians actually believed themselves to have been in existence *before* the Moon was formed: hence the term 'Proselenes'. The Moon always was, and still is, used as a measure of time. Our week is a lunar measure; among some communities (the Moslems, for instance) the Fast of Ramadan ends when the crescent Moon is first seen.

For a long time the supposed inhabitants of the Moon, or selenites, were believed to be fifteen times as tall as an average man; even the lunar trees and bushes were elevated in like proportion. This strange idea was undoubtedly based on the great length of the lunar day, which lasts fifteen times as long as ours. According to Flammarion, before white men reached Australia its existence was known owing to the brightness of a portion of the earthshine, which was much brighter than could be caused by reflection from the ocean.

Everybody has met people who have declared that 'it is unlucky to see the Moon through glass', who 'turn their money over' when the crescent is first seen. The Full Moon, being highest at midnight when everything is still and deserted, is supposed to raise ghosts in old ruins and churchyards.

In the time of Kepler men were much occupied with the mystical 'music of the spheres'; the highest note was assigned to the Moon, merely on account of her proximity.

As for the dark markings on the Moon's spotted face, we no longer regard them as the features of a man banished to the Moon for the crime of gathering wood on a Sunday, or that they are the face of Judas, but some people still believe they are the reflection of our own seas and continents. Even more widespread is the idea that the phases are due to the shadow of the Earth hiding part of the bright surface. Arthur Mee once saw a level-headed business man solemnly gazing at a lunar eclipse through a piece of smoked glass!

Some people, again, affirm the Moon to be nothing more than an old comet; others are much occupied with Joshua's famous 'long day', when the Sun and Moon are supposed to have stood still until the battle was decided! Even such a brilliant mathematician as the celebrated Laplace wished to improve upon Nature and suggested that the Moon would serve us much better as a luminary if she revolved around the Earth once a year instead of once a month. This 'permial moon' idea was demolished by M. Liouville, in 1845, who showed that such an arrangement would be unstable, while Whewell demonstrated that for the Moon to revolve around us once a year she would have to be removed so far away as to only look one-sixteenth as large as she now does.

And so we could go on: there is no end to the folly of humans with regard to our satellite. If the Moon is eclipsed it is regarded as due to a dragon eating the Moon, an idea prevalent in the East; the Moon is turned into blood; it is a sign of divine displeasure, or the Moon has wandered from her course.

Slowly but surely science is rooting out these relics of man's long childhood; and with the coming of age of the race superstition must eventually disappear. We no longer regard unusual celestial events, eclipses, comets, meteors, the appearance of the crescent Moon as anything but what science affirms, natural and predictable, subject to law and capable of explanation. The few examples cited of the folly of our ancestors should clearly indicate the sure, if slow, advancement of human achievement and genius.

Appendix V

LUNAR OBSERVERS OF THE PAST

We consider that a short biographical section will be of value to readers of the present work; it will serve as a résumé of selenographical history, and should also prove useful for reference. At the same time, it must be borne in mind that this list is by no means exhaustive, and stress has been laid upon practical observers rather than mathematicians. The list of living observers is admittedly incomplete; there are now so many skilful and enthusiastic lunar workers that it was obviously impossible to mention more than a very few. For convenience, astronomers have been arranged in the chronological order of birth, apart from the living observers, who have been dealt with alphabetically.

(1) ASTRONOMERS BORN BETWEEN 1564 AND 1700

GALILEO (1564-1642). Galileo Galilei, to give him his full name, is best remembered as being the first to apply the telescope to the heavens, though he was also a physicist and mathematician of the highest order. His 'optick tube', magnifying thirty times, was sufficient to reveal the lunar mountains, craters and *maria* well; and besides constructing a rough lunar map, he tried to measure the heights of some of the peaks. His method and results were very inaccurate, but he concluded that some of the mountains were as much as 5 miles high, which is at least in the right order of magnitude. He also discovered one of the lunar librations. Galileo held chairs first at Pisa, then at Padua University; but his defence of the Copernican System brought him into conflict with the Church, and in 1633 he was forced publicly to 'curse and detest' the false opinion that the Sun is the centre of the solar system. Subsequently he was confined to his own house; blindness was added to his troubles, and he died in 1642, the year in which Newton was born.

SIR WILLIAM LOWER. Lower, certainly the first British lunar observer, lived in the little Welsh village of Traventy. In 1611 he received one of Galileo's 'perspective cylinders', and studied the Moon with it. Unfortunately he seems to have left no drawings, and almost nothing is known about his life.

JOANNES RICCIOLI (1598-1671). Riccioli, a Jesuit professor of astronomy and theology at the University of Bologna, was a lifelong opponent of the Copernican Theory. His lunar map, issued in 1651, was based mainly on the observations of Grimaldi, and is only remembered because of Riccioli's system of naming lunar formations after eminent men of science. It does not appear that Riccioli himself was a notable observer.

MICHEL VAN LANGREN (Langrenus, 1600-1675). Van Langren, one of the early telescopic observers, was trained as an engineer and mathematician. By birth he was Belgian. At the age of thirty he was appointed Court Astronomer to the King of Spain, where he remained for twenty years. While in Spain he completed a map of the Moon, and planned to draw up thirty charts showing the different phases, though apparently never did so. On leaving Spain he returned to Brussels, and for the rest of his life devoted himself to engineering projects.

JOHANN HEWELCKE (Hevelius, 1611-87). Hevelius, a city councillor of his native Danzig, was one of the most active of the seventeenth-century observers. He did not lack money, and was able to build an observatory on the roof of his house, equipping it with the finest instruments available. He measured star positions, and observed the Sun and planets, but he is chiefly remembered as being the first to produce a reasonably accurate map of the Moon. He realized that the 'seas' are in reality great plains, and he gave values for the heights of lunar mountains which were far more accurate than Galileo's. His system of nomenclature, however, was clumsy; that of Riccioli soon superseded it, and only ten of Hevelius' names are now in use. Hevelius' observational career more or less ended in 1679, when his observatory was destroyed by fire.

FRANCESCO GRIMALDI (1618-63), Professor of Mathematics at Bologna University, was a sound lunar observer, and was mainly responsible for the map usually associated with his friend and tutor, Riccioli. Grimaldi is best remembered, however, for his discovery of the diffraction of light.

JEAN DOMINIQUE CASSINI (1625-1712). Cassini, one of the most eminent of early planetary observers, was born at Nice of Italian parents, and in 1650 was appointed Professor of Astronomy at Bologna University. In 1666, however, plans were made in France for the establishment of a national observatory; and three years later, King Louis XIV invited Cassini to Paris to direct operations. The observatory was built promptly, and finished in 1671; and Cassini became so attached to his new situation that he adopted French nationality. He also married a Frenchwoman, and spent the rest of his life in his adopted country. Besides constructing a lunar map that is of definite value (a few copies of it are still in existence), Cassini greatly improved the theory of librations. His other works, too, were of the highest importance; for instance, he determined the axial rotation period of Jupiter with great accuracy, and discovered four of the satellites of Saturn, as well as the division in the rings now named after him.

(2) ASTRONOMERS BORN BETWEEN 1700 AND 1800

TOBIAS MAYER (1723-62). Tobias Mayer was born in Württemberg. His father was a wheelwright, and the boy received very little education. However, he soon taught himself enough to become a professional draughtsman, and at the age of 28 was elected to the chair of economy and mathematics at the University of Göttingen. Three years later, in 1754, he became superintendent of the Göttingen Observatory, and worked there until his death at the early age of 39. He is chiefly remembered for his lunar tables, much the best of their time, which were used extensively by the British Admiralty. Mayer also produced an 8-inch lunar map, which remained the only reliable chart of the lunar surface until the time of Beer and Mädler.

SIR WILLIAM HERSCHEL (1738-1822), justly termed the 'Father of Modern Astronomy', first president of the Royal Astronomical Society, and discoverer of the planet Uranus, hardly comes within the range of this summary, as he did not do a great deal of lunar observing. However, he paid attention to the Moon from time to time; he believed that he had seen active volcanoes, and that the habitability of the Moon was 'an absolute certainty'.

JOHANN HIERONYMUS SCHRÖTER (1745-1816). Schröter should undoubtedly be considered the founder of modern selenography. He was born in Erfurt, and studied law at Göttingen; after living in Hanover for some time, where he made the acquaintance of the Herschel family (though William Herschel was already in England), Schröter was appointed chief magistrate of Lilienthal, near Bremen, where he remained almost to the end of his life.

From his early days Schröter had been a lover of astronomy, and on his appointment at Lilienthal he hastened to equip himself with an observatory. He obtained several telescopes made by Herschel, but the largest ever in his possession was a 19-inch reflector made by Schräder, of Kiel. This instrument was completed in 1793, and, at the time was the largest in Germany.

Schröter was no mathematician, but his enthusiasm for observation was unquenchable, and for thirty years he worked patiently away, drawing, measuring and checking. All the planets came under his scrutiny, but his most important work was concerned with the Moon; though he never produced a complete chart, he made hundreds of drawings, which are of the highest value. He also made height measurements far more reliable than those of his predecessors. Schröter's work has often been belittled, and it is perfectly true that he was not an expert draughtsman, but everyone who has examined the two great volumes of his *Selenotopographische Fragmente*—as we have done—will hold him in the highest esteem.

Tragically, Schröter's observatory was burned down in 1813, when French troops invaded Germany; the brass telescopes were plundered by the soldiers, who mistook them for gold, and all Schröter's books and unpublished observations were destroyed—an irreplaceable loss. The old astronomer, his life's work more or less wrecked, organized the transfer of the remains of his equipment to Göttingen, but died three years later.

Franz von Gruithuisen (1774-1852), born in Bavaria, took a medical degree at Landshut University, but subsequently turned to astronomy, and was appointed Professor of Astronomy at Munich in 1826. That he was an excellent observer cannot be doubted; but unfortunately his imagination was so vivid, and his ideas so extravagant, that even in his lifetime he tended to bring ridicule upon himself. For instance, he announced the detection of a 'lunar city' walled in by 'dark gigantic ramparts', whereas the area concerned contains little more than low, haphazard ridges. It was Gruithuisen who originally put forward the meteoric theory of lunar crater formation.

Johann Heinrich Mädler (1794-1874). Mädler's name is inseparably linked with that of Beer; between them the two astronomers provided the basis of all subsequent selenographical work. The amount they accomplished was amazing, particularly in view of their modest equipment; for most of their lunar studies they used a $3\frac{3}{4}$-inch refractor.

Mädler, a Berliner by birth, became a teacher; Beer came to him for astronomical instruction, and the two struck up a close friendship, eventually building an observatory at Beer's Berlin house. Between 1824 and 1840 they kept the Moon and planets under continuous observation, and in 1837 issued the immortal 'Mappa Selenographica', following it up with a book, *Der Mond*, containing a complete description of the surface. In 1840, however, Mädler left Berlin to become director of the Dorpat Observatory in Estonia; and, strangely enough, he seems to have done little more lunar or planetary work, devoting himself instead to much less profitable speculations about stellar motions.

Peter Andreas Hansen (1795-1874), the distinguished Danish mathematical astronomer, was born at Tondern, in Schleswig, and became apprentice to a Flensburg watchmaker. In 1823 he secured the post of assistant at the newly-founded Observatory of Altona, and two years later succeeded Encke as Director of the Seeberg Observatory, where he remained for the rest of his life. His lunar tables, published in 1857 at the expense of the British Government, were adapted for use in the *Nautical Almanac*, and his services to astronomy were recognized by two awards of the R.A.S. Gold Medal. Hansen suggested that the centre of the lunar globe was not coincident with the centre of gravity, so that all remaining water and air had been drawn round to the far side; but this theory has been shown to be absolutely untenable.

Wilhelm Lohrmann (1796-1840). Lohrmann was born in Dresden, and became a land surveyor there. He became interested in astronomy while still only a boy, and determined to construct a lunar map more accurate than the best produced up to that time (Mayer's). The scale was to be $37\frac{1}{2}$ inches to the Moon's diameter. The first four of the twenty-five sections appeared in 1824, but unfortunately Lohrmann's sight began to fail, and the map was left incomplete. He did, however, issue an excellent 15-inch map of the whole disk in 1838. His great map was eventually finished and published by Schmidt, nearly forty years after Lohrmann's premature death.

Wilhelm Beer (1797-1850), a Berlin banker, was the junior author of the immortal

Der Mond, although his name usually appears before that of Mädler. It is true that Mädler did most of the observing; but Beer's own share was quite considerable, and must on no account be disregarded. He does not seem to have done much more astronomical work after Mädler's departure for Dorpat, and died in 1850, almost a quarter of a century before his friend.

(3) ASTRONOMERS BORN BETWEEN 1800 AND 1850

WILLIAM RADCLIFF BIRT (1804-81). This English amateur was one of the most active lunar observers of the last century. It was he who reported to the British Association for the proposed large lunar map, although the committee formed to carry out the project was not reappointed after 1869, and very little was actually done. Birt was also the founder and president of the Selenographical Society, which was very active for several years, and issued a journal which is a mine of information. Unfortunately the death of Birt, coupled with the resignation and departure of the secretary (Neison) proved fatal to the Society, which soon disbanded. The B.A.A. Lunar Section, formed in 1890, carried on the work, and now issues a periodical, *The Moon,* which may perhaps be regarded as the direct descendant of Birt's old *Selenographical Journal.*

LEWIS RUTHERFURD (1816-92), an American barrister who turned his attention to astronomy at the age of 30, was one of the pioneers of lunar photography. His photographs remained the finest in existence for many years.

JOHN COUCH ADAMS (1819-92) was not an observational selenographer, but greatly improved lunar theory. He was a Cornishman, who achieved fame while still in his twenties by his brilliant investigations into the perturbations of Uranus, which led to the discovery of a new planet, Neptune. He served as president of the Royal Astronomical Society in 1851, and afterwards received the appointment of Director of the Cambridge Observatory. He was undoubtedly one of the most outstanding mathematicians of the last century.

JULIUS SCHMIDT (1825-84). Selenography owes much to this great German astronomer. Between 1840 and 1866 he was the only observer engaged in systematic lunar work, and but for his labours there would have been a long gap in the records. He started to observe the Moon while still a boy, and continued to do so right up to the year of his death. For some years he acted as assistant at various German observatories, but in 1858 the Athens Observatory was reorganized, and Schmidt accepted the post of Director. It was in Greece, therefore, that his main lunar work was done; in fact, he remained there for the rest of his life, as after his eventual retirement he continued to live in his Athens house. Schmidt was an untiring observer, and it is very fortunate that Lohrmann's records passed into his hands.

It was in 1866 that Schmidt made the startling announcement that Linné, recorded by earlier observers as a conspicuous crater, had vanished. This strange disappearance resulted in the general awakening of interest in selenography, so that henceforth Schmidt did not have to labour unaided. Twelve years later he issued his great map, 72 inches in diameter, which will bear comparison with almost any modern chart; this was published at the expense of the Prussian Government, at the instigation of Field-Marshal Von Moltke.

MORITZ LOEWY (1833-1907), Austrian by birth but French by naturalization, was for some years Director of the Paris Observatory. His earlier work dealt mainly with stellar and instrumental astronomy, but he made a lasting contribution to lunar studies by his formation of the great Paris Atlas, in collaboration with Puiseux.

HENRY DRAPER (1837-82), the son of an English doctor who had emigrated to the United States, is best remembered for his stellar photographic work; but he also photographed the Moon, and some of his pictures are of great value. Draper's death, at the early age of 45, was tragic and unexpected. The Harvard catalogue of stellar spectra was published as a memorial to him, speeded considerably by the generous financial help given by his widow.

It is of interest to note that Draper's father, Dr. John W. Draper, himself, produced some lunar photographs as early as 1840, which must be some of the first ever taken. However, they were only an inch or so across, and showed no detail worthy of mention.

THOMAS GWYN ELGER (1838-97). In 1890 the newly-formed British Astronomical Association established its Lunar Section, and invited T. G. Elger to become Director. The choice was a happy one, as Elger had already acted in a similar capacity for the Liverpool Astronomical Society, and was known as a skilful and enthusiastic lunar observer. By profession he was an engineer, but had also trained as a draughtsman, so that his lunar drawings were of the highest order. Elger directed the Section most efficiently until his death, in 1897, when he was succeeded by Walter Goodacre. Two years before he died Elger issued a book, *The Moon*, which contained a description of the surface, and an outline map of exceptional clarity. The book is now out of print, but the map, revised by Wilkins, was re-issued in 1951, and remains most valuable.

JOSEPH JOACHIM LANDERER (1841-1922), a leading Spanish selenographer, was born in Valencia, and lived there for most of his life. He published many drawings and papers in French and Spanish periodicals, and in 1910 issued a book, *La Evolución del Globo Lunar* ('The Evolution of the Lunar Globe').

CAMILLE FLAMMARION (1842-1925). Flammarion must certainly be regarded as the greatest of French astronomical writers, and did much to popularize the science which he loved; but he was also an eminent observer, and drew up a map of the Moon. He trained as an engraver, but subsequently joined the computing staff of the Paris Observatory, and later established his own small observatory at Juvisy, where he made many important observations of the Moon and planets. He was also the founder of the Société Astronomique de France. It is pleasant to record that Mme. Flammarion still lives at Juvisy, where Wilkins visited her in 1950, and both Wilkins and Moore in 1953.

HERMANN KLEIN (1844-1914). Klein was born in Cologne, and remained there for most of his life, eventually becoming Director of the Cologne Observatory. His researches covered many fields (he is perhaps best remembered for his excellent Star Atlas), but he was a particularly assiduous lunar observer, and it was he who first drew attention to the apparent change in Hyginus N.

JULIUS FRANZ (1847-1913) commenced his astronomical career at the Königsberg Observatory, and in 1897, on the retirement of Dr. Galle, assumed the directorship of the Breslau Observatory, which he held until his death. His principal work was in connection with the Moon's figure and librations; and his measures of the positions of surface formations remain invaluable.

(4) ASTRONOMERS BORN AFTER 1850

EDMUND NEISON (Nevill, 1851-1938). Neison provides a link between the present day and the great figures of the past. He was born in London over a century ago, and at the age of 25 published his monumental work, *The Moon*, containing a two-foot map (really a revision of Beer and Mädler's) and a complete description of every formation then named. This book can still be obtained occasionally, and is of the greatest value. Neison then acted as secretary of the Selenographical Society, but resigned in 1882 to become Director of the newly-founded Natal Observatory at Durban—and, so far as can be ascertained, his career as a selenographer came to an abrupt conclusion. We have been unable to discover any lunar notes or papers issued by Neison during the last fifty-six years of his life, and it seems improbable that any exist. Neison died in South Africa at the age of 87.

SAMUEL ARTHUR SAUNDER (1852-1912) was educated at St. Paul's, and went on to Trinity College, Cambridge. When he was 25 he became mathematics master at Wellington College, and remained there until six months before his death. His main astronomical interest was in the Moon, and his measures of fundamental points on the surface rank, with those of Franz, as the most reliable ever made. He was president of the British Astronomical Association in 1903-4, and served as a secretary of the Royal Astronomical Society between 1906 and the year of his death.

PIERRE PUISEUX (1885-1928), son of a French mathematician, was attracted to astronomy at an early age, and for many years worked at the Paris Observatory. In collaboration with Moritz Loewy, he took a large number of photographs and used them to compile the famous Photographic Atlas; Puiseux was entirely responsible for the accompanying text. He also wrote a book, *La Lune et la Terre*, which appeared in 1908.

LEO BRENNER (1855-1928) was born in Trieste. He came of a military family, and became an officer in the Austrian Army, but his interests lay more in the pursuit of science, and he retired from the army comparatively early. Fortunately he was not beset by any financial difficulties, and built himself an observatory at Lussinpiccolo, where he and his wife made important lunar and planetary observations between 1893 and his death, thirty-five years later.

WALTER GOODACRE (1856-1938). Goodacre, second Director of the British Astronomical Association Lunar Section, was born at Loughborough, but at the age of 7 came to live in London, where his father had founded a business concern. After his education was complete, Goodacre entered the family business, which he managed with great success until his eventual retirement in 1929.

He was attracted to astronomy from boyhood, and for a time directed the Lunar Section of the Liverpool Astronomical Society. Upon the death of Elger, in 1897, he was appointed to a similar position in the British Astronomical Association, and held it until a year before his death. He was president of the B.A.A. in 1922-4, and a life Fellow of the Royal Astronomical Society.

In 1910 he issued his 77-inch map of the Moon, the result of many thousands of personal observations, in which he made full use of Saunders' measured points. This was followed twenty years later by his book, *The Moon*, containing a reduced copy of the map. Unfortunately this important work was privately published by Goodacre at Bournemouth, where he had gone to live, and only a comparatively few copies of it were made, so that it is now exceedingly rare.

PROFESSOR WILLIAM HENRY PICKERING (1858-1938), one of the most distinguished of American lunar and planetary observers, was born in Boston, and educated at the Massachusetts Institute of Technology, where he subsequently became instructor in physics. He then went to Harvard Observatory, and was largely responsible for the setting-up of the Peruvian station of Arequipa, where he and A. E. Douglass made important observations of Mars and the Moon. He also assisted Professor Lowell in establishing the Flagstaff Observatory, and he founded an observatory at Mandeville, in Jamaica, where he took the plates used to form his celebrated Photographic Atlas of the Moon. It was in Mandeville that he died, at the age of 80. Among his other discoveries must be mentioned that of Phœbe, Saturn's ninth satellite.

JOHANN KRIEGER (1865-1902), son of a Bavarian farmer, turned his attention to astronomy and established the Pia Observatory, in Trieste. In 1898 he published the first volume of a lunar atlas, containing many fine personal drawings; but ill health caused him to abandon the project.

RUDOLF KÖNIG (1865-1927), an Austrian business man, was also a mathematician and amateur astronomer of no mean ability. His chief contribution to selenography was his completion and editing of the unfinished sketches left by Krieger, published in 1912. König himself intended to produce a lunar atlas, but this project, like Krieger's, was prevented by his sudden death.

ERNEST WILLIAM BROWN (1866-1938). As the work of E. W. Brown dealt entirely with lunar theory, and he was in no sense a practical observer, his labours fall rather outside the range of the present book; but there can be no doubt that his lunar tables will remain the basis of all future work in this direction for centuries to come. He was a native of Hull, but spent many years in America, some of them at Yale University. During his lifetime he received the highest honours of the scientific world, including the Gold Medal of the Royal Astronomical Society.

PHILIPP FAUTH (1867-1943). Fauth, a well-known German lunar and planetary observer, built his own observatory at Kaiserslautern, in 1890, but later transferred his equipment to Grünwald, near Munich. He published a large number of lunar drawings, and also three books, one of which (*The Moon in Modern Astronomy*) has been translated into English. Unfortunately Fauth's blind adherence to the absurd theory of glaciation led him to misinterpret his own observations, and he was very inclined to ignore the work of others completely. However, the keenness of his sight and the excellence of his drawings cannot be doubted.

KAREL ANDĚL (1884-1947), Czechoslovakia's leading selenographer, was born near Prague, and became a schoolmaster there. He founded the Czechoslovak Astronomical Society, and published a lunar map, as well as a book on the Moon.

ROLAND L. T. CLARKSON (1869-1954) was a native of Suffolk, and lived for most of his life in Ipswich. He was a skilful and active observer not only of the Moon but also of the planets.

DR. BERNARD LYOT (1897-1952). Lyot's name must certainly rank with those of the world's greatest astronomers. He was born in Paris, and after studying at the University became a lecturer there; but although he had been interested in astronomy since boyhood, it was not until 1920, when he became deputy assistant at the Observatory of Meudon, that his work in this field commenced in earnest.

It would be beyond the range of this book to review more than a fraction of his work—even if such could be done in a few pages—and his lunar studies occupied a minor place; but his researches upon the nature of the Moon's surface are of the highest importance, and the lunar photographs taken by him and A. Dollfus at the high-altitude Pic-du-Midi Observatory are unlikely to be surpassed. (Several of them are reproduced here.) The R.A.S. Gold Medal was only one of the numerous honours conferred on Lyot by scientific societies all over the world.

In 1951 Wilkins had the pleasure of visiting Lyot at Meudon, and had hoped to meet him again in 1952, when he and Moore were again invited to the observatory to work with the 33-inch refractor. The news of Lyot's tragic death in Africa, as he was preparing to return home after observing the total solar eclipse, came as a tragic shock to us on our arrival at Meudon. His loss, both to his friends and to the scientific world, is most keenly felt.

DR. SAMUEL MORRIS GREEN (1920-42). In 1937, Dr. S. M. Green joined the British

Astronomical Association, and showed at once that he was an observer of the highest promise. His drawings placed him at once among the leading modern selenographers, and his planetary work was of equal value. Unfortunately, the War intervened; Green joined the R.A.M.C., was commissioned as a lieutenant, and killed on his first day of active warfare. His death, so early in his career, was tragic indeed.

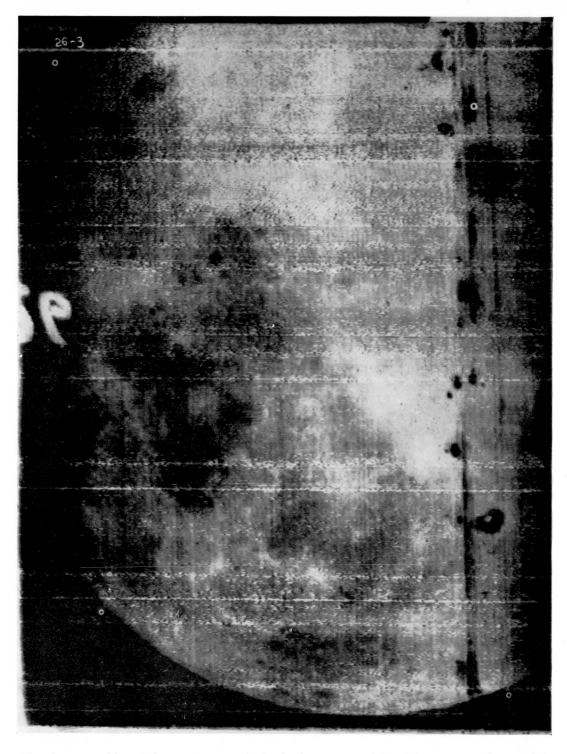

15. The Far Side of the Moon; a televised picture transmitted by the Russian vehicle Lunik III, in October 1959

Appendix VI

THE FAR SIDE OF THE MOON

In October 1959 the Russian vehicle Lunik III successfully photographed a large part of the far side of the Moon, and transmitted these photographs back to Earth by means of complex television techniques.

This was the culmination of a series of Soviet experiments which had begun earlier in the year. In January, the rocket vehicle Lunik I passed within 4,000 miles of the lunar surface, and sent back valuable information; in September, Lunik II actually landed on the lunar surface, probably in the region of the crater Archimedes (though no precise information has been obtained). Lunik III, however, represented an even greater triumph, since the photographs were better than anyone could have expected.

By the end of 1960 the Russian astronomers had completed their studies of the photographic results, and a team headed by Professor J. N. Lipski, of the Sternberg Institute in Moscow, published a comprehensive atlas of the newly-examined regions. The results show that, as expected, the averted hemisphere is basically similar to that which we have always known, though—again as predicted—there are fewer maria.

Various familiar features are also shown; notably the Mare Crisium, together with limb maria such as Humboldtianum, Marginis, Smythii and Australe. Of the new features, particularly notable are the well-defined dark plain now known as the Mare Moscovianum (Moscow Sea), which is about 186 miles in diameter and is thus comparable in size with the crater Bailly, and the craters Tsiolkovskii and Lomonsov.

Mare Australe has been shown to extend on to the far side of the Moon, while Mare Smythii is more rounded; south of it lies a mountainous region. Mare Marginis is elongated, and has an indentation on the side opposite to Mare Crisium. Like Mare Smythii, it too extends on to the averted portion. Mare Humboldtianum has what the Russians term 'an unusual pear-shaped outline'. The whole of the region near the western edge of the far side of the Moon has a reflecting power intermediate between those of mountainous regions and maria, and is similar to that of the region between Tycho and Petavius.

Analysis of the thirty or so photographs taken from Lunik III is now complete; the limb-charts drawn by Wilkins were used for purposes of correlation. In the future, further photographs, showing more detail, will no doubt be obtained; meanwhile the Lunik success represents an outstanding triumph, and no praise can be too high for the Soviet team which made it possible.

AA*

КАРТА ОБРАТНОЙ СТОРОНЫ ЛУНЫ

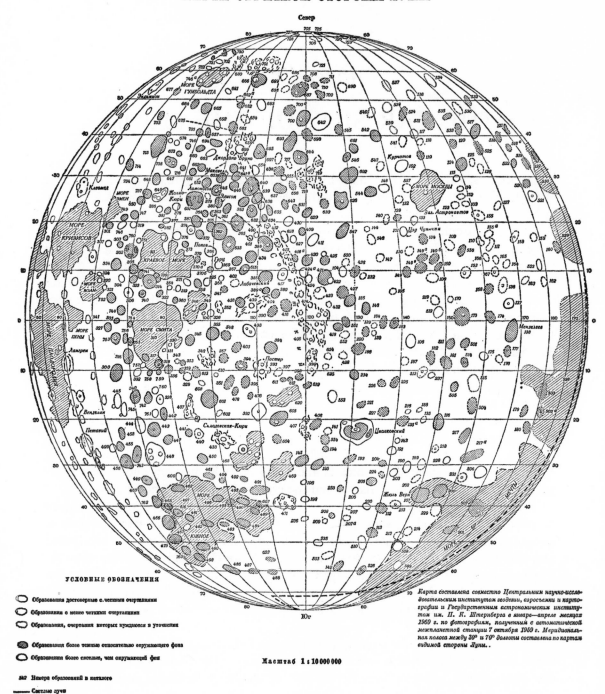

Масштаб 1 : 10 000 000

Карта составлена совместно Центральным научно-исследовательским институтом геодезии, аэросъемки и картографии и Государственным астрономическим институтом им. П. К. Штернберга в январе—апреле месяце 1960 г. по фотографиям, полученным с автоматической межпланетной станции 7 октября 1959 г. Меридиональная полоса между 30° и 70° долготы составлена по картам видимой стороны Луны.

Since the present book is intended primarily for lunar observers, it is pointless to give full details of the new regions, but a copy of the chart drawn up by Lipski and his colleagues is included for the sake of completeness. An exhaustive description of the features shown on the Lunik photographs has been made available in English.

INDEX TO FORMATIONS IN THE MAP

'L.R.' indicates that the formation is shown in the two special charts of the libration zones; 'N.P.C.' or 'S.P.C.' that it is shown in the North or South Polar Chart.

BIBLIOGRAPHY

The following books, devoted entirely to the Moon, have been published in Great Britain during the last hundred years:

1873	*The Moon*	R. A. Proctor	General, devoted largely to Lunar Theory.
1874	*The Moon*	J. Nasmyth and J. Carpenter	Popular; also description of the 'Volcanic Fountain' theory.
1876	*The Moon*	E. Neison	Description of Map.
1895	*The Moon*	T. Gwyn Elger	Description of Map.
1903	*The Moon*	W. H. Pickering	Text to Photographic Atlas.
1908	*The Moon*	G. P. Serviss	Elementary description.
1913	*A Day in the Moon*	T. Moreux	Popular.
1930	*The Moon*	W. Goodacre	Description of Map.
1936	*The Moon in Modern Astronomy*	P. Fauth	Glaciation theory.
1944	*The Imbrian Plain Region of the Moon*	J. E. Spurr	Volcanic theory.
1945	*Features of the Moon*	J. E. Spurr	Volcanic theory.
1949	*The Face of the Moon*	R. B. Baldwin	Meteoric theory.
1949	*Lunar Catastrophic History*	J. E. Spurr	Volcanic theory.
1949	*The Shrunken Moon*	J. E. Spurr	Volcanic theory.
1953	*The Moon*	G. Gamow	Popular.
1953	*Guide to the Moon*	Patrick Moore	Popular description and observers' handbook. (Revised 1957.)
1954	*Our Moon*	H. P. Wilkins	Popular description and observers' handbook.
1959	*Strange World of the Moon*	V. A. Firsoff	Technical.
1960	*The Moon*	Z. Kopal	Popular.
1961	*Surface of the Moon*	V. A. Firsoff	Technical.
1961	*Structure of the Moon's Surface*	G. Fielder	Technical.

Of these books the first nine are out of print, though second-hand copies may often be obtained. From 1944 onwards the list includes some books published only in America, but which are easily obtainable in Great Britain; the works by Spurr, Baldwin and Gamow come under this heading.

BIBLIOGRAPHY

Many books on astronomy contain long sections devoted to the Moon. Such are: Hutchinson's *Splendour of the Heavens*, 1923, where the chapter is by W. Goodacre and includes his map; and Dent's *Astronomy for Everyman*, 1953, in which the lunar chapter is by H. P. Wilkins.

INDEX

(Lunar formations are not listed, as they are given in the index to the map on pages 374 to 382.)

385